Discovering Washington's Historic Mines

Volume 1: The West Central Cascade Mountains

PUBLISHED BY
Oso Publishing Company
31328 N. Brooks Creek Road
Arlington, Washington 98223

ISBN 0-9647521-2-3

Printed and bound in the United States of America.

First printing 1997.

Manuscript editor: Ina Chang
Proofreader: Teri Kieffer
Design and production: James D. Kramer design services, Everett, WA 98208

This book is dedicated to those who lived and made this history, and to the people and organizations that have preserved and interpreted it for our use and enjoyment, now and in the future. Without their unselfish contributions, this book would not have been possible.

Disclaimer

Mines, mining, and mining claim locations can be dangerous, with numerous natural and artificial hazards. By accepting and using this publication and the information contained herein, the user agrees to relieve the authors and Northwest Underground Explorations, its officers, and/or assignees of any liability from the use of any information contained in this publication. The user also accepts responsibility for any liability incurred by family members or guests from the use of any information contained herein.

The authors and Northwest Underground Explorations do not encourage or condone trespass on private or otherwise restricted properties without express prior and proper permission from the rightful owners of said property.

Contents

Darrington   1

Monte Cristo   9

Mountain Loop Highway   47

Sultan Basin
75

Silver Creek to Silver Lake
87

Index   112

Miller River and Money Creek   144

Foss River   168

North Bend   176

Preface

When we consider the history of Washington State after the discovery of the area by Captain George Vancouver on a splendid summer day, we often dwell on the lumber, farming, and fishing industries that have long been the mainstay of the state's economy. Rarely do we consider the state's mining industry. And yet, Washington remains one of the top 10 producers of gold in the United States—a century and a half after mining began here. Why is so little known about the state's mining history? Perhaps it is partly because many early mines were very small operations, located in remote, mountainous areas. When these enterprises were discontinued, most of the material goods were salvaged from them, nature took its course, and the mines, along with the trails leading to them, became overgrown and forgotten. Much of the prospecting and early mining in the state took place from the late 1880s through the 1920s. Many small, marginal mines continued to operate through the 1930s, until the federal government prohibited mining for all but critical metals at the outset of World War II.

When I moved to this state from Chicago, Illinois, in 1961, I was enthralled with the mountains that I found here and wanted to see them "up close and personal." I was advised that the very scenic Monte Cristo/Mineral City area in the central Cascades would satisfy my thirst. And satisfy it did! I found the scenery and solitude that I had sought, but I also found much more. Everywhere I looked I noticed mines and their attendant machinery and building ruins. When I looked for information about what had led to this legacy, I found little in print that could provide an accurate picture of the miners or their era. People had many stories about what the miners did and who they were, but these were incomplete and often conflicting.

I began to research the Monte Cristo area. Information came slowly at first, but eventually a torrent of data began to flow my way. The result was my book *Monte Cristo,* which was published in 1979 by The Mountaineers. It describes the history of Monte Cristo from the discovery of gold there until 1979. As time passed, I continued to gather information and explore mines in Monte Cristo and other areas, and I eventually joined up with Northwest Underground Explorations, a loose-knit group of men and women who shared my desire to learn more about the mining past and experience the thrill of "getting underground." The group gathered information, gained expertise, and accumulated a large mass of data. The result is this book, which details the history and location of the mines and tells the stories of the people who attempted to wrest the stubborn minerals from the rocks in which they lay.

You might wonder why we haven't explored and researched every single mine and prospect in Snohomish County and King County for this book. That would take many, many years of long, tough hikes and brush-beating, plus countless years of research. Then we would still have to try to separate facts from the piles of misinformation, keep up with revisions made in roads and trails, and evaluate new theories of what might or might not have happened. Since Northwest Underground Explorations was founded in 1988, dedicated members have located, explored, and researched as many mines as possible. Much of the information we found was either vague or downright wrong. We spent months, and in some cases even years, on just a few mines or stories. Among the best sources were local citizens; when we were lucky enough to find one still alive and mentally capable, an old-timer who had lived through it all, that person became our "gold mine." We found Joe Cook, who grew up in Monte Cristo and was one of its last miners. He was a wonderful man who wanted to keep alive the heritage of the early days of our counties, and we hope that we have contributed to his wishes in a way that would make him proud. And there was John Maloney, Jr. (the son of John Maloney, Sr., who was instrumental in the Great Northern Railway's successful crossing of the Cascade Mountains), who told us about early mining in the Skykomish area. Helma Wolgemuth (daughter of John Jackson, pioneer prospector in the Silverton area) was not only a great source of information but an inspiration to all of us, with her knowledge and vivid memories of growing up in the little mining town of Silverton. Elof Norman, author of *The Coffee Chased Us Up,* and his sister Ely recounted the many adventures that they had while growing up in Monte Cristo. These people added color, romance, and a human dimension to the history of the entire area.

We of Northwest Underground Explorations hope to share with you some of the thrill of discovery that we have experienced over the years. While we're always ready to "climb a mountain to crawl into a hole," we don't recommend that everyone do this. You might be satisfied by simply driving or hiking to a mine, exploring the area around it, gathering mineral specimens, and enjoying the wonderful scenery. The decision about whether to enter a mine is a very personal one that must be made by each individual at the mine entrance, or adit. Some of the mines are quite safe to explore, while others are exceedingly dangerous. You must be willing to accept the risks involved—the possibility of personal injury or worse—before you decide to "go underground."

We trust that this publication will help educate the public about the contributions that the early miners made to this state. May you enjoy the awesome splendor of Washington's mountains and wonder at "how they did it" when you encounter a piece of machinery weighing many tons on top of some remote, high ridge in the central Cascades.

Philip R. Woodhouse

Introduction

Gold! Why does the mere mention of the word create such longing in some people? What is its addictive attraction? What is it about this simple yellow metal that drives people to lust for it? Covet it? Leave their families and homes in pursuit of it?

In Ian Fleming's novel *Goldfinger,* the villain Auric Goldfinger explains his passion to James Bond. "All my life I have been in love. I have been in love with gold," he says. "I love its colour, its brilliance, its divine heaviness. I love the texture of gold and I love the warm tang it exudes when I melt it down into a true golden syrup. I love the power that gold alone gives its owner...the magic of controlling energy, exacting labor, fulfilling one's every wish and whim and, when need be, purchasing bodies, minds, even souls. . . . I ask you, is there any other substance on earth that so rewards its owner?"

Goldfinger may be a fictional character, but we suspect that a little of the passion he so eloquently speaks of exists in all individuals. Most certainly it existed in the hearts of Meriwether Lewis and William Clark, the explorers who first visited our state in 1805. It existed in the heart of Dr. William Frazier Tolmie, who is said to have been the first white man to see glaciers on Mount Rainier in 1833. This passion probably flamed in the heart of Joseph Morel, a teamster employed by the Hudson's Bay Company at Fort Colvile,[1] when he made the first discovery of gold on the Columbia River around 1845.

For these explorers, and for many who followed, gold was a dream filled with hope and promise. Some people described the pursuit of this dream as a sickness, a "gold fever" that drove them to relentlessly pursue the "big strike" from one remote location to another, enduring all manner of hardship and degradation. Always searching! Always hoping! Always knowing that their dream was just over the next hill, or in the next stream, or maybe, just maybe...on that far-off mountain on the horizon.

These were the seekers who traveled through the early history of our state. They were here when Arthur Denny, William Bell, and Carson Boren located claims on the east side of Elliott Bay and established the town of Seattle on February 15, 1852. They were here when coal was discovered by Dr. R. M. Bigelow near the present site of Renton on the Black River in 1852. They were here when Washington became a territory on March 2, 1853, and Major Isaac Stevens was appointed governor.

One of Governor Stevens's first accomplishments as governor of the Washington Territory was to send George B. McClellan[2] to explore the Cascades in search of possible mountain passes to facilitate travel from eastern to western Washington. In October 1853, McClellan met with Governor Stevens at Fort Colvile to report the results of the expedition. In addition to telling the governor about possible travel routes, McClellan also mentioned that he had found minor traces of gold in the Yakima River. Somehow this information leaked out and caused a rush of prospectors to the central part of the state. Most of these prospectors had already been at the Columbia River, having come through the Rocky Mountains to get to the gold strike made earlier by Joseph Morel near Fort Colvile. Others came up through the present state of Oregon from the goldfields of California. These prospectors then began to explore the rest of the eastern and northern portions of Washington as well.

In 1857, new gold discoveries were made in eastern Washington and southern British Columbia, causing a rush of prospectors and would-be miners to these areas. The "gold rush" to eastern Washington led to some clashes between the prospectors and the local Indians. The army was sent in to

---

[1]   Fort Colvile [sic] was established as a fur trading post by George Simpson, an agent of the Hudson's Bay Company, around 1825. It was located near Kettle Falls and was named after Andrew Colvile, an officer of the company. On June 15, 1859, General W. S. Harney, commander of the recently created military department of Oregon and Washington, established a military fort 14 miles southeast of the Hudson's Bay Company's post of Fort Colvile. He named the installation Fort Colville, apparently deriving the name from the Hudson's Bay Post but perhaps misspelling it.

[2]   The same George B. McClellan who later achieved fame as a Union general in the Civil War.

resolve the problem, and battles broke out between the Native Americans and companies of soldiers from Fort Walla Walla, which was located near the present site of the city of the same name.[3] The conflicts with the Native Americans were resolved by treaty in 1859, but unfortunately this resulted in the resettlement of most of the original native peoples[4] on various reservations during the next five years.

Over the next three decades, many gold strikes were made or reported to have been made, causing new "gold rushes" into different parts of the territory. Some of these discoveries included placer deposits at Peshastin Creek on Blewett Pass, at Swauk Creek near the present-day town of Liberty, at Ruby Creek in Whatcom County, and in the Sultan Basin in Snohomish County. The discoveries at Ruby Creek and the Sultan Basin signaled the real beginning of mining in western Washington and gave birth to many new settlements with names that are familiar today.

In 1869, a prospector's camp was established on the Skykomish River. It was named Gold Bar after a small gold strike found in a nearby river gravel bar. During the same period, Amos D. Gunn laid out a plan for the construction of a town near much of the gold and silver mining activity. He named it Index, after a nearby mountain. In this same locale, other important mining camps sprang up, such as Galena and Mineral City, both located along Silver Creek.

In the early 1870s, gold placer deposits were reported along the Sultan River, but they were not heavily worked until around 1878. Some of the first settlers were a group of Chinese prospectors who painstakingly worked to glean small amounts of gold flakes from this area. In 1880, John Nailor and his wife established a homestead at the present-day townsite of Sultan.[5] Nailor was later appointed the first postmaster.

As word of the rich deposits of gold spread in the 1880s, lumber companies from the East Coast began to take notice of the availability of timber in Washington State, where the forests were virtually untouched and seemingly endless. Many timber claims were available, and large stands of this timber were close enough to Puget Sound that logs could be transported easily to waterfront lumber mills. The milled lumber could then be exported by ship. This very economical process made these stands of timber extremely desirable to rich timber men like Frederick Weyerhaeuser and like Charles L. Colby and Colgate Hoyt, who were members of the executive committee of the Northern Pacific Railroad and business associates of the famous financier John D. Rockefeller. Colby and Hoyt had traveled to Puget Sound from the East Coast, reportedly to investigate possible land purchases. But the real purpose of their trip was to establish a tidewater port at the location where they believed that James J. Hill's Great Northern Railroad would establish its West Coast terminal.

Initially, the men decided that the most promising place for the port would be at Anacortes because the Great Northern was surveying the Skagit Valley for the Cascade Mountain crossing. Colby and Hoyt planned to buy the land very cheaply and then sell it at a huge profit when the port town was built. Their intentions were discovered, however, and the cost of land in the Anacortes area skyrocketed. This, coupled with the fact that the Great Northern changed its plans and decided to cross the Cascades via Stevens Pass, prompted Colby and Hoyt to reconsider their venture. While in Washington, they were contacted by an acquaintance, Henry Hewitt of Tacoma, a wealthy timber man and landowner. Hewitt introduced Colby and Hoyt to the Rucker brothers, who were also involved in the

---

[3]   Walla Walla was the largest city in the Washington Territory until it was surpassed in size by Seattle around 1880.

[4]   The Native Americans had no concept of "owning" the land. The land was a blessing, given by the Great Spirit for the use and stewardship of all the people who occupied it. Many of the early clashes between the Native Americans and the white settlers resulted because of this basic difference in concepts. The settlers seized the land that the Indians perceived was not theirs to take.

[5]   The town was actually named after Tseul-tud, a chief of the Snohomish Tribe.

xvi   Discovering Washington's Historic Mines

lumber industry and who owned a large tract of land at Port Gardner.[6] The Ruckers tried to convince Colby and Hoyt that their tract of land would be perfect for the port. Colby and Hoyt were not certain that a partnership or this tract of land was in their best interests, but their feelings changed after July 4, 1889. On that date, a prospector named Joseph Pearsall staked a gold claim in the nearby mountains to the east of Port Gardner. The claim was rumored to be rich—maybe very rich.[7] Colby foresaw a probable gold rush and immediately sent mining engineers and geologists to the area to determine the potential for wealth. These men reported to Colby that the site, later named Monte Cristo, looked extremely promising and that the potential for gold and silver recovery was exceptional. They also reported that although the cost of recovering the minerals would be enormous, these expenses would soon be recouped and tremendous profit would be realized. Colby and Hoyt made their decision.

Hoyt contacted his personal friend and business associate John D. Rockefeller and convinced him of the potential of investing in the Port Gardner area and also in the acquisition of claims and property at the location of the Pearsall gold strike. Colby and Hoyt formed a syndicate, with the assistance of Henry Hewitt, that was financially backed by Rockefeller. The syndicate began pouring money into the area. They planned to purchase mining claims and build a concentrator at what was now called Monte Cristo, build a smelter at Everett, and build a railroad from Monte Cristo to the smelter. The syndicate bought into the Monte Cristo Mines in late 1891 and by September 1893 had completed the concentrator, the smelter, and the railroad from Everett to Monte Cristo.

The influx of capital and Rockefeller's participation in the enterprise generated much interest— after all, Rockefeller's reputation was that he never made mistakes. If Rockefeller was investing millions, this had to be a sure thing! This thinking lured speculators from every part of the country.

At the same time, many more claims were being filed in the Sultan Basin and other locales. Rumors abounded of plentiful gold, silver, iron, and copper deposits. More than 200 claims were filed in the Monte Cristo area alone. Fortune hunters continued to pour into the territory. Bustling mining camps sprang up everywhere, and prospectors and miners rushed from site to new site like honey bees flitting from flower to flower. Gold fever was rampant. Tales of rich finds multiplied, causing greed not only in the hearts of the would-be miners but also in the hearts of the already rich and their corporations.

These rumors of riches attracted other gold rush opportunists in addition to prospectors and legitimate investors. There were gamblers, prostitutes, and thieves. There were swindlers who easily duped inexperienced prospectors and investors who were blinded by greed and the dream of "getting rich quick."

The dream was alive and well for the next few years. Then a subtle change began to take place. The first discoveries of gold on the west side of the Cascades were placer deposits found in the streams and rivers. This type of gold deposit was fairly easy to recover, usually requiring only a sluice box and a gold pan. These placer discoveries were soon worked out and depleted, and the prospectors who had searched for the placer gold became disheartened and disillusioned. Some packed their gear and went home, some went north to British Columbia, and some went to find work in the Monte Cristo area. The gold discoveries at Monte Cristo and a number of other areas were lode discoveries that required intense preparation, much manpower, and great expense for recovery.

A great number of settlers had moved into western Washington by this time, and these migrants sought work laboring on the seas, in the fields, in the forests, and also in the mines. This provided a constant source of labor, but most of these people were unskilled and not used to toiling underground in the mines. Skilled workers were few in number and for the most part could not be counted on as long-term employees because of the severe winter weather and the primitive living conditions at the mines.

---

[6]   Port Gardner was later renamed Everett.

[7]   This claim was the initial discovery of gold at Monte Cristo.

This surreal-looking photograph of the Kromona Mine in the Sultan Basin shows how severe the winters were in the mining districts. In the foreground, note how the snow is tearing the side wall away from the building as it creeps down the mountainside. (Sky Valley Historical Society Collection)

The men who did stay lived and worked in the worst of circumstances. The mine entrances were usually located at very high elevations, which meant they had to make steep, sometimes dangerous climbs. There were living quarters at some of the mine entrances, but these were usually poorly constructed and equipped with only the barest of necessities, and the miners sleeping inside had to withstand bone-chilling temperatures. The miners were even required to provide their own blankets for sleeping on the bare floors of these so-called "bunkhouses." Cooks were provided, but they were often unskilled and had limited supplies to work with.

The conditions in the mines themselves were not much better. The men were forced to contend with flooding and poor safety conditions. They had to work at their own risk, at low wages, and without health or disability insurance. For these men, the dream of the "big strike" certainly faded quickly.

These poor conditions resulted in much dissatisfaction among the workers, but their complaints went unheeded by the the mine overseers and owners. The attitude of the mining companies appeared to be: Don't worry about how the workers are fed, housed, or cared for, as long as the ore is being ripped out of the mountain and processed as quickly as possible; there will always be other workers standing by to replace those who are lost along the way.

Labor problems were not the only troubles brewing in the mines and at the encampments. Severe winters brought heavy snows that shut down mining operations. This forced the companies to discharge large numbers of workers, and later a new group of workers would have to be hired and trained.

Spring brought moderate temperatures, causing some of the heavier snow accumulations to break loose and start avalanches. These avalanches often destroyed the buildings and equipment at the mine entrances. Sometimes certain levels of the mine would become flooded, making passage through the tunnels impossible until the water was pumped out. Rock slides in the summer months could be just as devastating as the winter and spring avalanches. All of these factors contributed to the constantly rising expenses just to operate the mines.

How the Cascades Were Formed The Cascade Mountains were formed in a variety of ways, primarily by the collision of continents or pieces of continents that drifted together while riding on the plastic mantle below the earth's crust. Such collisions are very gradual, occurring over millions of years, and can have several different results. One of the masses might ride above the other, subducting the second land mass beneath it and sending it into the depths of the mantle to be remelted and recycled. The masses, if they strike a grazing blow, might grind against each other in a slip fault, in which one mass grinds horizontally against the other, for millions of years. Or, as in the case of the Cascade Mountains, the masses might both remain afloat and squeeze into one another with enormous force. This action causes each to bulge both upward and downward. The upward bulging causes the land mass to rise farther and farther above mean sea level. When the uplifting becomes severe enough, the rock will begin to crack, and weathering will start to take its toll on the rising land mass. Water percolating down through the cracks begins a relentless disintegration of the land.

As the land is thrust higher and higher, it rises to elevations where the weather is more severe and the winters are longer than in the lowlands. This accelerates the weathering of the rocks; valleys, some populated by glaciers, begin to form. Ultimately, the mountains rise so high that they interfere with the prevailing weather patterns and create their own climate.

In the case of the Cascade Mountains, another factor is also at work. The floor of the Pacific Ocean is subducting beneath the continent just off the Washington coast. As it grinds its way down into the subabyssal depths and remelts, it is charged with superheated water and becomes lighter than the surrounding rock. This causes some of it to rise and establish conduits as it extrudes upward onto the already tortured, uplifted landscape. These rising magmas form the volcanos that punctuate the Cascade Range from Canada to California, including Mount Rainier, Glacier Peak, Mount Baker, Mount Adams, and, of course, Mount St. Helens.

The eruption of Mount St. Helens in 1980 attests to the fact that this is an ongoing process. The frequent earthquakes in Washington State also bear testimony to the forces at work beneath our feet. The mountains continue to rise and the weather continues its attempt to level them out. The two opposing forces created the environment in which minerals have been deposited that have enticed, and continue to entice, so many people.

In 1892, 1893, and 1896, floods washed out small sections of the Everett and Monte Cristo Railroad[8] which had to be rebuilt each time at great expense. In the fall of 1897, rapidly melting accumulations of heavy snow again swelled the rivers until they overran their banks. This time, however, so many sections of track washed out along the Everett and Monte Cristo Railroad that the shipment of ore from the Monte Cristo Mines was shut down until 1900, when Rockefeller invested more money to rebuild the rail line. This venture was getting expensive, even for Rockefeller.

---

[8] There is some confusion as to whether it was "Railroad" or "Railway." *Poor's Railroad Manual,* published in 1893, listed the line as the Everett and Monte Cristo Railroad. On this authority, this book uses "Railroad," even though many of the advertisements and schedules of the line used "Railway." Following the reorganization of the line in 1900, *Poor's Railroad Manual* listed the line as the Monte Cristo Railway.

The rebuilding of the damaged railroad and the resumption of ore shipments from Monte Cristo generated new optimism. In 1902, engineers reported that there were still huge deposits of ore located in the Monte Cristo mining area. This news resulted in a new gold rush of sorts, which brought another influx of prospectors, miners, and the usual riff-raff associated with the mining camps. Again, rumors of wealth ran rampant.

But something was not right. In 1903, the Rockefeller syndicate began to sell off its mine holdings. Rockefeller was actually able to profit financially from this venture because he reinvested the proceeds from mining properties into more profitable forest lands, with their bountiful timber resources.

Mines began to change hands, and the new owners found that the lode ore near the surface, which had been so readily available in the early days, was now depleted. Tunnels had to be driven to much greater depths to recover the ore. This was expensive. The deeper the miners dug the tunnels, the less ore they found and the more problems they encountered. Contrary to all of the geologist's and mining engineer's reports, the ore deposits were not consistent. They had been shifted in various directions by natural earth movement, or faulting, and the miners encountered many dead ends where the faults caused the ore veins to disappear. When they reached one of these dead ends, they would have to stop tunneling at that spot and then dig a new tunnel until they again located the ore body. More expense!

In addition, the ore recovered from these greater depths was generally of low grade and very complex. It contained a combination of many different minerals, which meant that more complicated and expensive methods of extraction were required. Costs were rising, but returns were diminishing.

In June 1906, a mining engineer named James D. Sword issued a report on the Monte Cristo mining area to the Anaconda Copper Mining Company. This report concluded that, because of the declining ore values and frequent interruptions, the area would probably fail to ever yield a net profit.

In January 1907, Mother Nature again played her hand and began to seal the fate of the struggling Monte Cristo mining district. It rained. And then it rained some more. Rock slides again blocked the tracks at tunnel #2 on the Everett and Monte Cristo Railroad, cutting off all rail shipments and transportation. While workers attempted to clear the rock slide, the wood framing in tunnel #1, the longest tunnel on the line, somehow caught fire, and the tunnel collapsed. This was the mortal blow. The railroad was not rebuilt until much later, and most of the mining operations at Monte Cristo shut down for good.

While the Monte Cristo operations represent the largest mining effort ever mounted in western Washington, there were many smaller and often more nefarious efforts throughout the area. Many of the "mining" promoters were little more than con men out to separate the unwary from their money. They would boost the image of a mining property by promising large amounts of ore within easy reach. They would promise that if only a little more money were poured into the efforts the returns would be enormous. After raising enough money, these shysters would vanish with their ill-gotten gains. Another situation that occurred either wittingly or unwittingly was the gathering of ore samples from a thin stringer vein that assayed very high in valuable metals. However, the promoters never mentioned that tons and tons of barren rock would have to be mined along with the thin stringer material to obtain these high values. This, of course, vastly reduced the total value of the final ore produced. Often, the rich stringer would disappear after only a few feet of tunneling. Hundreds of short prospect tunnels in the Cascade Mountains attest to this. Many of the people who prospered from the mining efforts were the merchants, the shysters, the promoters, and the purveyors of mining equipment who came to "mine the miners." These people preyed on the mining towns that sprang up to serve the mines. Their prices were often greatly inflated and caused the miners to quickly spend their earnings. Such were the circumstances that often gave mining and miners a bad name.

Over the next few years, some minor attempts at reopening mining in the area were fruitless—no bodies of ore were found that could be recovered profitably.

By 1917, all available men and materials had been enlisted for the war effort in World War I. Whatever equipment was left at Monte Cristo was scavenged, and the town was abandoned.

After the war, few mining operations were left anywhere in western Washington, primarily because it was no longer profitable. However, during the Great Depression of the 1930s, many unemployed men attempted to earn a meager living by using the methods of the early prospectors—sluicing and panning the gravel in the streams and rivers throughout Washington.

Today, many people make a weekend hobby out of following a strange urge to take a shallow pan, fill it with stream gravel, swirl it around, and look for golden colors flashing back in the sunlight. GOLD FEVER!!!

The Law and You

As you enter the different mining areas, you might wander onto federal land managed by the U.S. Bureau of Land Management (BLM) or the U.S. Forest Service (USFS), land owned by the State of Washington, or privately owned land.

The Mining Law of 1872 grants U.S. citizens the right to explore for, discover, and claim valuable mineral deposits on federal lands. It also grants the BLM authority to administer the law. Certain federal lands are not available for claiming, such as national parks, national monuments, designated wilderness areas, and administrative areas, such as campgrounds.

Under the law, a citizen can obtain either a patented claim or an unpatented claim. A patented claim is one for which the federal government grants a deed or passes "actual title" to an individual, as long as that individual claims the land within parameters set by the law. The land is then treated like any other private land and is subject to local property taxes and laws. An unpatented claim is one in which an individual, after locating valuable mineral deposits as defined in the law, is granted the right to extract and remove the minerals from the land. The individual receives only the right to remove locatable minerals, *not* full title to the land. The land remains under the legal jurisdiction of the federal government.

Washington State sometimes leases rights to extract minerals from its land to individuals who meet certain criteria. The proceeds of these leases go to various state trusts, such as the State School Trust. The land is not available for patented claims. Mining leases on Washington State–owned lands are regulated by the Washington State Department of Natural Resources (DNR) according to the Mining Law of 1872 and state laws and restrictions. You can find these laws and restrictions in the Washington Administrative Code (WAC 332-16) and the Revised Code of Washington (RCW 79.01). Additional information can usually be obtained from the DNR, state geologists, and geological surveys.

So how do all of these laws affect you? You are probably going hiking, not looking for a site to stake a claim! However, you might be interested in collecting a few mineral specimens or maybe even doing some prospecting with a gold pan along the way. Can you collect or not?

On federal lands, you might come across a patented or unpatented claim. The law requires the owner of the claim to properly mark its boundaries with visible monuments and to post a Notice of Location at the "discovery" site. You might also find signs indicating a "mining claim" and an "ORMC number"—a serial number assigned to the claim by the BLM when the claim is recorded. If you happen upon one of these monuments or claim signs, this probably indicates that the claim is active. DO NOT, under penalty of law, remove any mineral specimens or prospect at these sites because someone owns the rights to—and probably jealously guards—the minerals. If you want to obtain permission from the claim owner to do some collecting or prospecting, you can write down the ORMC number and contact the county auditor's office in the county where the claim is located, or contact the Oregon/Washington State office of the BLM in Portland. (They won't provide specific information over the phone, so you'll probably have to write to them or visit their office.) It might also be helpful to know the meridian, township, range, and section numbers of the claim location. You can obtain this information by looking at a geological survey map of the area. Both the county auditor and the BLM offices maintain records of mining claims, and these records are available for public inspection. In these documents, you might find the name and address of the current owner.

If the spot where you want to collect or prospect is not under claim or in a restricted area such as a national park, the Forest Service doesn't object to your picking up a specimen or two, as long as you are sensitive to any impact the activity might have on the environment. Mineral and fossil collectors are usually allowed to remove small quantities of materials as long as the specimens are for private collections or will be used for educational purposes. You are allowed to remove these specimens only from the surface of the ground or by "panning" the present-day stream gravels. You are not allowed to pan for gold in any stream in an area administered by the National Park Service. You are also not allowed to remove any vegetation, operate any power equipment for the purpose of excavation, or bring any mining equipment into a national park.

> **Note** Some areas might be closed by the Forest Service to any prospecting or mineral collection. There are many reasons for this, not the least of which is environmental impact, so "be safe rather than sorry." If you are unsure about the status of a particular area, contact the nearest Forest Service or BLM office and inform them of your intentions. They will be more than happy to advise you.

> **Artifacts** One of the many reasons to seek out old, abandoned mines is to view the artifacts that sometimes litter these sites. Many people are driven to pick up these trinkets as souvenirs and take them home. Others seem equally driven to destroy such artifacts, either by shooting at them, rolling them down the mountainside, or otherwise despoiling them. Remember, if everyone who visited a site before you had treated the remnants in this way, there would be nothing there for *you* to see. By the same logic, if you remove items from the site, visitors who follow you, possibly even your children or grandchildren, will have nothing to see. In addition, it is against the law to remove anything from federal land (an unpatented mine site) or from private land (a patented mine site).
>
> These artifacts tell a story all their own. By examining them, a person can date a site, understand how it was mined, or simply contemplate how these massive pieces of cast iron were conveyed to such a remote location. If artifacts are removed and taken to someone's home, they eventually become just another pile of junk to be discarded with the trash.
>
> The same holds true for natural artifacts inside many of the mines. These include the speleothems, stalactites, and stalagmites—the curtains and columns of mineral deposits that the descending waters have carried, drop by drop, into the man-made cavity. These are very fragile and can be destroyed by the slightest touch. Keep your hands off them, and they will be there to delight others for decades to come. Even if you were to remove them and take them home, most would dry out and crumble to dust in a few days.

Rockhounding is reportedly allowed on Washington State land as long as you do not disturb the "surface" of the land and the area is not currently under mineral lease. Gold panning is not allowed unless you have a placer mining contract for the parcel of land you want to prospect. These contracts are negotiated with the Washington State DNR. The state has been trying to institute a recreational rockhounding permit system, but at the time of this writing it has not been put into effect. If you have any questions regarding rock collecting or gold panning, you should contact the Geology and Earth Resources Division of the DNR in Olympia at (360) 902-1450. The DNR can also provide you with free printed materials about rockhounding and prospecting that are quite informative.

Washington State lands might not always be marked by boundary signs or otherwise identified. To learn if a particular parcel of land is state-owned, you will need to get a geological survey description, including the meridian, township, range, and section number(s). You then have to contact the Land Records Office located in the basement of the DNR Building in Olympia. If you provide them with the accurate location, they can tell you whether the land is state-owned and if there are any existing mineral leases.

One last word of caution: The Washington State Department of Fish and Wildlife (DFW) is responsible for protecting the state's fish and wildlife and is concerned about recreational activity that might impact these resources or their habitat. The DFW has prepared a pamphlet called *Gold and Fish* that can be obtained from any of its offices. The booklet was designed to protect our streams and rivers from disturbance, especially during sensitive periods when certain fish species are in their spawning cycles. It tells you which streams and rivers are open to prospecting, when they are open, and what equipment you can use. You must have a copy of this booklet ON YOUR PERSON if you are panning for gold in any Washington stream or river.

Finally, please respect the rights of private landowners! ALWAYS seek prior permission, ideally written permission, before entering private land, and NEVER remove anything from private land without obtaining the express consent of the owner.

Good luck, and enjoy your outing!

Preparing for a Mine Trip

Although we do not recommend that you enter the mines listed in this book, we know that some of you will feel the urge to do so anyway. This section will help you prepare to "go underground" as safely as you can. Remember that there are as many different safety concerns as there are mines. The conditions differ from mine to mine, and a lot of common sense is required to understand how to deal with them. Some mines are in hard rock and present relatively little danger during exploration. Some are in decaying, crumbly, mineralized rock, and can be very, very hazardous. Some mines are partially caved at the entrance, and sliding down the backside of the collapsed material into the tunnel can land you in water as deep as your armpits. Some mines contain winzes—shafts that are bored straight down from the horizontal tunnel. Stepping into one of these could be your last step—ever. Winzes are particularly hard to locate when they are under water through which you are wading. Some tunnels are low, and you must squat to get through them; others are spacious.

Exploring stopes—cavities where the ore has been removed—can present a whole other set of dangers and problems. Stopes are very irregular in shape and follow whatever angle the ore lay at in the vein. They can be enormously wide or tortuously narrow and can lie at shallow or very steep angles. The air in either tunnels or stopes might be low in oxygen or contain noxious gases. The human body is used to breathing air with 20.8 percent oxygen. Air containing 16 percent oxygen can cause a person to become disoriented, and air containing 14 percent oxygen can cause unconsciousness due to oxygen deprivation. If any of this scares you, it should: Entering mines is a risky business.

But if you've decided to go in anyway, how do you prepare for the experience? First, forget any notion that you might have gotten from movies or TV about what a mine is like. There is no light in a mine. It is a totally dark, stygian black hole in the ground. Without light, you are not going in, and if you lose your light inside, chances are you're not coming out! The rule of thumb for exploring underground is that each person should carry three independent sources of light at all times. Make certain that batteries are fresh and/or carry a spare set. A spare bulb is not a bad idea either. This can often be carried inside the lamp behind the reflector, depending on the make and model of lamp. A headlamp is best, because it leaves your hands free and the light is always pointing where you are looking. Hand-held lights do well also, but they limit your ability to examine and explore. Candles can serve as an emergency light to get you out in a pinch. (Remember to bring dry matches or a reliable lighter.)

Second, never enter any mine alone. Furthermore, stay together while underground. Make sure that each person is properly prepared and equipped for the journey.

You should also consider personal protection. First in this category is a hard hat. It won't protect you if the mountain caves in on you, but it will protect you from small rocks that tumble down from high places such as shafts or stopes. It will also serve you well if you accidently raise your head when there is a very solid chunk of mountain in the way. The hat should fit snugly but not too tightly. It should not fall off if you tilt your head from side to side or forward and backward. Mounting the headlamp on the hard hat is the best strategy for underground travel, because you have your light where you need it and you are protected as well.

Footwear is the next concern. Many of the mines contain water at varying depths. A pair of 10-inch or 12-inch rubber pacs or dairy boots will usually serve, but some mines might demand hip or chest waders for entry. If you enter mines requiring these last items, remember the winzes discussed above! Often you must visit a mine more than once to fully explore it. The first trip allows you to assess the situation and determine what you will need, and the actual entry and exploration will occur on subsequent trips. If you plan to do technical climbing in a mine, the rubber boots might not suffice, and climbing boots might be the best solution.

Mines are usually cool, remaining at about 45 to 50 degrees Fahrenheit all year long. Some mines that have air flowing through them can get very cold in the winter and can form ice that will complicate exploration. In any case, bring warm clothing for your underground excursion, be it in summer or winter. Thick gloves can be helpful as you make your way through sticker-infested brush while hiking to the mines and while exploring the mines.

If there are several people in your group, walkie-talkies with at least a 1-mile range can add to the safety and enjoyment of the trip. Keep in mind that walkie-talkies will NOT allow you communicate with the outside world, only among yourselves—and under some conditions, not even that. This brings us to the issue of carrying a cellular phone to call for help in an emergency: Forget it—leave the cell phone at home. Cellular phones work only when they are in an area, or "cell," that is covered by a computer-controlled transmitter/receiver with its attendant antennas. Two recent rescues involving cell phones in the Cascade Mountains were a fluke, because the accidents occurred near the Snoqualmie Pass area, where there is an active cell. In virtually all of the mine areas mentioned in this book, the phones are useless. Carrying such a device will only give you a false sense of security and possibly embolden you to overextend your activities beyond your capabilities. Don't do anything that you will not be able to walk away from.

Whenever you leave for a mine-exploring trip, let someone know where you are going and when you plan to return. Bring along the same "10 essentials"[9] that you would take on any hiking or climbing trip. If something unforeseen happens to you or your party, you might be out in the wilds longer than you expected.

The mines mentioned in this book are "hard rock"[10] mines that were dug in an attempt to locate metallic minerals. Washington State is also peppered with coal mines. Do not enter coal mines under any circumstances! They might contain methane (an explosive gas), carbon monoxide (a complex asphyxiant—very toxic and deadly), or carbon dioxide (a simple asphyxiant). Be certain of the type of mine that you are entering. Report all open coal mines to the local law enforcement agency or fire department, or to the Bureau of Surface Mining in Denver, Colorado.

---

[9]   According to The Mountaineers, the 10 essentials are: extra clothing, extra food, sunglasses, knife, fire starter, first aid kit, matches, flashlight, map, and compass. Northwest Underground Explorations has found that replacing the compass with an altimeter works better for mine exploration.

[10] The term "hard rock" does not mean that a mine is necessarily safe. Some "hard rock" mines are bored into very unstable, crumbly material. Be cautious at all times.

Hike Ratings

Because our readers will have varying abilities and experience when it comes to hiking and mine exploration, we have rated the hikes according to a simple system—from A through E for distance and 1 through 5 for difficulty. Note that this should not be confused with the mountaineering scale, which is similar. If you are familiar with the mountaineering scale, do not attempt to compare it to the ratings used in this book.

RATING	DISTANCE
A	Less than ¼ mile from your vehicle
B	Between ¼ and 1 mile from your vehicle
C	Between 1 and 2 miles from your vehicle
D	Between 2 and 4 miles from your vehicle
E	More than 4 miles from your vehicle

RATING	DIFFICULTY
1	A very easy walk from your vehicle. Little uphill hiking is involved.
2	A slightly more difficult walk. You might encounter muddy or rocky trails, with elevation gains of up to 500 feet.
3	This level might require you to do some rock scrambling, with total elevation gains of up to 1,000 feet. You might do some off-trail scrambling that requires elementary route-finding skills.
4	This level might involve precipitous rock scrambling, hiking on steep rock slopes, and off-trail hiking. Good route-finding skills are required. Serious missteps on trips with this rating could be life-threatening. Elevation gains might be as much as 2,000 feet.
5	The most difficult rating. You will often be required to climb steep slopes of loose rock and talus. Heavy brush might impede your way as you hike off-trail. Good route-finding skills are mandatory. Elevation gains between 2,000 and 4,000 feet will be required. Life-threatening possibilities abound...so be prepared!

These ratings are only a guide. If a hike appears to be too much for you before you reach your goal, it is always safer to turn back and save yourself for another day. Also consider when the sun will set. Turn back in time to reach your vehicle while ample daylight remains. Remember, it is far darker in the forest, and darkness comes earlier there than in open country.

Locations of Mining Districts

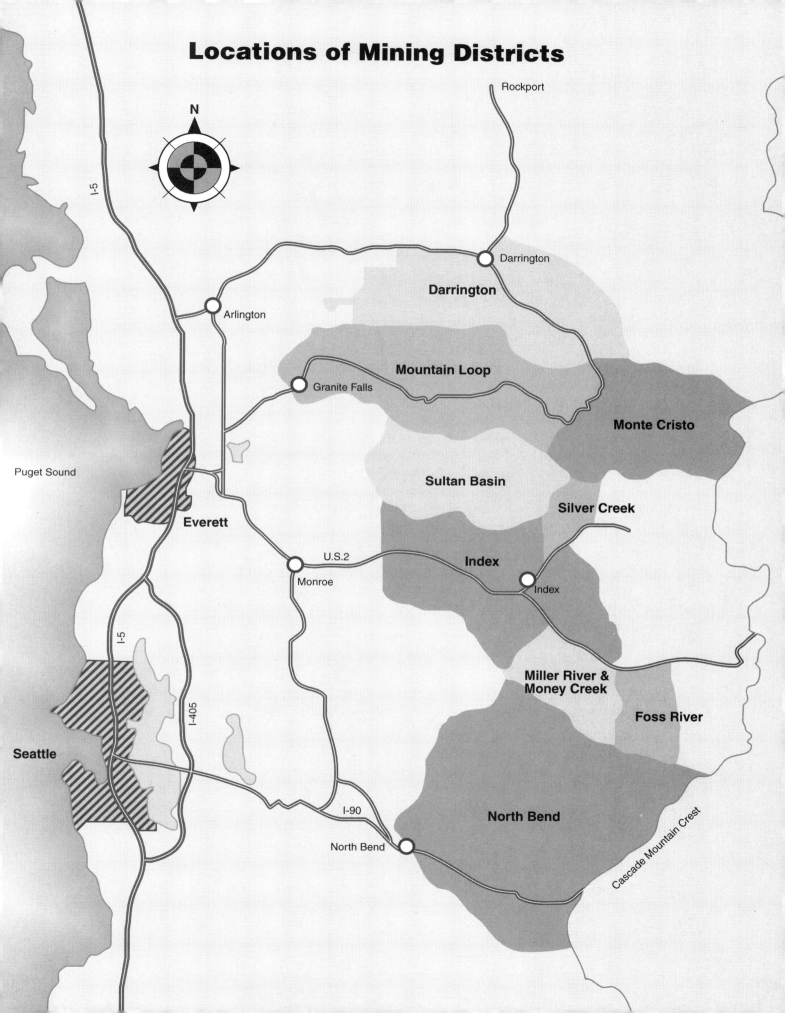

Rockport

N

I-5

Darrington

Darrington

Arlington

Mountain Loop

Granite Falls

Monte Cristo

Puget Sound

Sultan Basin

Silver Creek

Everett

U.S.2

Index

Monroe

Index

Miller River &
Money Creek

I-5

Foss River

I-405

Seattle

I-90

North Bend

North Bend

Cascade Mountain Crest

Darrington

The community of Darrington lies in the foothills of the North Cascades, 549 feet above sea level and approximately 80 miles from Seattle along Route 530. It is nestled in the lush Sauk and Stillaguamish river valleys and is surrounded on three sides by rugged mountain peaks. The most impressive of these landmarks is Whitehorse Mountain, which majestically climbs 6,852 feet into a seemingly endless, deep blue Washington sky. Other impressive peaks in the area are Whitechuck Mountain, Mount Pugh, Three Fingers Mountain, and Jumbo Mountain. The town of Darrington itself is situated on the flat ground between the Sauk River and the headwaters of the North Fork of the Stillaguamish River.

The Sauk River originates in the Monte Cristo Massif to the south of Darrington and flows northward until its confluence with the Skagit River at the town of Rockport (formerly Sauk City).[11]

History

The area was originally inhabited by the Sauk-Suiattle Indians and remained unexplored by white people until 1870, when the site was reportedly visited by a party of Northern Pacific Railroad surveyors.[12] These surveyors, with their Native American guides, were searching for a mountain pass to establish a direct railroad route to Lake Chelan. The area remained virtually unchanged until 1889, when gold was discovered at Monte Cristo, some 30 miles southeast of the present town of Darrington. The gold strike at Monte Cristo resulted in a rush of prospectors and miners into the surrounding areas. Some of these people also explored the Sauk River in their search for a shorter, more direct route to Puget Sound. A primitive wagon road was constructed along the banks of the Sauk River from Sauk City on the Skagit River to Monte Cristo. The road was soon well-traveled and later became known as the Sauk River–Monte Cristo Pioneer Trail. The future town site of Darrington was located on this trail and was originally used as an overnight camping spot by these early travelers.

Around 1890, prospectors discovered gold on a hill across the Sauk River from the Darrington campsite. This area was later named Gold Mountain. Many claims were filed by these hardy folk, who became the original settlers of Darrington.

The town of Darrington served as a jumping-off point for many of the people heading into the Cascade Mountains for mining and other endeavors. This scene depicts a pack train being formed for such a trek. Notice the three young children packed aboard the white horse, second from the right.

---

[11] From the town of Sauk City, a puncheon road was constructed into the mining camp of Monte Cristo in the early 1890s. Flat-bottomed river steamboats transported supplies and people up the Skagit River to Sauk City, the farthest point up-river that they could travel. The supplies were off-loaded there and transferred to tote wagons for the trip up the Sauk River to the mining camps.

[12] While surveying one valley up toward the Cascade Crest, these surveyors reportedly found the brush so dense that they cut down trees in their path to make their way through.

Over the next few years, copper, gold, silver, and lead were discovered on Jumbo Mountain and Whitehorse Mountain, fueling rumors and dreams of great wealth. Mines such as the Keywinder Group, the Hunter Group, the Coffin, the Mallet, the Bluebird, and the Bornite were worked in search of riches.

The town of Darrington was in a constant state of change during these early years. Mines would play out and people would leave for richer prospects elsewhere. On other occasions, new strikes would be reported and would bring a fresh influx of miners. The area also attracted promoters bearing promises of wealth and rumors of "big business" that would transform Darrington into a boom town of wondrous proportions. These promises never really materialized, and over the years the mining activity in the area slowed to almost nothing.

In the late 1890s, when the mining industry was still in full swing, the miners and developers decided that they needed a better way to transport their ore and bring in supplies other than by wagon over rough, slow roads. They sent a delegation to the Seattle and International Railway Company (later purchased by and known as the Northern Pacific Railroad) and tried to convince the company of the need for a railroad spur. The railroad listened and, greedily anticipating much wealth from doing so, struck a deal to extend its rail line from the town of Arlington up the Stillaguamish River to Darrington. Construction began in the summer of 1900, and the railroad finally reached Darrington on June 5, 1901.

By bringing in the railroad, the townspeople unwittingly ensured the town's salvation. During this period, people began to realize that the real wealth was to be had by harvesting the vast timber reserves of the nearby forests. The arrival of the railroad allowed the first heavy sawmill equipment to be brought in, and a mill was soon established.

From these early beginnings, a successful logging industry developed that overshadowed and outlasted the gold rush. Darrington might not be as boisterous now as it was during its mining and logging heydays, but it is still filled with pioneer spirit.

What to See

The area around Darrington is easily accessible by car because it lies astride State Route 530, 19 miles south of the town of Rockport and 28 miles east of the town of Arlington. Darrington is also at one end of the Mountain Loop Highway that runs over Barlow Pass and connects with the town of Granite Falls to the southwest. For the casual tourist, a drive through this area affords some picture-postcard moments, especially on a clear summer day. For more adventurous souls, there are opportunities to hike, climb, and explore the spectacular mountainous terrain.

Getting There

You can reach Darrington by driving east from the town of Arlington. Arlington lies on State Route 9 just 4 miles from Interstate 5. Consult a Washington State highway map to select the best approach to this area. Once at Darrington, you have the choice of several routes into the surrounding countryside. These will be discussed in the sections that follow.

Geology

Pick your favorite geologic time frame or your favorite rock type, and this area is likely to contain examples of it somewhere. Whitehorse Mountain is composed mostly of pre-Tertiary volcanic rock containing some interbedded limestone and other sedimentaries. Gold Mountain, located to the east across the Sauk River, is composed of low-grade pre–Upper Jurassic metamorphic rocks consisting of breccia, greenschists, and other similar materials. Just east of Gold Mountain, above Dan Creek, is a mass of basic rocks (as opposed to acidic rocks), characterized by their dark color and represented by gabbro and serpentine, as well as both volcanic and sedimentary Carboniferous/Permian rocks. These meet the surrounding rock at a thrust fault that exhibits an oval shape.

A pack train is ready to head for the mountains. This photograph was taken in front of the Darrington Store and Post Office.

For the Rockhound

Travertine (honey onyx) and chatoyant feldspar have reportedly been found in the vicinity of Darrington and on Gold Mountain. Asbestos can also be found in Asbestos Gulch on the side of Jumbo Mountain. Other rocks in the area are Tertiary granitics, pre–Middle Jurassic sedimentary and volcanics, and an intrusion of Tertiary dunite forming a north-south band about $1/2$ to $1/3$ mile wide in Paleocene/Cretaceous nonmarine rocks lying just east of Three Fingers Mountain. Since many of the ore deposits in the western Cascades are located on the boundary, or contact zones, between differing rock types, it is easy to surmise that this area was conducive to the formation of such lodes. The valley floors are generally covered with stratified glacial outwash gravels and silts that might or might not reflect the local rocks, because many could have been transported into this area.

The Mines

Bornite Mine

Rated at C-3. This is one of the best-known mines that still exists in the Darrington area. It was originally owned by the Bornite Gold and Copper Mining Company of Bangor, Maine. The mine is located on Liberty Mountain about 12 miles south-southwest of Darrington up Clear Canyon and Copper Creek Canyon on the approach to Windy Pass.

Mining operations began in earnest on this copper claim around 1903. Over the next several years, the owners, gambling on suspected rich copper reserves, reportedly invested $300,000 in search of the main ore body. The operation was a marvel of engineering and included a wooden surface tramway running from Darrington to within a half mile of the mine. From this point, an aerial tramway spanned the remaining half mile of deep canyon to the mine adit.

The mine boasted the latest equipment, including air drills, and a crew of more than 100 miners worked in continuous shifts. By 1908, the tunnel penetrated more than 3,000 feet into Liberty Mountain.

The Bornite mine in its heyday. Started in 1903, it used a 13-mile combination aerial and surface tramway to bring in the ore. The building in the photo was believed to be located across and above the road from the present-day Clear Creek Campground. A town, also called Bornite, sprang up around the mine while it was in operation. By 1910 the eastern investors had withdrawn their money and the Bornite was abandoned. (Darrington Historical Society)

All of this expenditure and exploration ultimately proved fruitless, however, since no commercially valuable copper deposits were discovered. Active mining ceased around 1910, and the claim was abandoned a few years later. In 1970, the mine was claimed by a new owner, the Bornite Exploration Company, but nothing came of this venture, and mining was again discontinued. The tunnel, as it exists today, bores through about 3,200 feet of dark, mineralless rock. About 100 feet from the end, it passes through a contact zone, beyond which the rock is banded and much lighter in color. The final 100 feet of the mine contain traces of green malachite, indicating the presence of copper-based ores. As you approach the mine area on the access road, you can see a high basin on the side of Liberty Mountain with streaks of gossan along its rear walls. From the location and heading of the tunnel, it appears that the miners were attempting to access the lode represented by these gossan stains. Remnants of the actual workings and old equipment serve as a reminder of the hard work and broken dreams of days long past.

A typical mountain scene in the 1890s in the hills of the Darrington district. Many people of that era played musical instruments, like the man and woman shown here. Many cabins similar to this one were built in the dark recesses of the Cascade Mountains to house those who came to seek their fortunes. (Snohomish County Historical Society)

To reach the mine, drive to the stop sign in Darrington as you approach from the west along State Route 530. Turn right onto the new section of the Mountain Loop Highway. Head south away from town for about 3 miles to the Frog Lake Forest Road #2060, and then turn right from pavement onto gravel.

> **Caution** This road becomes more rugged and difficult the farther you travel. We recommend that you use a high-clearance vehicle to avoid getting stranded. This road can easily damage the underside of a lower-clearance vehicle, and it can damage any car's paint job.

Stay to the right when the road divides immediately after leaving the highway. You'll cross Asbestos Creek after about 2 miles, and after about 5 miles the road splits, with #2060 continuing straight up the valley and another, unnumbered road veering to the right. Take the right-hand fork, which will take you out of Clear Creek Valley and into the Copper Creek Valley.[13] Continue along this track as far as you can. This is the bed of the old surface tram that the Bornite Mining Company built between Darrington and the Bornite Mine. When you can drive no farther, park and begin hiking along the same grade. After 1 to 3 miles, depending on how far you were able to drive, you will come upon the lower camp of the old Bornite Mine. It will be easily identifiable by the presence of three cabin sites, massive concrete foundations and cable anchors that once supported the aerial tramway cables, and the winding machinery to move the cars along them. The cast iron remains of several heavy air drills lie in the brush along the trail, and other types of debris are scattered everywhere.

At this point, you are very close to Copper Creek, and through the trees you might have glimpsed the grand waterfall just up the valley. After leaving the lower site, you will climb to this waterfall!

> **Warning** The rock on the waterfall offers a good grip, but it is very steep. A good pair of hiking or climbing boots is a must. If you do not feel comfortable climbing this type of terrain, end your journey here and save yourself for another day. (You can circumvent the waterfall somewhat by climbing to the right or left side of it through dense brush.[14])

This is open country once you leave the lower camp, and routefinding is very easy. It is always a good idea, however, to stop periodically while heading up and look behind you to see how the area will appear when you return. You will gain a lot of elevation quickly, and once you reach the top, you will see that you are headed toward a pass at the head of Copper Creek. You are looking up into Windy Pass. Continue toward the pass, and look for the tailing pile of the Bornite Mine on the left side of the valley, not far below the headwaters of the creek.

With the view becoming grand about you, continue to climb toward the mine dump, either directly through the brush (before sighting the mine tailings) or up the creek until you are directly below the tailing pile. Ascend the dump, being careful of its loose condition, and observe the many artifacts along the way. When you reach the top, you will come face to face with the adit. You are standing 3,200 feet from the far end. This tunnel is bored in very firm rock and presents little danger of collapse; however, the choice to enter is yours and yours alone.

---

[13] At this point, stop and look up at the mountain ahead of you that separates Clear Creek to your left from Copper Creek to your right. This is Liberty Mountain. You will see a basin high on the mountainside with streaks of rust-colored gossan staining its cliffs. We have theorized that the Bornite Mine was being dug to strike this ore lode at depth below this basin.

[14] A pair of gloves and long pants are suggested, especially if you plan to ascend through the brush.

Warning The tunnel forks near the end. The left fork was in the process of being blasted when mining was discontinued. The final charge of dynamite is still in the blasting holes—UNFIRED. Do not, under any circumstances, touch or in any way disturb this material. Old explosives become touchy; if you set off the dynamite, you will be blown to bits!

Just inside the entrance of the mine are many artifacts, such as broken drill bits and various broken pieces of cast-iron machinery that remain from the early attempts to operate this mine. Just outside the adit, you will find more modern debris characteristic of the most recent mining attempt here.

Head down the way you came or pick a different route to search for additional artifacts on the mine's dump. In any case, your goal is to return to Copper Creek and descend the waterfall. It will look much steeper going down than it did coming up. You can also try the brushy sides of the stream to avoid the open rock of the stream bed. Find your way back to the lower encampment, located just to the left of Copper Creek a short distance from the bottom of the falls. Follow the trail back to your vehicle.

Bluebird Mines

Rated at C-3. These mines are a series of small tunnels located on the west face of Gold Mountain overlooking the town of Darrington. They all tapped a curious vein of copper ore that ran parallel, and close to, the face of the mountain.[15] None of the tunnels that we visited go very deep into the mountainside. Most of them crosscut a short distance straight into the hill, encounter the vein within a few feet, and drift left and/or right along it. Some fine samples of chalcopyrite ore have been found hand-stacked in front of one of the tunnels. You can see the remains of a wooden chute that dropped the ore down to a collection point below the mines.

Miners pose at the adit of one of the Gold Hill mines near Darrington in the early 1900s. This might have been one of the Bluebird Mine adits. (Collection of Loyal Sherwood, descendant of the original Knutson family of Darrington)

It is difficult to describe how the mines can be reached, because there is frequent logging activity in the vicinity, and the road conditions and locations are constantly changing. The tunnels are mostly at an elevation of 2,000 to 2,500 feet in steep, thin forest cover on the side of the hill. An altimeter can

---

[15]   This puts them in the oxidized zone, which is near the surface of the rock. Oxidation is one of the elements of mineral concentration, which might account for why the veins are there.

be helpful in guiding you to the right spots. The tunnels are small, however, so do not look for large mine dumps—there aren't any. You can reach the area via a logging road that leaves the old Mountain Loop Highway across the Sauk River from Darrington *if* it is ungated and passable. To reach the old Mountain Loop Highway, head north toward the edge of town on State Route 530. As you approach the Darrington Ranger Station, take the road off to the right and cross the bridge over the Sauk River. At the far end of the bridge, turn right onto the old gravel highway. The area presents some interesting challenges for the curious, but the hillside is steep and contains many small cliffs hidden in the forest. Most of the tunnels are in solid rock, and some are partially flooded. Do not enter any tunnels if you are not properly equipped and willing to take the risks. The metals found here were gold, silver, copper, and nickel derived from the ore minerals chalcopyrite and pyrrhotite. The gangue was broken country rock.

Whitehorse Mountain, Jumbo Mountain, and Gold Mountain contain many other mines than the ones mentioned here. The Sam Strom Mines, the Neste Group, and the mines in Wellman Basin are all somewhat difficult to find; checking out a copy of Hodges's *Mining in the Pacific Northwest* would be a good start for the serious mine hunter. Some of these mining claims are on privately owned land, so it might be a good idea to stop by the Snohomish County Assessor's office to determine who owns what before you go.

These buildings were typical of those at many mines in the Darrington area. Most were crude but sturdy in construction and generally lacked paint. (Snohomish County Historical Society; collection of Loyal Sherwood, descendant of the original Knutson family of Darrington)

Monte Cristo

Including Goat Lake and Weden Creek

The Monte Cristo Mining District is situated about 40 miles east of Everett in the central Cascade Mountains. The area ranges in elevation from 2,100 feet in the lower valleys to 7,800 feet on the loftiest mountain peak. The topography is rugged, with steep, crenelated ridges separating valleys that contain roaring creeks and waterfalls, rushing rivers, and placid lakes. Lush forests carpet the lower valleys, while numerous alpine basins, located near or above timberline, are filled with meadows of wildflowers. The steep, gullied mountainsides easily expose traces of the mineral wealth that the miners sought in the 1890s. The weather is typical of the Cascades—spectacular azure blue skies on the best of summer days and savage storms in the winter months. Between these extremes are many wet and cloudy times. But the clouds can provide an experience all their own, with mountain peaks playing hide-and-seek and occasional shafts of sunlight capriciously illuminating patches of mountainside.

Monte Cristo as it appeared in about 1907. The steam plume from the concentrator indicates that milling was in progress at the time. The concentrator was crushed by heavy snows in the great winter storms of 1910. Wilmans Peak dominates the skyline behind the town. (Enid Nordlund Collection, Asahel Curtis photo)

In Glacier Basin, Glacier Creek takes form at 4,300 feet amid the awesome crags of Cadet Peak, Monte Cristo Peak, and Wilmans Peak and then gushes over Glacier Falls into the valley below. On the opposite side of Wilmans Peak, '76 Creek is born in '76 Gulch and flows toward its confluence with Glacier Creek to form the South Fork of the Sauk River at the town site of Monte Cristo. Nestled in a high cirque above Glacier Basin at 5,200 feet, between Monte Cristo Peak and Wilmans Peak, is the Wilmans Glacier. Other lofty peaks in the area are named Addison, Foggy, Prospectors, Silvertip, and Toad. The principal mines in the '76 Gulch area were the Independence of 1776, the Liberty, the Lincoln, and, 2,700 feet above Monte Cristo, the Comet. The Glacier Creek Valley boasted the Rainy; the Justice; the Golden Cord; the Mystery #1, #2, and #3; the Philo; the Pride of the Woods; and the Pride of the Mountains. Just above the town of Monte Cristo were the O&B and the Boston-American. Many other mines dotted the area and bore names such as the Emma Moore, the Uncle Sam, and the Lalla Rookh.

Monte Cristo Mining Area

Sloan Peak

Cadet (Ruby) Lake

Bedal Peak

North Fork Sauk River

Penn Mining Co. camp (early)

Foggy Mine

Osceola Pass

Goat Lake

Cadet Peak

Foggy Peak

Penn Mining Co. camp (later) □

Pride of the Woods Mine

Pride of the Woods Mine

Pride of the Mountains Mine

Monte Cristo Peak

Keyes Peak

Columbia Peak

Mystery Mines

Glacier Creek

Wilmans Peak

Comet Mine

Hopeful Mine

Twin Peaks

Twin Lakes

Blanca Lake

Troublesome Creek

Elliot Creek

Gate

Addison Ridge

Monte Cristo

76 Creek

Prospector's Peak

Wilmans Pass

Twin Peaks

Poodle Dog Pass

Boston-American Prospect

Hubbart Peak

Sheep Mountain

South Fork Sauk River

Toad Mountain

Silver Lake

Silvertip Peak

Mackinaw Mine

Del Campo Prospect (lower)

Silver Creek

Twin Peaks

Mount Dickerman

Weden Creek

Barlow Pass

Palmer Creek

Gate

Twin Bridges

Northwest Consolidated Mines

Weden Lake

Sheep Gap Mountain

Crested Buttes

Stillaguamish Peak

Buck Creek

Lewis Peak

Foggy Lake

Del Campo Prospect (upper)

Del Campo Peak

Gothic Peak

Headlee Pass

Perry Creek

South Fork Stillaguamish River

Vesper Peak

Sultan River

N

Scale
(in miles)

1   1/2   0   1   2   3

The Bedal sisters, Jean and Edith, with their pack horses at the headquarters building of the Penn Mining Company base camp near Goat Lake, which lies in the valley immediately northeast of Monte Cristo. This photograph was taken in the early 20th century when the sisters ran a pack train between Darrington and many remote mountain locations. (John A. Juleen photo)

Monte Cristo

The valley to the north of Monte Cristo contains one of the truly pristine mountain lakes in the area, Goat Lake. Originally called Oulliette Lake, it was renamed for the many mountain goats that call this valley their home. The original name, however, was anglicized and provided the name for Elliott Creek, which drains the lake to the South Fork of the Sauk River. Several groups of prospectors staked claims and worked mines in this valley, among them the Coffin family. All members of the family owned mine claims, including the daughters; they were among the very few women in the area who did. The largest concern in the valley was the Penn Mining Company, which established the Foggy Mine 1,500 feet above the lake on the northern ridge of Cadet Peak. All supplies had to be carried in on wagons from the Everett and Monte Cristo Railroad at Barlow Pass. No rail line was ever built into the valley. Goods destined for the mine had to be toted to the shore of Goat Lake, loaded onto a barge, floated across the lake, and then dragged on wooden sledges up the steep rock and snowfields below the mine.[15] This task was assisted by a steam winch located at the mine, part of which is still there. The peaks that define this valley are Addison, Foggy, Cadet, Sheep, and Sloan.[16]

To the southwest of Monte Cristo is Weden Creek, a mining area in its own right. The Mackinaw (Mercantile), Northwest Consolidated, and upper and lower Del Campo Prospects were bored in this area. Weden Creek gets its start in the snowfields of Del Campo Peak. Here Foggy Lake drains down the mountainside into Weden Lake and eventually flows into the South Fork of the Sauk River just downstream from Monte Cristo. Major mountains surrounding this valley are Del Campo, Sheep-Gap, Silvertip, and Toad.

---

[15] To facilitate this, a warehouse was built at Barlow Pass on the Everett and Monte Cristo Railroad, where goods were stored until the tote wagon could fetch them.

[16] At 7,800 feet elevation, Sloan is the loftiest peak in the Monte Cristo Massif.

A pack train ready to ascend the trail to the Del Campo Prospect in 1912. The man in the dark shirt and suspenders is Jim Kyes, foreman of the mine. From the left is his eldest son, Leo; little Elsie Banta; Mrs. Banta; Leo's sister, Velma; James Kyes; Jimmy Kyes; Jim's wife, Elizabeth Kyes; Diego Kyes; and two unidentified persons. The group stands alongside the Monte Cristo Railroad tracks. (John A. Juleen photo)

History

In the spring of 1889, Joseph Pearsall, a mountain goat of a prospector who was busy locating claims in the Silver Creek district to the south, climbed up Hubbart's Peak to get a better view of the surroundings. He saw more than he bargained for: To the north, beyond a high ridge, he spotted something golden and glittering in the afternoon sunlight on a distant mountain. He and a pair of companions made an excursion to gather samples of ore along the glittering ridge, which he had assayed. His suspicions were confirmed: It was galena, a sulfide ore of lead, [17] heavily laced with silver. It was what he had been searching for.

The first claim was staked in the valley on July 4, 1889, and was named the Independence of 1776. This was quickly shortened to '76. The valley and the stream running through it were named '76 Gulch and '76 Creek. Still more minerals were found in a basin farther north, [18] and additional claims were staked. By the summer of 1890, several locating parties were plying the hills in this new district, and more locations were staked in the valley and even high on the mountainsides and peaks.

The name of the area was suggested by Fred Wilmans, one of the three Wilmans brothers. These brothers were mining and financial men with whom Joe Pearsall had allied himself in the quest for wealth. To entice men of means to invest in the area, Fred Wilmans found a name that exuded wealth and mystery, from a book that he and his brothers had all read several times: Alexander Dumas's *Count of Monte Cristo*. The name, along with other factors, brought an influx of capital to the area. Mining companies were established, a crude puncheon road was built from Sauk City (Rockport) to Monte Cristo, and supplies poured in. A sawmill was constructed, and work on the mines began in earnest. The town also began to take shape on the hogback between Glacier Creek and '76 Creek. By September 1893, a railroad had been blasted up the Stillaguamish River, over Barlow Pass, and up the South Fork of the Sauk River to the town. Even before the arrival of the railroad, aerial tramways were erected between the lofty mine locations and the valley floor, where a 300-ton-per-day ore concentrator was under construction. The valley was a beehive of activity.

---

[17] While galena is gun-metal silver in color, the vein that Pearsall found was covered with a layer of limonite, or gossan, the rusty result of the weathering of the iron sulfide ores. This made the vein golden in hue.

[18] This basin, later named Glacier Basin, was first visited by Fred Wilmans, Joe Pearsall, and Frank Peabody, who climbed through a col, or high pass, between Wilmans Peak and Columbia Peak and descended across the Wilmans Glacier, a feat not many would attempt today.

This portion of a much larger photograph, taken in 1894, shows Monte Cristo to be a typical mountain mining town with its unpainted buildings and rude pathways. The 300-ton-per-day concentrator is the large building on the left, just behind the town. In the right-hand corner, a person walks along the main track of the Everett and Monte Cristo Railroad. The rail line on the trestle in the center is the switchback to the concentrator. The main street, called Dumas Street, is paved with planks and puncheon. (Frank LaRoche photo)

The Penn Mining Company established a huge mine 1,500 feet above the head of Goat Lake. It tunneled clear through the mountain and bored upward seven levels, almost to the top of the ridge. Despite all this activity, no ore was ever shipped from this valley.

Along Weden Creek, the Northwest Consolidated Mine operated an exploratory venture at the turn of the century, while the Del Campo Mining Company made its attempt in the 1910s. The Mackinaw Mine first ran tunnels into the base of Silvertip Peak in the 1890s and then moved the operation down the valley nearer to the Sauk River. The miners dug large tunnels there and exposed the only known nickel prospect in the area. This site was explored as recently as 1969 by a Canadian mining firm. No ore of any import was ever shipped from this valley either.

The Monte Cristo concentrator began operation in 1894, and ore was shipped on a regular basis until 1896, when a massive flood destroyed the railroad. The road was rebuilt, and ore again was shipped in 1897 until, in November, the railroad was again washed out.[19] This time it remained in an unusable state until all the properties and companies in the district were firmly in the hands of the Rockefellers, who had put up much of the original capital to build the facilities in the area. The rail line was rebuilt in 1900, and the mines operated until their 1903 sale to the Smelter Trust (then the Guggenheims, now ASARCO), which promptly ceased all its operations at Monte Cristo.

The area never again attained the level of activity and excitement that it had experienced at the turn of the century. Mining was carried out at a vastly reduced level by small companies and individuals until 1920, when the last major mining attempt in the area, the Boston-American Mine, was shut down.

---

[19]   M. Q. Barlow, the design engineer of the railroad, for whom Barlow Pass is named, fought against running the line through the canyon of the Stillaguamish. The money interests prevailed, and Barlow quit in protest. Barlow was right; the river took the line out again and again.

Since that time, the area has mostly catered to tourists and curiosity seekers, along with the occasional prospector and mining engineer. Monte Cristo was accessible by railroad until the early 1930s. In the early 1940s, the automobile road was built as a mine-to-market road into the town along the old railroad right-of-way.

The Mine-to-Market Act, enacted in 1939 and repealed in 1975, required local road-building jurisdictions to construct roads across federal land on which potentially productive mines had been located. This act provided access to critical war materials located in the area. The road was soon extended from the town to just below Glacier Falls, allowing convenient access to this scenic area.

The concentrator at Monte Cristo shortly after its construction in 1894. Steam and smoke emanate from the 200-horsepower Corliss steam engine that powered the plant. This was the farthest point that the Everett and Monte Cristo Railroad traveled into the mountains. The structure to the left of the chimney is the terminal for the lower aerial tram from the Comet Mine located 2,700 feet of elevation above the valley. (Herman Siewart photo)

What to See

This area has it all: opportunities for mountain biking, mine exploring, scenic hikes, mountain climbing, camping, fishing, and photography. For a Sunday stroll with the kids, hike from Barlow Pass up the old Monte Cristo Road for a while. This road is also an excellent mountain bike trail. Stop and fish the stream, and enjoy the forest and wildflowers along the way. Climb into Glacier Basin above Monte Cristo to bask in the alpine meadows set amid braided Glacier Creek and surrounded by some of the grandest peaks in the Cascades. Or go further still and climb the peaks themselves. Ruins of the mining days abound, with old cookhouse dumps and tramway machinery slowly decaying at the mining sites. Just when you reach a spot that you're sure no one else has ever seen, a mine tunnel or a large piece of gear will appear, reminding you that others have come before.

For the Rockhound

Spectacular specimens of quartz crystal have been found in this area, especially above Foggy Lake opposite Del Campo Peak and in the Glacier Basin area. You can find black mica, or biotite, on a massive scale in the Glacier Basin area beneath Wilmans Peak. On the mine dumps and along the aerial tramways, you can find heavy chunks of glistening ore. It might not glisten when you first find it because it has weathered over the years, taking on the rusty hue of limonite, a hydrated iron oxide. Break the heavy sample open to reveal its true colors. The ore might consist of galena, arsenopyrite, pyrites, chalcopyrite, and, rarely, stibnite. Much of the ore is in a massive state, but on occasion euhedral crystals can be found.

For the Railroad Enthusiast

Traces of the old Everett and Monte Cristo Railroad can still be found. Mostly, you can see evidence of the old grade where it has not been replaced by roadway or washed out by the river. You might even find a railroad spike or other artifact along the route of the long-vanished tracks. The beam of the original engine turntable at Monte Cristo is still there—and it still turns!

Getting There

Getting to Monte Cristo today is either a pleasure or a chore, depending on your point of view. The map that accompanies this chapter illustrates how to approach Monte Cristo from the west. You can also approach the area from the north via the Mountain Loop Highway from Darrington. Drive through the town of Granite Falls and up the Mountain Loop Highway to Barlow Pass. The pass should not be difficult to locate because the paved road ends there, and signs normally mark the spot. Join the many other visitors, and park at the pass.[20] Monte Cristo lies 4 miles beyond a massive gate blocking the road that was built after the original road washed out in the 1980 winter floods. The road is now semiprivate; you might encounter vehicles along the way, so use caution. You can either walk or bike into the town. The road is not steep, with the exception of two short hills on the way in.

About $3/4$ mile beyond the gate, you will cross the major washed-out area of the road, which as of this writing had been repaired by the Monte Cristo Preservation Association and others. A mile beyond the gate you will reach Twin Bridges, the first of two crossings of the South Fork of the Sauk River. (To reach the Northwest Consolidated Mine or the Del Campo Prospect, you would leave the road at this point and take the trail to Gothic Basin.) Continuing along the old railroad right-of-way, you will circumnavigate two washed-out sections of the old road. About 2 miles beyond the gate, you will reach Weden Creek Station; a small sign marks the spot. It was from the rail station at this point that the pack trains of horses would leave the valley for the mines in the Weden Creek area, which lies across the Sauk River. At $2^{1}/_{2}$ miles beyond the gate, the road climbs Hap's Hill[21] as it leaves the railroad grade and begins a series of gentle undulations along the valley. At 4 miles, you will reach the old town site of Monte Cristo with its small cluster of modern-day cabins. This is the jumping-off place for hikes into the surrounding alpine scenery, for exploration of the mining past, or for climbing the lofty peaks that surround you.

Geology

Most of the Monte Cristo area is, technically, a type of pluton called a batholith. A batholith is a mass of formerly molten rock that, millions of years ago, was forced under enormous pressure into the layers of existing rock miles below the earth's surface. At this depth, the molten mass cooled very slowly. As it cooled, stresses were set up within the mass that would later form cracks and fissures. The batholith that makes up the mountains of Monte Cristo was formed during the Lower Tertiary period, about 60 million years ago. At the boundaries, or contact zones, between the batholith and the surrounding rock, chemicals native to the two materials gradually commingled to form new, sometimes exotic, minerals.

As the eons passed, the land beneath the batholith began to rise due to pressure caused by tectonic plate movements. The Cascade Mountains were beginning to form. As the layers of rock above the batholith eroded, water began to seep into the cracks that criss-crossed it. At the same time, hydrothermal (hot water) solutions were forced up from below, carrying dissolved minerals into the same cracks and depositing them as they cooled. Gradually, the rock above the mass was almost completely removed by the inexorable weathering process, and the hydrothermal upwelling ceased. The primary force was

---

[20]   You can park along the road or in a small parking area up a spur road to your left just as the pavement ends.

[21]   This hill is named for Happy Annen, who was instrumental in establishing Mount Pilchuck State Park.

now the water that descended the cracks, carrying oxygen throughout the minerals deposited there and aiding in the concentration of the minerals in lens-shaped bodies along the veins. The minerals in these cracks formed the veins of ore that we now encounter in the Monte Cristo area. The vein materials contain a high percentage of iron, and they weather at the surface to form limonite, a hydrated iron oxide, or rust, that stains the vein's surfaces. The prospectors looked for this stain to help locate the mineral wealth beneath. They called it "iron hat," "iron cap," or "gossan." This is what Pearsall spotted from the flank of Hubbart Peak in the spring of 1889—a thin layer of gossan over a crystalline vein of argentiferous, or silver-bearing, galena, that gave the appearance of gold in the late afternoon sun of that day.

The Mines

> **Note** The road into Monte Cristo is closed, so you must hike or bike the first 4 miles to reach the town site. The difficulty ratings begin *at the town site.*

Boston-American Prospect

Rated at A-2. At the town site of Monte Cristo, you will notice a mine dump low on the side of Toad Mountain[22] immediately above the old railway turntable. This is the site of the Boston-American adit, the last major effort to commercially mine the Monte Cristo mountains. The company was founded in 1913 and was a consolidation of several mining firms in the area. The name derives from the American Mining Company and its treasurer, F. W. Boston. The O&B Mine already existed much higher on the side of Toad Mountain, and the newly formed company planned to run a crosscut tunnel to contact the ore at a great depth below the O&B tunnels. This was a standard mining strategy, to encounter the ore as low as possible and then work upward, using gravity to bring the ore down as the miners bored upward through the vein. Alas, the operators never found a rich vein, and they eventually abandoned the tunnel.[23] The ore at Monte Cristo tended to diminish as the veins were traced farther and farther from the surface, until they pinched out altogether. The short hike to the Boston-American mine dump rewards you with a fine view of the town site and the many surrounding mountains. Little mineral content is to be found here, because little was ever encountered in the tunnel.

The final day of mining at the Boston-American came just before Christmas in 1919. Four men had remained at Monte Cristo expecting to spend the winter months working on the tunnel. One day they awoke to discover that an avalanche had roared down the flank of Toad Mountain the night before, totally demolishing the headhouse, the building at the entrance of the mine that held all their tools and blasting supplies. Realizing that it was fruitless to remain in this remote location with no work and more severe weather ahead of them, they decided to trek out of the valley. This was a very dangerous proposition because the railroad was kept open only to Silverton, some 17 miles down the tracks. The snow had fallen heavily that year and remained fairly soft and difficult to traverse. The four men had only two pairs of snowshoes among them, so they rigged two additional makeshift pairs for their journey out. They began their hike at 2 a.m., while the snow was frozen at its hardest, and made an exhausting though uneventful march down the tracks to Silverton.

---

[22] This mountain is named for the rock on the right side of the peak as viewed from Monte Cristo. It is shaped like a toad about to hop up the mountainside.

[23] One mining journal went so far as to accuse the Boston-American Company of fraud, saying that they were out to "mine the public, not the ground." This was a reference to their aggressive money-raising efforts and lack of ore production.

O&B Mine

Rated at C-4. "O&B" stands for Oliver and Ben, the names of the original locators of the property in 1891. The ownership of this area was once hotly contested and even resulted in gunplay at one point. No one was killed, but the sheriff had to be called in to quell the disturbance. The mine had varying success at producing ore over the years as it changed owners numerous times. Several carloads of hand-sorted ore were shipped to the smelter in 1895, but regular production never took place at the mine. A small aerial tramway was constructed from the mine down to the base of Toad Mountain in anticipation of a big ore strike, but it was seldom used.

The lower adit of the O&B mine in 1966. This mine, located near Silver Lake, produced some very rich ore, which was hand-sorted before being sent by aerial tramway to Monte Cristo in the valley below. Some mining records indicate that only one carload of ore was ever shipped, although others tell of more. (Phil Woodhouse photo)

Monte Cristo

The mine is located far up on the side of Toad Mountain above the Monte Cristo town site. It was recorded with the county auditor on August 11, 1891. The best, and certainly most scenic, way to reach it is by hiking toward Silver Lake over Poodle Dog Pass. Begin by leaving the Monte Cristo Road just after crossing the Sauk River as you approach the old town. Hike the Silver Lake Trail, stopping often to drink in the views as you ascend the side of the valley. Upon reaching Poodle Dog Pass, turn abruptly to your right and scramble through the brush while staying on top of the small ridge. You will soon find yourself in splendid meadows looking down at Silver Lake on your left and out to the Monte Cristo Massif on your right. In August, these meadows are resplendent with wildflowers, while ice floes might still remain in Silver Lake. Continue along the ridge toward the rocky bulk of Toad Mountain until you see a small lake below you on your right. This is Cultus Lake. [24] Descend to the shore of this tiny lake, and continue to hike toward Toad Mountain, contouring as you leave the lake. You will soon come upon the mine dump of the O&B Mine.

---

[24] "Cultus" is a local Native-American word meaning "useless."

After examining the dump, you can hike up it to the two upper levels of the mine. The mine had tunnels on three levels, and the stopes where the miners blasted the ore from the vein opened to daylight above the upper tunnel. This area is now caved and resembles a trench cut through the rock. If you locate this "trench," notice the regular notches cut into its walls. These originally held the timbers, or stulls, that supported the miners as they worked this area of the mine.

You can find minerals here, especially pyrites, arsenopyrite, and chalcopyrite. Look for them on the dump, or follow the path of the aerial tramway to find the "ones that got away"—the pieces of hand-sorted ore that were bounced out of the tramway cars on their way to the valley below. The metals sought here were copper, gold, and silver to be derived from the ore minerals chalcopyrite, arsenopyrite, pyrite, galena, sphalerite, and realgar. The gangue was quartz and calcite.

Independence of 1776 Mine

Rated at C-4. This was the first mine claim staked in the Monte Cristo region. It was located and staked on July 4, 1889, which accounts for the name. It was quickly abbreviated to the '76 Mine.

Begin your hike in the old town site near the railroad turntable. Walk toward Wilmans Peak, cross the footbridge over '76 Creek, and hike through the town site past the ruins of the buildings. (You will be walking up Dumas Street.) Soon you will arrive at a junction, where you will have four roads to choose from. Take a sharp right onto Mercedes Street, and follow it to '76 Creek; then follow the trail along the near side of the stream. Walking just above '76 Creek, you will soon come to the Lincoln Mine site. A large log lies parallel to the creek at this point; either climb the log or ascend the bluff adjacent to it. From the Lincoln Mine, the trail climbs steeply for a while and then again contours just above the creek. When you reach a point where you are right next to the creek and approaching the Sidney Mine tailing pile,[25] turn abruptly to your left and scramble up the side of the gully through brush.

Continue up the valley, slowly wending away from the creek. You will cross an area of fallen timber. Ahead of you will be a large talus slope coming from the prominent gully on the side of Wilmans Peak. Make a climbing traverse of this talus as though you were planning to climb the gully, but do not turn upward. Instead, after crossing about half of the talus, you will see the mine dump of the '76 Mine above you and far up the valley. As you cross the talus slope, you will be able to see the small mine dumps of the Hannah, Emma Moore #1, and Emma Moore #2 properties across the valley on the other side of '76 Creek. The Hannah prospect was staked on June 19, 1890, and the Emma Moores were staked on August 31, 1889. Continue climbing to reach the mine. There is an abandoned entrance just to the left of the main adit, partially hidden by brush. Two other tunnels lie up the gully immediately to the right of this adit (as you face the adit).

One of the interesting features of this mine was the air piping in the tunnel, which was about 8 inches square and made of wood. Most of this has decayed and now lies on the floor of the mine. Careful examination reveals the fine cabinetry skills used to fabricate this pipe, with its chamfered joints and airtight seams. The tunnel is small, and this pipe, which was suspended from the ceiling, did not allow much headroom for moving through the passageway. Around 1900, a steam drill—boiler and all— was hauled to this mine, and several hollow-core drill holes were made at right angles to the tunnel in an attempt to locate additional ore bodies. Apparently none were found, or else no attempt was ever made to tunnel to them.

You can find ore in this area, mostly arsenopyrite and some galena, located primarily on the mine's dump. The gully that ascends to the upper tunnels of this mine was the glittering band that Joe Pearsall

---

[25] You will see signs of a grade parallel and just above the water level of the creek. If you reach the Sidney Mine, backtrack about 75 feet before climbing the bank.

spotted from the side of Hubbart Peak to the south. But all of the surface deposits of galena have been stripped away. You can find other samples in the gully leading up to the mine's other tunnels, but watch your step: The gully is steep and, if wet, very slippery. The metals sought here were gold and silver, to be derived from the ore minerals of argentiferous galena, chalcopyrite, pyrite, arsenopyrite, and sphalerite. The gangue consisted mostly of tonalite.

Comet Mine

Rated at D-5. The highest mine in the Monte Cristo district was the Comet, located 2,700 feet above the town site at 5,400 feet above sea level. It was one of the properties established by the Wilmans brothers, the first financiers in the district. The mine was recorded with the county auditor on July 20, 1891, and was active in the halcyon years of the late 1890s. Ore was shipped down a 10,000-foot aerial tramway to a receiving station near the concentrator above Glacier Creek. A 500-foot tunnel pierced Wilmans Peak from '76 Creek to Glacier Basin. The initial span of the tramway leapt over a yawning chasm on the mountainside while dropping 700 feet to the facilities below. One of the cables remained in place until 1977, when winter snows brought it down. The last structure of the bunker that held ore for delivery to the tram collapsed in 1958; while it was still standing, it could be seen from the town site in the valley below. It was said that on a clear day you could see a bend in the Columbia River from the mine's lofty perch. Located on the only level piece of rock on the side of Wilmans Peak, the buildings consisted of a bunkhouse, cookhouse, ore bunker, and outhouse. The ledge resembles the prow of a great ship about to set sail from the cliffside.

Looking down the Comet Mine's aerial tramway right-of-way in 1984. This view is from the site of the mine's tram station 2,700 feet above the town site. The tram's brake wheels are shown in the foreground. The Monte Cristo town site is the light-colored area at the top of the picture just left of the cliff. The thumb of rock in the center of the photo is the 110-foot Old Man of the Mountain. (Phil Woodhouse photo)

It was difficult to maintain supplies of fresh food and drink at the cookhouse. Without refrigeration or the ability to obtain a steady supply of ice, the miners had to transport perishables to the cookhouse daily. This was not a huge problem, because the tram could transport food and other supplies up as well as carry ore down. One exception was the supply of milk, because the bulky milk containers, which arrived daily on the train, did not fit in the tiny Hallidie tram buckets and would fall out and smash on the rocks below. This problem was solved for a time by the cook, who rode the tram down and then rode it back up to the mine while clinging for dear life to the tram bucket and the milk jug. However, one day a whipping tram cable sheared off one of the cook's ears. After that, the practice was stopped and the miners had to do without their daily milk.

Monte Cristo

While no photographs of the Comet Mine's Hallidie tram are available, the aerial tram in this photograph is virtually identical to it. The similarity extends even to the "X" towers. Hallidie trams were of simpler construction than the Bleichert trams because only a single, moving cable was required to both carry and move the cars. The cars were fastened permanently to the cable at equal intervals, similar to a modern ski lift. The cars could not carry nearly the weight that those of the Bleichert trams could, however, because of the light weight of the carrying cable. The cable had to be flexible enough to wind around the driving and brake wheels at either terminal. (From an 1890s mining journal)

The ore taken from the Comet was mostly arsenopyrite and galena, both of which contained the valuable silver the miners sought. When the bottom fell out of the silver market in 1893, the ore was mined for its gold content. Not many samples of ore can be found at this mine because of the steepness of the terrain. Any samples that went over the side are far down in '76 Gulch by now. The gangue was mostly country rock and kaolinite.

The climb to the Comet is not for novice hikers and certainly should not be attempted by anyone with a propensity toward acrophobia. The climb can be made without climbing paraphernalia, but it is very treacherous. Take plenty of water for this trek,[26] especially late in the year, because after the snow is gone all the streams on the mountainside dry up. The ascent begins at the old Monte Cristo town site. The first destination is the remains of the tramway transfer station at the base of the Count of Monte Cristo Rock, also called the Old Man of the Mountain. This 110-foot, thumb-shaped outcrop of rock standing above a steep gully at 4,700 feet on the side of Wilmans Peak is a favorite destination for rock climbers. You can approach it from several different directions. You can climb the arete, or hogback, that extends down the side of the peak to the old town site. If you stay on the crest, you will reach the transfer station at the point where the ridge joins the peak.[27] You can also hike into '76 Gulch via the trail that begins at the town site, passing the Lincoln Mine and Sidney Mine along the way. At the Sidney

---

[26] Bring at least a half gallon per person, or more if it is unusually hot.

[27] This route might be brushy and entail climbing through dense timberline forest, but it is relatively safe.

Mine, turn abruptly uphill away from '76 Creek on a way trail and walk into the timber and brush. After a short distance, turn up-valley again and cross a large amount of downed timber as you gradually ascend a great talus slope that emerges from a steep gully. Ascend the gully until you reach an elevation of 4,600 feet. Turn left and climb precipitously up the side of the gully to the transfer station.

> **Warning** Be extremely careful of loose rock as you scramble up, especially in the gully and during the final climb to the station.

Another way to reach the transfer station is to start at the town site and take the old trail toward the Justice Mine (see the Justice Mine section below) and then ascend the gully just after breaking out of the woods. This way is very brushy, however, and it might be suitable only during the early part of the year when there is enough snow in the gully to cover the brush but not so much that the danger of avalanche exists. Also note that there could be too much snow in the gully approaching the Comet bunker when snow is present in the first gully; since the first part of this climb is on the north side of the ridge and the gully to the Comet is on the south side, you might be able to climb the snow on the shaded, north part of the route and then emerge on the south side to find it relatively snow-free. Good luck!

Once you reach the transfer station, it's only 700 vertical feet to the bunker. But what a 700-foot climb it is! After resting, gathering your wits, and satisfying yourself with the breathtaking scenery, resume your climb by going straight up toward the looming mass of the cliff above you. This might feel like a hopeless task, but, as if by magic, an old miner's trail will appear as you approach the scarp's base. Turn right and follow the base of the cliff, which parallels the gully, until it leads you back into that gully. As of this writing, a piece of very rusty steel cable runs directly up the center of the gully to assist in the ascent. Once you complete this part of the climb, it is a relatively easy scramble up the gully to the site of the bunker.

> **Warning** Remember, you will descend along this same route. Before you attempt each phase of this journey, determine if you will be able to make a comfortable return. If not, do not proceed. Turn around occasionally and look behind and below you. This is what you will face on the return trip. Also, a good pair of lug-soled boots is recommended for this climb.

Once you reach the ledge of the Comet Mine, you will feel a great sense of accomplishment. Short of ascending one of the surrounding lofty peaks, this is about the most exhilarating climb that you can make in the Monte Cristo area. But, alas, you will also discover that the mine is hopelessly collapsed beneath the relentless pressure of rock from above. At the time of this writing, the upper set of tram brake wheels still clung to the bunker amid the decaying timber.

Justice Mine

Rated at B-4. This mine was one of the Wilmans brothers' ventures. It proved to be a productive property until they tried to dig too deeply into the mountain: Like other mines at Monte Cristo, the ore tended to run out about 500 feet from the surface. The mine changed owners several times, and production resumed in 1907 and again in the 1920s, but without success. The Boston-American Mining Company was the last to attempt mining operations here. The company built a new concentrator at

Monte Cristo and a tramway from the mine to the concentrator. No ore was ever shipped down that tram. One of the mine's tunnels was bored under a large rock slide to a point 400 feet below the Mystery #3 Mine. The ore in this tunnel was considered too low in quality for mining.

A trio of explorers at the Justice Mine in the mid-1930s. The adit is immediately behind them in this picture. From the left are Jean Bedal Fish (one of the Bedal sisters who ran pack trains in this area), Margaret Hilmo, and Gladys Ohlhoff. (Gladys Ohlhoff photo)

The Boston-American Mining Company erected this aerial tram from the Justice Mine to a new concentrator at the tram's lower end. (It is the building at the end of the line of towers.) This tram borrowed much of the abandoned machinery from previous trams in the area. The collector station of the original long trams from the Mystery Mines and the Pride of the Mountains Mine is the building to the right of the line of towers. (Enid Nordlund Collection)

To reach this mine, cross the footbridge over '76 Creek and hike up through the Monte Cristo town site as directed in the Independence of 1776 section. Upon reaching the multiple "Y" at the end of Dumas Street, ignore the other three roads and take Glacier Street (the second road from the left), which continues directly ahead. Within a few feet, you will notice a clearing in the forest immediately below the street with some metal debris lying about. This is the site of the ore concentrator that handled 300 tons of the precious material per day in the mid-1890s. If you descend to this site, you can see some of the equipment foundations and some of the railroad trestle uprights. This was the farthest that the railroad ran up this valley.

Just beyond the concentrator site is a large bevel gear just downhill, off the trail, which probably ran a gyratory rock crusher. Far down in the trees beyond the gear you will see a large ore cart. This is one of the mule-powered surface tram carts that transported the ore from the aerial tram collector station to the concentrator. The surface tram was covered to allow for winter operation, and it was electrically lighted, with power generated by one of two dynamos connected to the 200-horsepower Corliss steam engine at the concentrator.

A short distance beyond the gear, you will see an old grade just below the trail. This is the grade of the old surface tram. Soon you will come upon a short spur in the grade leading to timbers jutting above the ground—the remains of the receiving station of the aerial tram that brought the ore from the Comet Mine. As of this writing, some of the small buckets of the aerial tram can still be found near here. They were left at this spot when the cable was salvaged many years ago.

A Corliss steam engine on display at an industrial exposition in the 1890s. The set of cams and push-rods on the side of the cylinders were the valve gear that controlled the steam to and from each side of the cylinders. This is similar to the 200-horsepower Corliss engine that ran the concentrator at Monte Cristo along with two DC electric dynamos. The valve gear was so tricky to maintain that an advertisement for an operating engineer for the Monte Cristo concentrator stated, "If you are not completely familiar with the valve mechanism of the Corliss Engine, you need not apply." (From an 1890s mining journal)

Continue walking up Glacier Street and notice remnants of the original wooden paving, decaying where it was laid in the 1890s. About $^1/_4$ mile after leaving Dumas Street, you will break out of the forest and join another roadway, which parallels Glacier Creek.[28] Hike up this roadway, and on the left you will see the charred ruins of the aerial tramway collector station. Samples of ore can be found here where they fell when the bunkers collapsed and burned. This station received ore from the Mystery #3 Mine and the Pride of the Mountains Mine on the other side of Glacier Basin. Continue uphill along this road until you encounter a large washout that has taken out almost the entire width of the road into Glacier Creek. Notice the debris eroding from the side of the washout. This is the remains of the Wilmans brothers' power plant for the Justice Mine. It was powered by water tapped at the top of Glacier Falls and con-

---

[28] This is the "Mine-to-Market Road" built during World War II to assist in the extraction of critical minerals from this area.

ducted to this spot via an 8-inch pipeline. At this point, look to your right, high up on the side of Wilmans Peak: You will see a stream of water that seems to emanate from the side of the mountain and follow a massive mine dump almost to the creek. The water is flowing from the adit of the Justice Mine.

Leave the roadway at this point or just a few feet down-valley, and head directly toward the mine. You can ascend through the brush or go through the clearer area, which is very swampy from the water that descends from the mine. Whichever you choose, your immediate goal is to reach the base of the mine dump, where the rock is dry, steep, and *loose*. Climb this dump, aiming for a point along the bottom of the cliff about 100 feet to the right of the water source.

> **Warning** When climbing any mine dump or talus slope with other hikers, try to stay abreast of one another to avoid rolling loose rocks on the other people. If you are above someone else and you loosen a rock, yell "Rock!" to those below you. Make certain that you are all trained to respond instantly to that cry of "Rock!" Immediately stop, look up, and dodge as necessary.

In the late 1930s, much of the building at the Justice Mine remained standing and was reachable via this ladder. Today you have to scale the rock itself, and the buildings are but a pile of rotted wood on the cliff side. (Gladys Ohlhoff photo)

After climbing 800 feet of elevation, you will arrive at the base of the cliff and intercept the old Justice Mine Trail, which used to climb across the brushy slopes from the forest but is now overgrown. Follow this precipitous track up along the base of the cliff and climb the cliff next to the waterfall created by the water emanating from the mine.

> **Warning** Make certain that you are comfortable climbing in this type of terrain before attempting this journey. The rock here is usually wet and slippery and covered with moss in places, which adds to the danger.

An alternate, less steep route leaves the old trail just after reaching the cliff, crosses the mine stream just below the waterfall, and ascends near the building ruins. In either case, you will find yourself on a man-made ledge blasted out of the mountainside. This was one of the mines founded by the Wilmans brothers. The adit will be very obvious once you reach the ledge. This crosscut tunnel reaches the vein several hundred feet in. The tunnel is in very hard rock and is perhaps the safest of all the Monte Cristo tunnels to enter.

> **Warning** If you choose to explore this mine underground, first read the section titled "Preparing for a Mine Trip" at the beginning of this book. Even though the tunnel can be considered relatively safe, it leads to areas that are decidedly dangerous.

In the mid-1930s, the Justice Mine buildings still retained some of their former shape. As seen here, the main structure was three stories tall and snugly fitted into the mountainside. Today it is but a pile of decaying timbers scattered down the slope. (Gladys Ohlhoff photo)

Adjacent to the ledge are the ruins of some of the buildings that stood at this mine. The cookhouse, bunker, bunkhouse, and headhouse were all located here. Be very cautious because of the decayed state of the wood and the many nails that protrude from it. It was in this cookhouse that a tragedy occurred in 1905. The cook was talking with several of the local boys, who had brought their rifles along. During a friendly tussle, one of the rifles discharged, and the cook was struck in the abdomen. He was rushed to Monte Cristo and placed on a locomotive, which began the long trip to a hospital in Everett. But before reaching Everett the cook died. His last words were "Don't blame the boy, it wasn't his fault." Another incident at this mine had a happier ending. During the night shift, one of the ore chutes became jammed with mineral and had to be broken loose. Two miners were seeing to this task when the ore suddenly broke loose, throwing one of the men off balance and sending him down the chute with tons of ore. Miners and ordinary citizens from town dug frantically at the base of the chute to remove the ore, fearing what they would find. Instead of a lifeless body, however, they soon came upon two feet, frantically kicking. Further digging freed the miner, who was bruised but otherwise unhurt.

You can find large amounts of mineral at this mine, most of it on the mine dump; you can pick it up as you ascend and descend the dump. For those adventurous enough to enter the mine, there is a vein of galena from which you can dig ore. Follow the adit crosscut through its gentle left turn, past the first drift to the right and the water pouring from the ceiling, until you reach the drift tunnel that intersects at right angles. At this point, you are standing beneath the three tunnels of the Golden Cord Mine, the adits of which are situated higher up the side of Wilmans Peak. They are connected to the tunnel in which you are standing by a series of raises. Turn right into the drift tunnel. Just before you reach the first ore chute, the galena vein is exposed on the right wall near the floor of the tunnel. A rock chisel and rock hammer are the best tools for removing the ore. Phil Woodhouse of Northwest Underground Explorations once accompanied a young boy to this mine and helped him extract some galena from this vein. When they returned home, they embedded a crystal of the galena in lead. The lad wound a tuning coil and assembled a crystal radio, the galena and lead serving as the detector to receive ordinary radio broadcasts. That was a school science project that he could truly tell a story about!

When returning from this mine, pay heed to the steepness of the terrain, and follow all the warnings previously mentioned. No matter how you arrived at the mine, it is easiest to descend on the side of the waterfall nearest the building wreckage for a short distance, and then cross the stream just below the waterfall to reach the mine dump for the final descent. Be sure to climb down the dump on the side of the stream away from the building ruins; it becomes much too steep on the other side.

The metals taken from this mine were gold, silver, arsenic, copper, lead, iron, and zinc. These were extracted from the ore minerals galena, chalcopyrite, arsenopyrite, pyrite, realgar, orpiment, and sphalerite. The gangue was mostly quartz and calcite with crushed tonalite.

Rainy Mine

Rated at B-1. Discovered and staked on June 9, 1890, this mine seems to have been fraught with problems from the beginning. The underground workings were extensive, but most of the tunnels were entered via a shaft, which had to be constantly pumped to keep it clear of water. An adit that was dug straight into the mountain didn't have to be pumped, but it didn't expose any paydirt either. The shaft accessed ore in a vein that ran beneath Glacier Creek.

The Rainy Mine was established early in Monte Cristo's history, but in the 1900s it changed ownership several times, and each owner had problems with it. In one case, the pumps used to dewater the mine kept breaking down, so the owner gave up and sold the mine. The new owner installed a compressed air bailer, only to have the compressor house burn to the ground. No ore was produced after that.

Begin your hike as you would to reach the Justice Mine, by hiking up through the town site of Monte Cristo and taking Glacier Street at the junction where Dumas Street ends. As you leave the woods and walk onto the Mine-to-Market Road, where you can see the mountains about you, look across Glacier Creek and notice an area with some reddish-colored soil scattered around it. This is the location of the Rainy Mine, which is situated across the creek from the old tramway collector station whose ruins lie immediately ahead of you.

To reach this mine, you have two choices: You can proceed from the location mentioned above and cross Glacier Creek—a job made easier by waiting until late in the year when the snow runoff is at a minimum. Or, instead of entering the town site as you approach Monte Cristo along the road, take the left fork that goes up the hill to the campground on the left. Continue over the massive rock slide and pick up the road again on the opposite side. You are walking along the railroad grade to the old ore concentrator, the farthest that the line ran up the valley. This road will enter the bed of Glacier Creek. Stay on the left side of the creek as you face up-valley, and rock-hop and/or bushwhack your way upstream until you reach the mine.

This mine is the only property at Monte Cristo to sport a shaft—a tunnel driven straight down from the surface. The shaft, currently filled with water, is boarded over and covered with dirt. Watch where you step. The shaft was bored 210 feet into the rock to access the rich ore beneath the creek bed. Consequently, it was always flooded unless efforts were made to pump out the water. Every time a new owner purchased the property, the first task was to pump out the shaft. All manner of equipment was used: buckets, pumps, and compressed-air bailers (now known as eductors).

> **Warning** The shaft here is a vertical tunnel that daylights at the surface of the ground.

A large amount of ore was shipped from this mine over the years,[29] but perhaps the most notable incident at this facility happened on June 6, 1905. Fred Peterson, one of the workers at the Rainy, was being hoisted from the bottom of the 210-foot shaft when the cable on the bucket broke, sending him plummeting into the blackness. Miraculously, he survived the fall, although both his legs were terribly smashed. Two men waiting their turn to be raised were struck but unhurt. A month later, Peterson was reported to be "getting around with the help of two good canes."

Near the shaft opening is an adit that pierces 800 feet into the mountainside. It was driven into unstable rock before it reached the solid rock of the cliff itself; entry is not recommended. About 80 feet inside this tunnel a raise was dug to the surface. The rock was so hard that much of the fumes and dust from blasting remained in the tunnel; for this reason the raise was bored as an air shaft.

The metals extracted from this mine were gold, silver, and arsenic. The minerals were arsenopyrite and pyrite.

Mystery Mines

Rated at C-4. When Pearsall, Peabody, and Fred Wilmans crossed the col from '76 Basin to Glacier Basin, these were some of the first properties they claimed. They were only the second group of white explorers in this region, and the first to enter Glacier Basin. The Mystery Mines were staked on August 30, 1889, and recorded with the Snohomish County auditor on September 25, 1889.

Since the ore was spectacularly evident on the cliff surfaces, these were also some of the first mines to be opened. Aerial trams from the Mystery Mines were first built by the Monte Cristo Mining Company in 1892 and proved to be dismal failures. By November 1894, the Trenton Iron Company had constructed a stout Bleichert Patent aerial tramway from the Mystery #3 adit to a collector station near the concentrator. This tram used long spans to cross the many avalanche paths along the mountainside.

The mines were bored using hand drilling and blasting until 1896, when an electric air compressor was installed at the Mystery #3 adit. The power lines were strung along the tram towers from a dynamo at the concentrator. The air-powered drills accelerated the pace of mining considerably. These mines produced most of the ore that was shipped from Monte Cristo. They shut down following the railroad washout in 1897, reopened in 1900, and then closed for good in 1903. They still contain a sizable amount of ore, but present-day costs and environmental laws make it unprofitable to pursue the ore.

---

[29] The ore tonnage from this mine has been reported at as high as 20,000. We have not verified this figure.

The headhouse of the Mystery #3 Mine during its construction (around 1893). Notice that the building was assembled before the windows and doors were cut. You can see the side of Foggy Peak at the upper left. (Enid Nordlund Collection)

The Bleichert Patent aerial tram is identical to those used throughout the Cascade Mountains. This one in Poland hauls ore from a mine high up on the distant mountain to a mill located behind the photographer. Note the loaded car on the left and the empty car on the right. (From a Polish book on aerial trams)

   Begin the climb to these mines as you would for the Justice Mine. At the washout in the road below the Justice, continue along the road to its end, a few hundred feet up the valley. You will find yourself at the base of a broad talus and rock slope. Looking up the slope, along the base of Mystery Hill (Mystery Ridge), you will see the mine dumps of the Mystery Mines. Choose your route up this rocky slope toward the mines. The country is open here, so finding your way will not be a problem.

Looking toward the entrance to the Mystery #3 tunnel. The portal is about 600 feet down the right-hand crosscut tunnel. The tunnel to the left was drifted along the vein. You can see one of the ore chutes from the stopes above at the drift's entrance, in the far left of the photograph. (Phil Woodhouse photo)

Warning When climbing any mine dump or talus slope with other hikers, try to stay abreast of one another to avoid rolling loose rocks on the other people. If you are above someone else and you loosen a rock, yell "Rock!" to those below you. Make certain that you are all trained to respond instantly to that cry of "Rock!" Immediately stop, look up, and dodge as necessary.

The long aerial tram at Monte Cristo in 1900 as viewed from directly below where the cables made a long span from the top of Mystery Hill to a tall, single pole tower on their way to the collector station. The long span was required to cross a wide avalanche track along the side of Mystery Hill. The collector station is the building immediately to the right of the pole tower. One of the tram buckets is traveling down and the other is traveling up in this scene. This photograph was taken from just below the Mystery #3 adit. (University of Wyoming, Josiah E. Spurr Collection)

Before you reach the mine dumps, you will probably encounter some of the aerial tramway cables lying across your path. These carried the tram buckets from the Pride of the Mountains Mine over Mystery Hill and down to the collector station near the town. If you are lucky, you might even find the remains of one of the aerial tram buckets. Other artifacts and mineral samples litter these slopes, so keep a sharp eye out for them.

When you arrive at the mine, you will be at the Mystery #3 tunnel, one of the longest at Monte Cristo. This tunnel bores about 3,500 feet beneath Mystery Hill, under Glacier Basin and into Cadet Peak. It served as a haulage tunnel, collecting the ore as it was dropped down the chutes from the Mystery #2, Mystery #1, Pride of the Woods, and Pride of the Mountains mines. The depression in the surface of the dump housed the upper tramway terminal, from which ore was transported to the collector station near the concentrator. You might notice that the ruins are charred. They were burned, leaving little of the wooden structure remaining at this site. You can see many cast iron artifacts, however, as well as some old, massive air drill frames. One look at the adit of this mine speaks volumes about the dangers of entering. The timbering has completely rotted away, leaving the loose rock hanging precariously over the entrance. Also, the mine is very muddy; if you decide to enter, tall rubber boots or hip waders might prove useful.

Looking down the Mystery #3 tunnel. The portal is 1,800 feet from this area. The stope above the tunnel could once be climbed 600 vertical feet to the workings of the New Discovery tunnel of the Pride of the Mountains Mine in Glacier Basin. (Phil Woodhouse photo)

Warning This is a very dangerous mine, but as luck would have it, it is one of the more interesting in the area. The choice to enter is yours.

From the mine dump of the Mystery #3, you will notice that more dump material lies above. This is from the Mystery #2 and Mystery #1 mines farther up the side of Mystery Hill. The Mystery #2 adit is almost completely collapsed and leads to a dangerous drop-off inside anyway. It is about 70 feet in elevation above the Mystery #3. If you attempt to climb above the Mystery #2 to the Mystery #1, be very careful—the Mystery #1 adit no longer exists as such. The Mystery #2 was stoped up into the Mystery #1 and opened the adit into a glory hole, where the stope opened onto the surface. Be very cautious as you climb into the last gully leading to the Mystery #1, because you will suddenly find yourself on the edge of the stope staring down 100 vertical feet into the abyss. One misstep and you will become a permanent part of this mine. This is an opportunity to see a stope without ever venturing underground, but be extremely careful. The gulch in which the glory hole is located is very steep and narrow, and it is littered with loose boulders. Only one person at a time should attempt to climb here.

This is a good area to find mineral samples because most of the ore removed from the area was mined here and shipped down the tramways from this point. You will find mostly galena, arsenopyrite, pyrite, and chalcopyrite. A lot of quartz and calcite crystals have been found here as well. These are on the mine dump and the surrounding talus slopes.

You can descend the way you came, or, if time allows and enough strength remains, you can continue up the rock slope to the saddle high above. Here you will be rewarded with a breathtaking view of Glacier Basin and Monte Cristo Peak on the other side. Equally spectacular is the view back down the valley from which you climbed. From this point, you can descend into Glacier Basin and hike the trail back to the town site. This makes a nice loop hike for the more adventuresome.

If you still have time and energy when you reach the saddle, hike along the top of Mystery Hill, finding your way along the animal and way trails there. You will soon come to the remains of the aerial tramway tension station, which maintained cable tension on the line that ran from the Pride of the Mountains Mine on the opposite side of the basin to the collector station near the town site. Here you will see the 8-foot-diameter, solid cast iron winding wheels around which the traction cables passed. Quite a bit of ore can be found here, as well as old machinery and cable remnants. The views of Glacier Basin and the valley below are also grand. If you reach this spot, do not attempt to descend toward the town site, because you will encounter sheer cliffs. Return to the saddle and descend into the basin or back down the rock slope.

The metals extracted from this mine were gold, silver, copper, arsenic, and zinc. The ore minerals were galena, chalcopyrite, arsenopyrite, pyrite, and sphalerite.

Pride of the Woods Mine

Rated at C-3. First staked on August 29, 1889, and recorded with the county auditor on September 25, 1889, this mine tapped the same vein as the Mystery Mines. While the Mystery tunnels were driven into Mystery Hill from the Monte Cristo side, the Pride of the Woods approached the vein from the Glacier Basin side. Eventually, the Mystery #2 and Pride of the Woods tunnels met inside Mystery Hill and were operated as a single mine. So complex were the ore bodies along this vein that one miner described them as resembling "a squashed spider."

Begin your hike as you would for the Justice Mine. After the washout in the road, continue several hundred feet to the road's end, and then along a narrower trail that continues to parallel Glacier Creek. Glacier Falls will be on your left, and the trail will begin to climb the side of Mystery Hill next to the falls. After leaving the road, you will notice the top of a pipeline in the middle of the trail beneath your feet. This pipe carried water from the top of Glacier Falls to power the Wilmans brothers' Justice Mine powerhouse near the road washout above Glacier Creek. Continue up this trail until you reach the top of the falls. This is a good spot to rest, gather your wits, and look out over the valley. Scramble out onto the rocks and enjoy the scenery.[30] As you look over toward the Justice Mine, you will notice the mine dumps of the Golden Cord Mine to the left and higher on the side of Wilmans Peak. This mine, representing the upper tunnels of the Justice Mine, was recorded with the county auditor early in Monte Cristo's history.

> **Warning** This is very vertical country, and a misstep can mean instant disaster. Stay away from the edge, and mind your children.

---

[30] Notice the small segment of Glacier Falls on your right as you face upstream. At the base of these falls, directly beneath your feet, is a small tunnel. This is the intake for the water pipe that ran down the trail to the Wilmans brothers' Justice Mine powerhouse. If the brush is not fully leafed out, you might be able to see the pipe itself just below the rock outcrop on which you are standing (on the downstream side).

On its last legs, one of the structures adjacent to the adit of the Pride of the Woods Mine sags with age as the winter snows begin to take their toll in the early 1930s. The dump of the mine is just beyond the tall tree to the right of center. This structure might have been a bunkhouse or office for the mine. (Gladys Ohlhoff photo)

After resting at the falls, continue upward on the trail—and we do mean upward! The next 400 vertical feet are mostly on steep, bare rock from which the thin soil has been removed over the years by countless feet and descending water. Sneakers can be used for this part of the hike, but hiking or climbing boots are preferred. These rocks might also be wet and slippery, so pace yourself accordingly. Do not leave the trail during this part of the trek, because a very steep cliff awaits you on the downhill side and its presence is not obvious when you are on the trail. During your climb, you will pass a sign that announces your entry into the Henry M. Jackson Wilderness Area. Senator Jackson was an avid outdoorsman, and the Monte Cristo area was one of his favorite haunts as a young man.

You will make an initial steep climb just above the falls followed by a brief respite and then another steep climb over bare rock. As the trail becomes less steep, you will emerge on the side of a splendid valley that lies between Cadet Peak on your left and Mystery Hill on your right. As you continue upward, the back wall of Glacier Basin will come into view. What you'll see, if the weather permits, is the Wilmans Glacier. Late in the year, you can see blue ice and crevasses; earlier on the glacier is covered with snow. Farther along the trail, you will encounter a jumbled coil of steel cable rusting alongside the trail. This was once part of an aerial tramway that stretched over the trail between the Philo Mine (staked on June 21, 1890) on the side of Cadet Peak to the tension station on top of Mystery Hill. This arrangement was set up in 1907 in a one-year, last ditch attempt to bring ore down from the Philo. Look carefully across the valley at roughly your current elevation and slightly down-valley, and you will see the mine dump of the Philo Mine—if the snow has already left the area.[31] As you continue hiking, your view will expand to take in most of Glacier Basin. The bulk of Wilmans Peak dominates to your right, while Cadet Peak walls the area on your left. Straight ahead, at the rear of the basin, rises Monte Cristo Peak. After a small rise in the trail, the Emerald Isle—a grassy island in Glacier Creek—will appear at your feet, with the braided Glacier Creek running through it, and beyond that the mine dump of the Pride of the Woods Mine.

---

[31]   The main adit of the Philo is directly behind a narrow waterfall.

The cookhouse for the Pride of the Woods Mine. Located in Glacier Basin, this cabin was home to 80 miners, 26 of whom are seen in this photograph from the early 1900s. Snow in the winter months could cover this place to the peak of the roof. The Xs mark where miners lost their lives earlier in the year in an avalanche. (Edward L. Meyer photo)

Between the trail and Glacier Creek is an old trash dump scattered amid the boulders containing broken china and rusting tin cans. This is the dump of the cookhouse/bunkhouse. The trail divides here, one branch descending to the creek and the other climbing toward the mine. The first steps along the upper trail are on an old wooden platform. This is the floor of the old cookhouse/bunkhouse, which housed 80 miners at one time. A covered walkway connected this facility to the mine along the path of the current trail. Continue along the upper trail to reach the top of the mine dump. The adit is caved, and no entry to this mine is possible. Remember, however, that you are on the exact opposite side of Mystery Hill from the Mystery Mines. The Mystery #2 and the Pride of the Woods are at almost the same level and connect inside Mystery Hill.

A building at the Pride of the Woods Mine in the early 1930s. The structure gradually collapsed as the snows bore down on it each winter. Notice the remains of the log building in the distance. (Gladys Ohlhoff photo)

You'll get a magnificent view of Glacier Basin from the top of this dump. Years ago, a photographer stood at this spot in the early spring to photograph the snowy splendor before him. Suddenly, an ominous thunder sounded from far up on the side of Cadet Peak across the valley. A massive avalanche of snow had begun high up on the mountain and was rapidly descending. Realizing that being across the valley didn't necessarily mean he was out of reach of the approaching white death, he grabbed his tripod-mounted camera and headed for the adit to seek cover. As he reached the entryway, a powerful blast struck him from the rear and sent him hurtling into the tunnel. He was briefly knocked unconscious; when he awoke, he was covered with mud, as was his camera. He collected his things and returned to the adit, discovering that he had been blown 50 feet into the mine. Back in the daylight, he saw that the snow had never reached his side of the valley. A cushion of compressed air had fired him into the tunnel like a cannonball. It is now known that avalanches can create air cushions and ride them down the mountainsides at speeds approaching 300 miles per hour. If you are hiking in this area early in the year, stay off, and far away from, the steeper mountain slopes.

Minerals of all types can be found in the mine dump—quartz and calcite crystals, pyrites, arsenopyrite, chalcopyrite, and galena. The material on the dump has become cemented together over time and is approaching the consistency of concrete. This makes it treacherous to climb the sides and difficult to dig for samples. A tool such as a geologist's hammer can make the task much easier.

If you have the time, continue hiking into Glacier Basin, being careful to find the almost lost trail in the brush and rocks that first goes down and then up again. You will soon reach an old grade on which the pipeline that carried water from Glacier Basin to this mine was laid. Most of the pipe can be seen down in Glacier Creek and on the Emerald Isle. Continue along this grade until you enter the basin. You will encounter Glacier Creek beneath the side of Lunch Rock. You can clamber onto the rock and eat lunch (hence the name) or explore the meadows of the basin. You can also continue climbing around the side of Mystery Hill toward Wilmans Peak to reach the saddle between Wilmans Peak and Mystery Hill. From here you can gaze down the valley to where your hike began. Another worthwhile trip takes you along the ridgetop from the saddle to the tramway tension station, high atop Mystery Hill.

The metals found at this mine were gold, silver, copper, iron, lead, arsenic, and zinc. These were extracted from the ore minerals galena, chalcopyrite, arsenopyrite, pyrite, realgar, orpiment, and sphalerite.

These 8-foot-diameter winding and brake wheels are situated atop Mystery Hill. There are two wheels on a common shaft, with each wheel being a single casting of iron. The shaft is 5 inches in diameter. These wheels controlled the speed of the tram that carried ore across Glacier Basin and down to the collector station above the concentrator. Notice the fellow holding the measuring rod on the right. Each major division of the rod is one foot. A second set of wheels, equal in diameter to these, was once located just to the right on a 3-inch shaft. The cable might have been wound in a figure-eight pattern around the wheel set to allow it 270 degrees of contact with the braking wheel. This would have lessened the chance of slippage when the brakes were applied. The brake drums are the flat surfaces above and below the pulley grooves. The lower drum has a small flange along its lower side to prevent the brake shoes from falling off. The brake material was hard wood (usually oak, ash, or maple), blocks of which were fastened to a steel strap that was wrapped around the drum. By tightening the strap, friction between the wooden blocks and the steel drum would be increased, causing additional braking action. Some of the original wooden blocks were found at this site and displayed charring along their contact surfaces, attesting to the energy released during braking. (Phil Woodhouse photo)

New Discovery Tunnel

Rated at C-3. First located in 1896, this mine taps the same vein as the Mystery and Pride of the Woods mines. A raise was driven 800 feet along the vein from the Mystery #3 to connect to the New Discovery. The closure of the mines due to the railroad washout in 1897 interrupted the construction of the raise. When the mines reopened in 1900, this raise was one of the first projects completed. It allowed ore to be transported from the New Discovery Tunnel to the Mystery #3 and then down the low-level aerial tram to the collector station. This eliminated the need to transport the ore over the high tram, which ran across the top of Mystery Hill. All work at this mine ceased in 1903.

Hike into Glacier Basin. When the trail divides at the Pride of the Woods cookhouse/bunkhouse, you have two choices: The first route continues into Glacier Basin, crosses Glacier Creek (difficult at high water), and climbs to the mine. The mine is just across the valley as you approach Lunch Rock while walking on the pipeline grade. It is a fair rock scramble, so use caution as you climb; even some of the large rocks are loose. The alternative route leaves the trail altogether at the previously mentioned trail division and descends to the left around the shore of the pond at the Emerald Isle. Begin climbing the rock slide on the other side of the valley as you walk toward Glacier Basin. You will encounter some brush as you approach the mine, but there are numerous paths through it. Maintain a gradual climbing traverse, and you will eventually reach the mine directly across from, and far above, Lunch Rock.

The New Discovery Tunnel got its name because it was not located until about 1896, long after the upper tunnels had been producing and shipping ore. In fact, the playing out of the ore in these upper tunnels prompted the search for new mines in the area, and this one was found on the same property. You will see two tunnels here, one on your left and one on your right as you face the mountain. The one on the left is the New Discovery Tunnel, which was bored more than 3,000 feet into Cadet Peak and was still in good ore when it was abandoned in 1903. Just inside this tunnel, a winze drops about 260 feet to a transition level that marks the upper workings of the Mystery #3. The two mines were connected underground, so the ore mined here could be passed down to the Mystery #3 and carried down the lower aerial tram. This was a serious consideration in winter when the upper tram often had mechanical problems due to freezing or avalanches. This tunnel is now very, very dangerous; do not attempt to enter it!

The tunnel on the right is an air shaft bored from the inside and from the outside (they met in the middle); it was intended to ventilate the upper stopes of the Mystery #3, which ran 800 feet up into this area. It is fairly safe to venture into this tunnel if you do not go beyond the collapse about 600 feet inside. You will note an elevation change of about $2^1/_2$ feet in the tunnel where the inside borers met the outside borers during construction. If you look carefully along the right side of the tunnel as you leave, at eye height, you will find the date "1901" very prominently inscribed in the wall.

The aerial tram originally began at the upper tunnels of this mine, 700 feet above the basin floor, and spanned the entire basin to the tension station on the top of Mystery Hill. In 1897, after the ore in the upper tunnels had played out, the terminal was moved down to this location; several of the big winding wheels can still be seen here. One rolled clear to the Emerald Isle, and you can see the remaining half of it in the camping area there. The headhouse at this mine experienced two major tragedies. At one point it burned to the ground. (There was no way to fight fires at these remote locations once they got going.) Another time, a massive explosion occurred just before the start of the early shift, blowing three men to bits.[32] The identities of the men could only be determined during roll call at the shift's end, when three men went unaccounted for. The blast wrecked most of the building and deafened a young boy who was visiting his father at work there. The lad was taken to Monte Cristo and sent down to Everett, where he was treated. He never fully regained his hearing and ended up attending a school for the deaf, even though he could still hear some sounds.

---

[32] In the era when Monte Cristo was operating, explosives were handled casually and accidents of this nature were common.

Minerals galore can be found on the dump at this mine. They are mostly pyrites, arsenopyrite, and chalcopyrite. Some quartz crystals have also been found here and in the surrounding talus slopes. Be careful when rockhounding on the steep slopes of the dump; like the Pride of the Woods dump, this dump has begun to cement itself into a solid mass, which makes climbing on its surface and extracting items from it very difficult. Again, a geologist's hammer is a most suitable tool for this task.

The metals wrested from this mine were gold, silver, iron, lead, antimony, copper, arsenic, and zinc. These were derived from the ore minerals galena, chalcopyrite, arsenopyrite, jamesonite, boulangerite, realgar, orpiment, sphalerite, and stibnite. The gangue consisted of quartz and calcite, along with country rock.

Pride of the Mountains Mine, Mukilteo Tunnel

Rated at D-4. This is one of the many properties that were staked by Fred Wilmans, Frank Peabody, and Joe Pearsall on their second visit to the area in the fall of 1889. So rich was this lode that a high tramway was built to it in 1894. The span across Glacier Basin from Mystery Hill stretched 1,100 feet and was one of the longest aerial tram spans in the world in its time. By 1896, most of the ore had been mined, and activity shifted to the New Discovery Tunnel farther down the vein.

This photo of the Monte Cristo aerial tramways was taken from just in front of the collector station looking up toward Mystery Hill. Notice that the right-hand, or short, tram begins at the Mystery #3 tunnel on the side of Mystery Hill, while the left-hand, or long, tram continues through the clearcut to the top of the hill, where the cars were transferred to a tram that carried them to and from the Mukilteo (upper) Tunnel on the side of Cadet Peak. An 1,100-foot free span was required to make this leap, making this one of the longest free spans of any aerial tram in the world at that time. The upper terminal of the short tram on the right was a terminal building on the side of the hill. This Bleichert Patent tram was built in 1894 by the Trenton Iron Works of New Jersey. The Bleichert Patent trams had stationary cables that carried the weight of the cars while "live" traction cables moved the cars along them. When the loaded side of the left-hand tram had the maximum compliment of cars attached, the system generated 16 horsepower; the speed was controlled by a braking system located at the tension station atop Mystery Hill. (Enid Nordlund Collection)

You reach these upper workings of the Pride of the Mountains Mine by climbing toward the New Discovery Tunnel and then contouring slightly up-valley toward Monte Cristo Peak to reach the steep rock slide. Ascend the rock slide toward the cliffs above. As you climb, notice a platform at the top of the rock slide to your left. A 100-foot tower was located here and was the last tram tower before the cables reached the top of Mystery Hill at the tension station. At 1,100 feet, this span was one of the longest in the world when it was built in 1893-94. Continue climbing until you reach the base of the cliff, where you will find a way trail. Follow this to your right, keeping close to the cliff base.

> **Warning** This is very steep country. You should wear proper climbing or hiking boots with good lug soles to prevent slippage on the slopes here. If you are not comfortable in steep environs, this area is not for you.

As you continue up along the base of the cliff, you can see outcrops of quartz crystals, along with ore of every description. This was one of the "broad, bold ledges of gold" reported by the Wilmans-Peabody-Pearsall party when they first staked claims here in 1889. Most of the surface minerals have been removed, but there is still plenty to see. Still ascending, you will come upon the remains of the upper aerial tram terminal and the cookhouse/bunkhouse. The substantial man-made pile of rocks at the terminal served as the anchor for the tram cables while the system operated from this lofty perch. The timbers of the cookhouse/bunkhouse were cabled to the side of the cliff because the avalanches in winter and spring would sweep away any unfastened structures on the mountainside. More ore and artifacts can be found here.

This 1900 view of Foggy Peak from the vicinity of the Golden Cord Mine neatly captures an aerial tram car on its cables mid-span between the station on Mystery Hill (off the photograph to the right) and the tall pole tower (off the photograph to the left). (University of Wyoming, Josiah E. Spurr Collection)

Climb a bit farther along the cliffside to the Mukilteo Tunnel, passing along the way a partly caved, water-filled lower tunnel and a totally caved intermediate tunnel. Both were driven into the mountain along the vein that you followed. Be careful as you approach this tunnel. There are a few places where the stopes from below reach daylight along the vein indicating that ore was mined from the tunnels below to the surface. Stay clear of these glory holes.

You can descend the same way that you climbed or you can continue along the cliff until you emerge onto the rock slide beyond. Early in the year, this slide will be fully covered with snow; if you are comfortable on steep snow (an ice axe and the ability to use it are mandatory), you can take this route. When descending this area, look for mineral and crystal samples in the talus. Some decent specimens of stibnite have been found here, with their characteristic interwoven, bladed crystals showing prominently. Upon returning to the floor of Glacier Basin, the trail back will be obvious.

The metals sought here were gold, silver, antimony, copper, lead, iron, arsenic, and zinc, which were extracted from the ore minerals galena, chalcopyrite, arsenopyrite, pyrite, sphalerite, stibnite, and realgar. The gangue consisted of quartz and calcite in crushed country rock.

Foggy Mine

Rated at E-5. Located 1,300 feet above the head of Goat Lake, this is one of the most difficult mines in this area to reach, at least in a single day.

By 1893 a group of businessmen from Pennsylvania had recorded a series of claims at the southern end of Goat Lake and established the Penn Mining Company to exploit them. They built a road from Barlow Pass to the Lake via the Elliott Creek Valley, which they used to carry supplies to their camp once the Everett and Monte Cristo Railroad was running. They built a small warehouse at Barlow Pass to hold the merchandise until the tote wagons could pick it up for transport to the base camp on the shore of Goat Lake. Throughout the years that the Penn Mining Company operated, it attempted to get a railroad spur line built from the Everett and Monte Cristo line to the Goat Lake Camp. This never happened, however, and the tote road remained the only way to haul freight in and out of the area.

Within a few years, it became evident that the location of the base camp was too exposed to the weather and the avalanches that roared down the valley's slopes in the winter and spring. The company built a new, more protected and substantial camp a short distance down the valley from Goat Lake at a location that would allow a railroad to easily reach it should one ever be constructed up the valley.

The effort that the Penn Mining Company put into its claims high above Goat Lake was stupendous. The miners bored deep into the ridge beneath Osceola Pass, pierced the ridge at two places, and prospected on seven levels, all connected underground by an incline and a six-level high winze. They hauled a boiler and steam engine 1,300 feet up to the lower tunnel to power a haulback tram to hoist supplies from the end of the lake up the snow patches to the mine. This was all to no avail, because in the end they never struck any veins with enough ore to make the enterprise economically viable.

To visit the mine, you must first hike to Goat Lake, a beautiful gem that was formed when a large rock slide blocked the valley eons ago. To reach the lake, drive to Barlow Pass as if you are heading to Monte Cristo. Don't stop at the pass, but continue via the gravel road toward Darrington. You will cross the Sauk River and then wind along its valley past Monte Cristo Lake (which is mostly swamp now). The road descends steeply next to the river, and soon after that you will cross Elliott Creek, which flows from Goat Lake. Just beyond this crossing, turn onto Forest Service Road #4080, which heads uphill to your right. If you have approached this junction from Darrington, the road will be about a half mile beyond the South Fork Campground along the Sauk River. Drive about a mile up this road until it is gated or blocked. The Goat Lake Trail begins on the right side as you look up the road.

A short descent will take you to the historic wagon road over which the supplies for the Penn Mining Company and its Foggy Mine were hauled from Barlow Pass to the company's headquarters camp and the mine farther up the valley. The way will be easy for a while, but after about 1 1/2 miles the trail crosses a large logged area, and the track might be difficult to follow. If you are on a mountain bike, this might be the time to stash it and continue on foot. Wend your way through the slash and brush until you again attain the easier track through the forest. At this point, you will have been following the course of Elliott

Foggy Mine
(isometric projection)

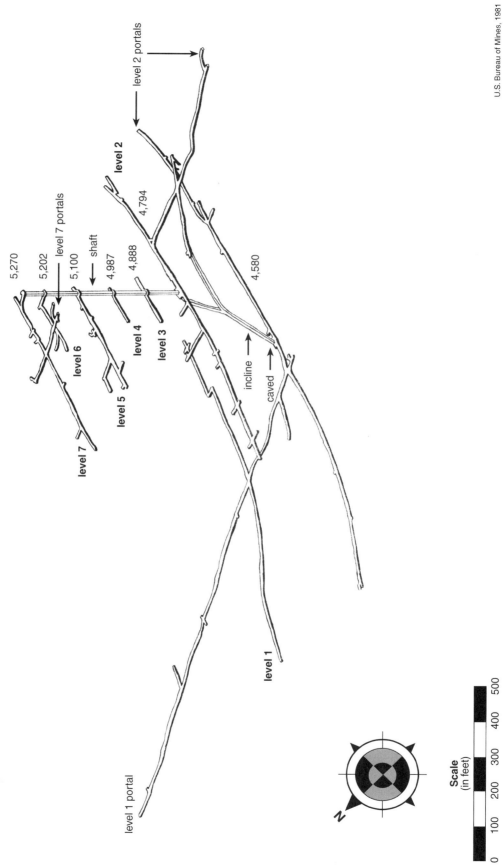

level 2 portals

level 2

4,794

5,270

5,202

level 7 portals

5,100

shaft

4,987

4,888

level 6

level 4

level 3

level 5

4,580

level 7

incline

caved

level 1

level 1 portal

N

Scale
(in feet)

0   100   200   300   400   500

U.S. Bureau of Mines, 1981

Creek for more than 3 miles, never straying far from its waters. About a half mile from Goat Lake, as you approach the landslide that impounded its waters and you see Elliott Creek cascading down the slide's face, turn abruptly left and follow a much narrower trail. At this point, you are directly across Elliott Creek from the Penn Mining Company's old headquarters camp. The road once crossed a bridge to reach the camp, but now access is difficult at best. Follow the narrow track upward over the rock slide until you suddenly regain the roadway, which switchbacks upward. Soon you will reach Goat Lake at the point where Elliott Creek begins, and you will be rewarded with the spectacular view up the valley across the lake. There is a wilderness campground just off the trail, where you can spend the night.

Located 1,300 feet above Goat Lake, the buildings at the adit of the main haulage tunnel of the Foggy Mine were constructed like ski jumps to divert the massive winter avalanches harmlessly over them. This technique apparently worked, because the buildings remained intact until they rotted away in the 1920s. This photograph was taken in the 1890s. (University of Washington, Penn Mining Company Collection)

If you look up the gullies at the head of the lake, you will be able to make out the mine dump 1,300 feet up on the mountainside below Osceola Pass. A pair of binoculars will be handy here. Follow the way trail around the left side of the lake until you reach the lake's head. Here the trail peters out, and you are left to cross a considerable amount of vine maple and other brush to reach the talus slopes beyond. Try to follow some of the natural seasonal water courses that often allow you to pass beneath, rather than through, the brush. At the talus slope beneath the mine, you will be able to clearly see the dump and the ledge that was blasted out above it.

The second main camp that was built by the Penn Mining Company below Goat Lake. The headquarters building is the large log cabin on the left side of the photograph. (University of Washington, Penn Mining Company Collection)

There are two ways to approach this mine. The first one depends on luck and skill at routefinding. The miners built a trail that ascends the cliffs on the left side of the valley as you face the mine. If you can locate this trail, it is relatively easy to reach the ledge and the mine adit. Barring that, you will have to make a more direct assault on the ledge. Your route will depend on how much snow still lies in the gully and how comfortable you are with climbing over steep snow and rock. The gully that runs just right of the mine makes a reasonable approach.

> **Warning** This is very unpredictable country. Good lug-soled boots are almost mandatory for this type of terrain, along with a good amount of common sense. Do not climb beyond your expertise. Remember to look back periodically to see what you will face coming down!

Upon reaching the ledge, you will find some of the old walls of the headhouse rotting away on the ground. On another part of the ledge are the remains of the boiler and steam engine that were used to hoist supplies up the snow and rocky slopes from the lake. The buildings in this area that were originally built outside the ledge were shaped like ski jumps that had their beginnings high on the cliffs above. This allowed the snow avalanches to pass harmlessly over them in the winter and spring. This approach apparently worked—we've found no records indicating that any buildings at this mine were ever swept away. The headhouse structure has since decayed and fallen far below, leaving only the heavier machinery behind.

The tunnel that you are standing in front of is the lower tunnel—the #1 tunnel—of the Foggy Mine. This is the haulage tunnel through which ore would have been transported from the mine, if any ore had ever been taken from the mine. Alas, none ever was, save for the small amount that was taken down periodically for assay purposes. The operators here had big plans. Since the railroad would not build a spur line into the camp, the Penn Mining Company made plans to bore a tunnel clear through Cadet Peak that would open high on the cliffs above Glacier Falls. An aerial tramway would then carry the ore down to the railroad at Monte Cristo. Such a tunnel would have been almost a mile long, but it was never realized. There are six additional levels of this mine, with level #7 almost at the top of the ridge just beneath Osceola Pass. You can enter level #1, but you had better plan to get very wet or else wear chest waders. There are at least two places in the mine where breakdown from the ceiling has dammed the water in the tunnel, making it a swimming proposition to continue.

The tunnel is quite long, almost passing through the ridge. Toward the back, it was connected to level #2 via an incline that has totally collapsed and is impassible. Level #2 *does* emerge on the other side of the ridge overlooking the Mayflower Glacier on the back side of Cadet Peak, Monte Cristo Peak, and Kyes Peak. Level #7 is also open above the glacier and can be reached via a trail from Osceola Pass only late in the year when that trail is usable.

You won't find much mineral here because not much was ever found in the mine, but careful hunting might turn up some specimens. No stoping was ever attempted in the mine due to the lack of ore.

The view of Goat Lake and the surrounding mountains is truly spectacular, however, and that fact alone makes the climb worthwhile. When you descend from the mine, try to locate the trail that starts down just beyond the wreckage of the steam engine. It will make your trip down easier and safer.

The early Penn Mining Company camp on the shore of Goat Lake. This was soon replaced by a more modern and substantial camp several hundred yards down the valley. This company's workings (the Foggy Mine) were situated 1,300 feet up the gully at the far end of the lake in the snow patches seen in the reflection. (University of Washington, Penn Mining Company Collection)

The metals found at this mine were copper, gold, silver, lead, zinc, antimony, and arsenic, which were derived from the ore minerals arsenopyrite, pyrite, chalcopyrite, galena, sphalerite, stibnite, and realgar. The gangue was quartz.

Mackinaw Mine

Rated at B-2. Also known as the Mercantile Mine, the Mackinaw is situated about a mile up Weden Creek on its eastern side. So unique is the mineralogy of this area that there is a mineral named for the mine, mackinawite. To reach this mine, begin as if you are going to Monte Cristo. After passing the gate and Weden Creek Station, you will travel along a straight stretch of road for about $1/2$ mile. About 150 yards before reaching the end of this straight stretch, take the side road that leads off to the right. It leads quickly to the river, where the bridge is out! You have to find your way across the Sauk River as best you can, a task made much easier by low water later in the year. Once you are across the river, regain the road and follow it up to the mine. This mine was last professionally explored in 1969 by a Canadian firm, and there are some artifacts lying about.

The tunnels here are driven in a classic contact zone, and the minerals display quite a bit of diversity. Nickel has been reported at this location, which has made this mine intriguing to miners and investors. Because of the contact zone location, the rock through which the tunnels are driven is very weak; as of this writing, the lower tunnel, driven in 1969, has already collapsed. The second level, located a rock scramble above the first, is open but in a very unstable condition. There are said to be tunnels much farther up the valley and below the present road that were worked by the original company earlier in the 20th century, but we have not discovered them, and no known trail leads to the tunnels.

You can probably find mineral samples in the vicinity of the tunnels; other mineral outcrops have been reported far above this area on the steep hillside.[33] This area has not been well explored, especially above the tunnels; part of the reason is the steepness of the terrain. Quartz crystals have been reported in gullies high above this mine and farther up the valley, as well as high on the mountainside.

The metals detected at this mine were copper, nickel, cobalt, gold, silver, and possibly uranium. These were reduced from the ore minerals pyrite, chalcopyrite, malachite, chrysocolla, garnierite, erythrite, pyrrhotite, chloanthite, cubanite, pentlandite, and mackinawite. The gangue was quartz, serpentine, and carbonates.

Northwest Consolidated Mine

Rated at C-4. Several small mining companies with properties on the flanks of Del Camp Peak joined forces to become the Northwest Consolidated Mining Company. In early 1909, J. C. Morton, the company's manager, announced that, upon resumption of railroad service to the property, ore shipments would begin. However, it was not until the autumn of 1916 that the company actually shipped its first carload of hand-selected ore to the Tacoma smelter. Earlier in the same year, the company finished building a small aerial tramway from its properties to the valley that allowed the transport of the ore to the railroad, but there is no record of any ore ever being shipped from this location. Little was heard of the company after that time. The veins proved too small and produced too little pay dirt to keep the venture operating.

This mine is located up Weden Creek on the western side, almost directly across from the Mackinaw. The approach to the property, however, is far different. Begin as if you were going to Monte Cristo, but after you pass the gate, stop just before crossing Twin Bridges. The trail starts in the small camping area there. This is decidedly a hiking trail, *not* a biking trail. The first mile of the trail is new; it was built after the tree that allowed crossing of the river at Weden Creek Station washed away. It follows the Sauk River, making small up-and-down excursions along the way. After a mile, you will enter an open forest and join the old miner's trail just across the river from Weden Creek Station. Follow the trail uphill.

You will soon learn what is meant by a miner's trail, as the next mile gains 1,500 feet of elevation. The views of the valley below and of the surrounding mountains become spectacular when the trail breaks out of the woods into open gullies on the side of Del Campo Peak. In the early part of the year, usually until late July, a large snow patch lies in the first gully. Crossing can be extremely treacherous. (A hollow, or snow cave, usually forms beneath this snow patch, so use caution when crossing.) Cross the first gully, regain the trail if necessary, and continue up through open country. You will soon cross a second and third gully. While in this area, look up the talus slopes above you. You will notice mine dump material, with its characteristic reddish color, mixed in with the talus rock. Leave the trail and follow the mine dump material to the small tunnels of the mine.

Samples of pyrites can be found in the mine dumps of these small tunnels, but perhaps the greatest treasure here is the view that you worked so hard for as you hiked up the trail.

Del Campo Mine

Rated at D-5. If you enjoyed the hike into, and the scenery viewed from, the Northwest Consolidated Mine, you'll be absolutely stunned by the hike into the Del Campo Mine.

---

[33] Impressive, clear quartz crystals up to 4 inches in length have reportedly been found far above the mine area. These include Japanese twins.

Monte Cristo

The Del Campo Metals Company appeared on the scene in 1910, with prospects on the flanks of Del Campo Peak about 3 miles below Monte Cristo. The lower claims were slightly higher in elevation and a mile farther up on Weden Creek from the Northwest Consolidated Mining properties, and the same trail was used to access both. The upper Del Campo prospect was situated about 1,000 feet of elevation above the lower and was located above Weden Lake in the gully beside the stream that drains Foggy Lake. The company hauled its supplies to the mine along the Monte Cristo branch of the Northern Pacific Railroad because regular train service was not in operation beyond Granite Falls. This isolation, combined with the fact that the lower crosscut tunnel never struck any ore and the upper drift tunnel returned a disappointing quantity and quality of ore, ultimately led to the failure of the Del Campo Metals Company.

To reach the lower tunnel, first hike to the Northwest Consolidated area. After crossing the gullies, the trail will continue upward through spectacular rocky meadows, with the view becoming more magnificent at every turn. About a mile past the Northwest Consolidated Mine, the trail passes below a beautiful waterfall and then makes an abrupt right turn and starts straight up the mountainside. Instead of making this turn, probe straight ahead through the small trees and brush to locate an overgrown trail. Follow this trail about 100 yards to the ledge where the upper buildings once stood. Cast iron debris on the ground will mark the spot.

The buildings of the upper Del Campo Mine appear to cling to the mountainside. These were built in the 1900s by James Kyes Sr., foreman of the Del Campo Mining Company, his brother Dan Kyes, and Sheridan McElroy. The adit is just off this photograph to the lower left and was accessed by the trail constructed along the cliff. Weden Lake is at the lower right. You can see Silvertip Peak through the trees at the upper left of this scene. (Enid Nordlund Collection)

From this vantage point, look down the steep, smooth rock below you; you will see many cast iron items lying about on a ledge about 40 feet below. The lower mine tunnel is bored from this lower ledge into the mountainside. Be careful as you make your way to this lower ledge; find ways around the steep rock. You might notice the remains of a pipe coming straight down the mountainside from somewhere above. This was the penstock that fed water to a Pelton wheel to provide power to operate the mine. As of this writing, the wheel is still at the site, but missing are the buckets that caught the water to make it spin. These buckets were usually made of bronze and were quickly salvaged when a mine was abandoned.

You can enter the tunnel (with caution, of course) because it is bored through hard, stable rock straight into Del Campo Peak. In fact, the rock is so hard that no mineralization can be found along its 800-foot length. The tunnel is so straight that you can still look out of the adit from the back of the bore. Apparently, the mine was crosscut toward some imagined vein deep within the mountain, a vein that the miners never encountered. Little, if any, mineral can be found here, because none was ever mined from this area.

The headhouse and mine tailing pile at the lower Del Campo Prospect tunnel in about 1912. This crosscut tunnel was driven straight into the mountainside but never struck ore. Today, you can stand at the back of the tunnel and still see the adit 800 feet away. Notice a spray of water just to the left of the base of the large tree. This was the tailrace for the Pelton wheel powerhouse. (Photographer unknown, but possibly John A. Juleen; Enid Nordlund Collection)

A water flume intake gathers water for power generation farther down the valley at the adit of the upper Del Campo Prospect below Foggy Lake and above Weden Lake. This mine never produced ore, but it is interesting because of its remote, scenic location. (Enid Nordlund Collection)

To reach the upper tunnel, do not take the hidden trail where the main trail turns abruptly upward; take the main path up near the course of the waterfall. The trail will continue upward for some distance, and eventually it will level off across what appears to be a small, man-made pond. You can see decayed wood-stave piping with its attendant steel hoops at this spot.[34] This is the headworks of the penstock pipe that provided water to the Pelton wheel at the lower tunnel. Continue along the trail until you reach lower Gothic Basin. You will recognize this point because the trail leaves the Weden

---

[34] As of this writing, some of the wood-stave piping was being used to fill the gaps in the trail where it passes the little water pond that served as the reservoir for the lower Del Campo Pelton wheel.

Creek Valley and passes through the top of the canyon wall into a small basin. Turn left here and walk past some small ponds to the edge of a bluff. Looking down, you might be able to see Weden Lake far below. Move along this bluff until you can safely descend a short distance to another meadowed ledge about 50 feet below. On the right side of this ledge is a man-made notch cut out just above a stream that runs through a steep gully. From the floor of this notch, which once held the buildings of the upper Del Campo Prospect, a precipitous trail leads to the tunnel, which is located in the gully immediately adjacent to the stream. It is so close to the stream that early in the year, when a lot of water is gushing down this waterfall, you can expect to get wet while entering the tunnel.

The tunnel is in hard rock and is relatively safe from collapse. This is a drift tunnel following the vein, but like the lower tunnel it never gave up much mineral, and no ore was ever shipped from this location. To find minerals in this area, leave the prospect and return to the spot where you entered lower Gothic Basin. Follow the prominent gullies up toward upper Gothic Basin, and after climbing a while, you will reach beautiful Foggy Lake. Del Campo Peak will be on your right, and Gothic Peak and Castle Rocks will be on your left. Climb to the ridge below the left side of Gothic Peak. If the snow is gone, as you approach the ridgetop you will be able to find good, clear quartz crystal specimens lying about on the ground.

Again, the highlight here is the scenery. From the top of the ridge, you can gaze 3,000 feet down into Sultan Basin and out across the mountain peaks to the west and south. Looking back across Foggy Lake, you can see the entire Monte Cristo Massif almost laid out at your feet. If you are so moved, you can ascend Gothic Peak from this ridge. Be sure that you have good hiking boots and are comfortable on steep terrain before trying the climb. Be sure to descend to the lower basin before trying to find the trail. The side of Del Campo Peak is very steep—don't take any shortcuts.

Mountain Loop Highway

Granite Falls to Barlow Pass

All the spectacular scenery that beckoned tourists, photographers, and artists to the rugged valley of the South Fork of the Stillaguamish River as far back as the early 1890s is still attracting visitors from around the world. Lying about 15 miles northeast of Everett at the terminus of State Route 92 is the community of Granite Falls. This is the beginning of the scenic Mountain Loop Highway that runs eastward into the valley through evergreen forests and rolling hills, along the meandering but sometimes raging Stillaguamish River, and past mountain streams. Along this route you also get views of famous Big Four Mountain (6,160 feet) and snow-clad Del Campo Peak (6,610 feet).[35]

Driving along the 30-mile drive from Granite Falls to Barlow Pass, many visitors become curious as they pass abandoned mine tunnels and decaying railroad relics. What went on here? Why? What is left?

The historic town of Silverton, 22 miles east of Granite Falls. Silver Gulch rises up in the distance. Copper was the treasure sought in this area. The Mountain Loop Highway now runs along the old railroad right-of-way running right to left at the bottom of this picture.

---

[35] The Mountaineers publish several books on the area, such as *Footsore 3, Trips and Trails 1, 101 Hikes,* and *Cascade Alpine Guide.* We also recommend *Monte Cristo Area: A Complete Outdoor Guide* by Majors and McCollum (Northwest Press, now out of print), if you are lucky enough to find a copy.

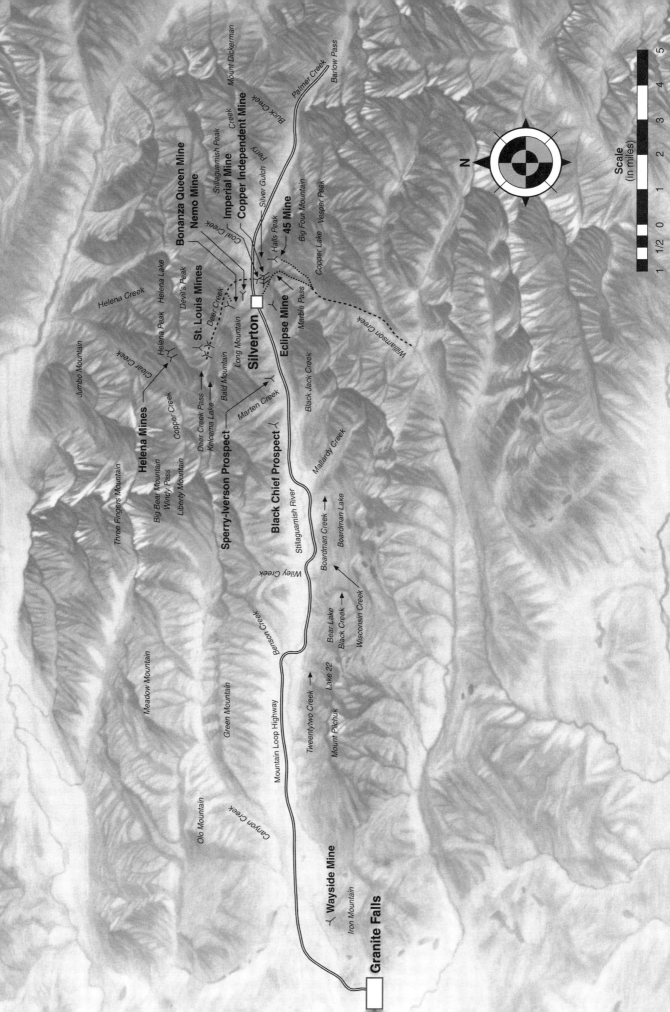

Mountain Loop Mining Area

History

In 1883, Joseph S. Enas became the first settler to locate near the present town site of Granite Falls, and in 1890 the first post office was secured, with John L. Sneathan as postmaster. In 1891, the town site was platted and consisted of 18 blocks. Also that year, a new mining district was formed around the town and the little farming, mining, and logging community was on its way to becoming an important part of the development of the Stillaguamish Valley. In December 1888, the first mineral claims were established in the area with the locating of the Pilchuck Iron Lode between Pilchuck Creek and the Stillaguamish River and the organization of the Pilchuck Iron Mining Company (with a capitalization of $500,000). In 1891, citizens of Granite Falls pledged $290 to build a trail to Silver Gulch to supply the miners and prospectors of the new and thriving mining camp of Camp Independence.[36]

The railroad was built through the town of Granite Falls and up the Stillaguamish Valley in 1892. It was funded by John D. Rockefeller and named the Everett and Monte Cristo Railroad. After it passed through Granite Falls, it entered the Robe Canyon of the Stillaguamish, where it passed through six tunnels on its way up the river. The railroad played a critical role in the mining and general economy of this area, because it was the only major carrier of goods and passengers from 1893 until 1925.[37] As we drive along this scenic byway, we will provide more historic anecdotes.

The town of Silverton in the winter of 1928. The small, dark building in the lower center of the picture was the railroad station.

Mountain Loop Highway

What to See

This area is particularly accessible because it is situated along both sides of the Mountain Loop Highway, which provides a paved driveway to the many splendors here. There are mountains to be climbed, mines to explore, and fish to be caught in the Stillaguamish River that carved it all (after the glaciers, of course). Small lakes dot the mountainsides along the way. Forest animals abound and can often be seen from your car, especially in the winter and spring before the throngs of people drive them deep into the woods. In the spring, the river can go on a rampage as the melting snows are funneled into the narrow gorges. In the fall, the vine maple and huckleberry bushes turn shades of fiery red, and deciduous trees lend their golden colors to the scene.

---

[36] The name Camp Independence was soon changed because the post office refused to recognize that name for fear it would be confused with Independence, Oregon. The new name chosen for the camp was Silverton.

[37] In 1925, the Hartford Eastern Railway, as the Monte Cristo line was then known, passed into the hands of the Rucker Brothers, who had leased it since 1915 and who operated it as a common carrier. By this time, roads were beginning to push their way up the valley of the South Fork of the Stillaguamish, and the line had competition. Little by little, as the roads were lengthened, the rail line was abandoned, with the last of it being discontinued in 1936.

The gateway to the area is the town of Granite Falls. Driving the Mountain Loop Highway from there, you will pass through the communities of Robe Valley and Verlot, and then on to the old mining town of Silverton. Although known mostly for its rock quarries, Granite Falls had some mines with substantial development work nearby. However, most of the significant mines in the area were located near Silverton in the Deer Creek and Silver Creek drainages.

For the Railroad Enthusiast

The Mountain Loop Highway roughly follows the path of the Everett and Monte Cristo Railroad through the valley of the South Fork of the Stillaguamish River. At some points, the road is actually built on the railroad grade as it winds its way along the river. If you look carefully, you can glimpse an occasional set of decaying trestle timbers from the highway. Along with the directions to the mines, this chapter also provides directions to some of the tunnels that were bored along the railroad mainline as it passed through the treacherous Robe Canyon. As the highway approaches Barlow Pass at its upper stretches, the road remains in the valley as the railroad grade climbs the mountainside to the left. You might want to park along the highway about a mile below Barlow Pass and hike the old grade to get the flavor of what the railroad passengers saw as they rode into this scenic area.

Getting There

Reaching this area is simplicity itself. From State Route 9, which runs north from the town of Snohomish, travel north past Frontier Village Shopping Center to the right-hand turnoff labeled "Granite Falls." This is State Route 92. Follow this road east to the town of Granite Falls, and then go east through the town on Stanley Street. If you have a trip odometer in your car, set it to zero at the town, because mileages from Granite Falls will be given in this chapter. If you don't have a trip odometer, take note of the odometer indication while at Granite Falls and practice your math skills as the miles accumulate.

Geology

The lower portion of the valley consists of Upper Jurassic and Lower Cretaceous sedimentary, along with some volcanic rocks. Magmas intruded along cracks in these rocks while they were still many miles below the earth's surface, carrying with them compounds rich in metals. As the area was upraised and cooled, these metallic compounds gradually concentrated in veins and seams along the fracture joints in the rocks. Contact zones between the sedimentary and igneous rocks provided the most promising locations for the formation of rich mineral deposits.

Farther up the valley, near the town of Silverton, the country rock consists mainly of Paleocene and Cretaceous nonmarine conglomerates and pre–Upper Jurassic metavolcanic rocks with some Tertiary granitic rocks. Into this country rock was intruded a vertical mass of Tertiary intrusive dunite, which extends from the Sultan Basin to the south and cuts the ridge immediately above the town of Silverton, continuing northward to the Kelcema Lake area. This intrusive structure (caused when molten rock was forced, under great pressure, into a major crack in the country rock) averages about $1/3$ to $1/2$ mile in width along its path as it outcrops on the surface. The major ore deposits of this region are located along the contact zones between this intrusive structure and the country rock. All the major mines in the Silverton area owe their rich ore deposits to this phenomenon. The valley bottom, along which the Mountain Loop Highway travels, consists of valley gravels and talus debris from the surrounding mountains. This debris generally reflects the rocks that form the valley walls along the way.

The Mines

Yankee Boy Mine

Rated at B-1. The closest mine to Granite Falls is the Yankee Boy Mine, located behind the high school (Section 18, T30N, R7E). After purchasing 40 acres of a patented homestead in 1920, A. G. Jacobson discovered signs of mineralization on the property and dug a 30-foot shaft, a 30-foot drift, and some open cuts on the vein. He also bored a 70-foot crosscut tunnel with the intention of cutting the ore body at depth right at the base of the mountain 350 feet below the outcrop and only 1,000 feet from the Hartford Eastern Railway.[38] S. W. Howe later leased the property and drifted an additional 900 feet during the next two years. A Mr. Peterson then took over the lease and finished extending the present tunnel until it was driven more than 1,500 feet back into the mountain. (A cave-in now blocks the main crosscut 250 feet from the portal.) The only known production was by a lessee named V. R. Foreman, who acquired the mine in 1933 and shipped a truckload of ore to the Tacoma Smelter.

The workings now include, in addition to the main 1,500-foot crosscut, a 30-foot-deep incline shaft (now flooded), a 50-foot exploratory tunnel 250 feet east of the incline shaft, and an open cut still farther east, all at approximately 650 feet above sea level and 260 feet above the crosscut at the base of the mountain. The crosscut was equipped with an 18-inch, 12-pound track, two 1-ton ore cars pushed by hand, electric lights, air line and ventilation pipe, air compressor, and fan. A hand windlass was used to raise ore and rock from the incline shaft. A bunkhouse, cookhouse for six men, compressor house, blacksmith's shop, and fan house were located at the main portal. This mine is on private property, and access is with permission only, so check with the owners before visiting.

At the town of Granite Falls, drive east on Stanley Street, pass the stop sign at Granite Street, and continue to the second stop sign. The school complex will be down the block to your left. Continue past the stop sign until you reach the end of Stanley Street. Park and continue, with permission only, on foot across private property to the first road, which turns off to the left. This will be overgrown and brushy. Continue along this old road for about 750 feet to reach a point roughly behind the high school. You will encounter the adit, still open, at this point.

The principal minerals of the mine were copper, gold, lead, and zinc, while the ore was malachite, sphalerite, pyrite, and galena. The gangue was quartz and calcite, contained in a shear zone of limestone and serpentine that was stained green with malachite. The gangue also contained some sphalerite.

Washington Zinc Mine

Rated at A-1. This mine is worth mentioning because of its mineralogy and accessibility. No visible vein minerals remain in these workings, although you can see broken, egg-size geodes in the ceiling, along with other unidentified materials. The adit is only 30 or 40 yards off a hard-surface residential road. The 300-foot tunnel is larger than those of other mines, possibly due to the vein width and height.

Just west of Granite Falls, leave the Granite Falls Highway and take Jordan Road for 6 miles to 143rd Avenue NE. Go 1/2 mile on 143rd. The portal to the mine is on the right, in the woods at the base of the hill. This mine tunnel is on private property and might be posted with signs. Obey and respect the instructions posted.

Lineal features of the tunnel are a 30-foot drift to your right, 90 feet from the portal. Ninety feet farther in is a flooded winze, also on the right. This winze appears to access a sublevel at quite some depth. On the left is a 5-foot pocket located 90 feet past the winze. Twenty feet beyond the pocket, the

---

[38] Formerly the Everett and Monte Cristo Railroad.

tunnel takes a 30-degree turn to the left, ending in a few yards, where either the tunnel roof, a raise, or a stope caved, blocking the unknown remainder of the workings.

According to a local story, one or more people reported to the sheriff that there was a body at the bottom of the flooded winze. Scuba divers were called in, but the investigation stopped when the report was deemed a hoax. Apparently these people had wanted to satisfy their curiosity about what was at the bottom of the winze, so they made up a story that might lead to the winze being pumped out. Exploratory adits can be found in the hillsides east of this tunnel all the way to King Lake.

> **Note** Across the river from the corner of Jordan Road and 143rd is an area that was once a coal prospect.

Wayside Mine

Rated at A-1. From the time ore was discovered here in 1892 by H. H. and James Humes to the mid-1900s, when Ram Mines Inc. finally closed it down, this mine was a major shipper of ore in Snohomish County. Located along the right-of-way of the Everett and Monte Cristo Railroad 1$^1/_2$ miles east of Granite Falls (in the southeast corner of Section 8, T30N, R7E), it comprised 15 patented claims on two mineral veins, the Phoenix and Red Bird, which were 900 feet apart.

This comprehensive photo of the Wayside Mine northeast of Granite Falls shows a typical mine of the 1890-1900 era. Just to the left of the upper center is the head frame, which supported the winding wheels that allowed the skip cars and man cages to be raised and lowered in the triple-compartment shaft, located immediately below the frame. The bottom of this shaft is over 400 feet below sea level. The grade (flat ledge) that runs horizontally between the water tank and the head frame is the railroad grade of the Everett and Monte Cristo Railroad. The boiler house is easily identified by the three smoke stacks protruding from its roof. (Snohomish County Historical Society)

Drive east from Granite Falls, pass the high school, and turn right on Gun Club Road toward the Miller Shingle Mill. Then veer right on the road to the rock quarry and park at the gate. After checking in at the quarry office (you will be crossing private property), proceed slightly to the left of the main road that leads up to the main quarry workings and find what appears to be an abandoned logging road.

This is the old railroad grade. Stay on the grade for about a half mile, beating the brush and alder trees out of your way as you go. Just before a large rock face that reaches down to the road (a railroad right-of-way) and has been stripped clean by a recent rock slide, you'll see the shaft.

> **Warning** At this point, be very careful: The vertical shaft is just behind you and to your right, in heavy overgrowth, and the collar is not covered. What you'll find is a VERY open three-compartment shaft that drops a dizzying 80 feet to the floor of drift #1 before plunging another 778 feet to the bottom. Dropping into this would not be a good way to treat the old body. PLEASE STAY AWAY FROM THE EDGE!!

Once you locate the shaft, toss down a rock or two and listen to it bounce off the sides as it plummets into the darkness. Then look over the side of the bank on the left, and note the mine rails and debris scattered about. Proceed past the rock face on your right and look closely on the other side; you might be able to find where the horizontal drift entered the hillside. During the Wayside Mine's heyday, the ore was raised from the shaft in two separate compartments. The shaft's third compartment was used as a manway. A large double-drum hoist lifted the ore and deposited it in a small car that ran it over the top of the railroad tracks well above the top of any train that passed. The car then dumped the ore over the grizzly screens into the mill, which was located against the side of the hill below the tracks. This plant was capable of processing up to 250 tons of ore per day, and over its lifetime produced about $500,000 worth of high-grade ore.

The principal metals were copper, gold, silver, lead, zinc, and vanadium, while the ore minerals consisted of chalcopyrite, pyrite, galena, sphalerite, and bornite. The gangue was mostly cherry quartz. You can find many ore samples over the bank from the shaft and on the rock ledge near the horizontal mine portal.

Red Bird Tunnel

Rated at A-2. The Red Bird Tunnel is some distance above the Wayside workings as you face the hillside. It is developed by a 300-foot tunnel with a short drift that is heavily shored at the portal. This tunnel apparently did not strike the ore body encountered in the Wayside workings, and it was probably abandoned.

Robe Canyon

Rated at E-2. This hike, down to the old railroad tunnels on the Everett and Monte Cristo Railroad line, shows you one of the biggest railroad blunders in Northwest history.[39] This railroad was built in 1892-93 by the Colby-Hoyt syndicate, backed by John D. Rockefeller. It was meant to supply the syndicate mines at Monte Cristo as well as other mines, mills, and communities along the way, but it became famous for its almost annual washouts and storm damage.

The trek starts 7 miles east of Granite Falls, where the Canyon Creek–Green Mountain Road takes off to the left of the Mountain Loop Highway. Park on the right side the road, and find the trailhead leading off into the woods. (In inclement weather, a good pair of waterproof boots is recommended.) Walk a few hundred feet to the top of the bluff overlooking the valley, and note the small, round pond at the southwest edge of the old clearcut. This was the mill pond for the Canyon Lumber Company's shingle mill, which was built in 1891 along with the town of Robe (named for Truitt K. Robe, its founder).

[39] For a better explanation of this blunder, see *Monte Cristo* by Philip R. Woodhouse, published by The Mountaineers, 1011 SW Klickitat Way #107, Seattle, Washington 98134.

Continue down the trail to the bottom of the hill, and follow the road; this was the old "Robe Wye," which was used to turn entire trains around in the absence of a turntable. As you near the river, you'll see that the wye joins the main line and continues west, adjacent to the Stillaguamish River, through the area where the town of Robe once stood. Cross a couple of streams, enter the canyon, and soon the eerie darkness of tunnel #6 will appear just down the trail and you'll see some spectacular scenery just ahead. Note the concrete track bed and retaining wall you are walking on, which continues clear through tunnel #6. This concrete bed was laid because the river, during heavy rain storms, would actually run several feet deep in the tunnel and wash out the track. This happened so often that it became necessary to rectify the problem once and for all. This was accomplished by casting the existing wooden cribbing support structure in concrete. You can see some of the original wooden supports because the concrete has slowly eroded.

This canyon once contained six tunnels ranging in length from 95 feet (tunnel #5) to 847 feet (tunnel #1). Tunnel #6 is the longest tunnel you will pass through and is now less then 250 feet long. That tunnel is followed by #5, which is now about 75 feet long. Tunnel #4 was next, but it was reduced to an open cut by the Northern Pacific Railroad in 1911 to cut down on the constant maintenance required to remove loose and fallen rock. This was done by blasting off the entire ridge of the canyon through which the tunnel had been bored and then laboriously, by hand, dumping the debris into the river. Climb over and around the rock pile that was once tunnel #4 and continue on, taking in the wild and beautiful gorge as you go. Note the long concrete arch over a rock chute that was at one time the road bed. This is a good place to call it quits and turn around, because this chute is steep and the rock unstable. It is not the place to lose your footing, because when the river is high it could mean a sleigh ride to the rapids below and an aqua adventure to death. To top it off, tunnel #3 just beyond requires the crossing of another chute that is more dangerous than the first one. Tunnel #3 is caved 150 feet inside anyway, so turn around and head back to the car; you will have walked 4½ miles round trip.

On the way back, it might be fun to ponder some of the rich experiences had by the workers on the construction crews, which at one time were 2,000 strong. To control vice and other crime along the line, the county commissioners refused to issue liquor licenses to saloons and dance halls along the right-of-way. This practice seemed only to encourage bootleggers and strong-arm violence that could not or would not be controlled by the law or by railroad camp managers. As a result, the saloons along the railroad carried liquor in defiance of the regulations, and robberies, prostitution, gambling, and drunken brawls were commonplace. This problem escalated to a point where some laborers finally decided enough was enough, and a large mob of men took the law into their own hands and stormed to a dive named the Monte Cristo Club, a saloon and dance hall 5 miles east of Granite Falls. They dynamited the building and ordered the proprietors and staff out of the area. They then turned their attention to another dive, The Branch of the Burning Bush, and threatened to destroy it to avenge the "rolling" of some of their fellow workers. (Rolling means robbing someone while he is drunk and unconscious.)

The interior of one of Silverton's saloons. Notice the embossed sheet-metal ceiling, which was typical of many commercial establishments in the 1890s.

Other Points of Interest

As you resume your trip east past Verlot and over a large steel-girded bridge, the road enters a winding canyon. You are now traveling on the old railroad bed for most of the way to Barlow Pass. As you near the 15-mile mark on your odometer from Granite Falls, pull over at Wiley Creek Campground on the left, on a point of land between the road and the river. Park and then walk across the road and look at the hillside at road level just downstream from the campground: You might be able to pick out the entrance to tunnel #7, the ill-fated "Mud Tunnel." It was here in 1892 that the railroad contractors tried to dig a tunnel through the hill to avoid the sharp bend in the river. But instead of tunneling into solid rock, they found that the hill consisted of only dirt and mud. Some workers actually refused to work in this quagmire for any price. One day, as the foreman walked back to the face where the men were working, he heard a suspicious low hissing sound. He had heard that kind of sound before, and since it was nearing the noon hour anyway, he quickly ordered the workers out of the tunnel for lunch. He then returned to the face for a better inspection. As he neared the face, he discerned a slight earth movement. Knowing full well what it meant—quicksand and an inevitable cave-in—he turned and started for the tunnel entrance. The sound behind him became a thunderous roar, and he ran for his life toward the entrance still some 250 feet away. As he reached the daylight, he turned and quickly clawed his way up the steep side of the bank with his fingers and knees. He reached safety just as tons of mud and sand shot out the tunnel's mouth.[40]

It is worth the short hike to the hilltop where the forest floor is flat and tree-covered. There on the flat plain is a giant crater roughly 80 feet in diameter and nearly 40 feet deep. This was the void left when the tunnel filled with sand. When offers of triple wages failed to entice men to work in this tunnel, the railroad decided to put in a shoo-fly[41] around the hill, which resulted in a very sharp 18-degree curve around the hill to the right and an even sharper 25 degree turn to the left,[42] making this the sharpest turn on the line and, according to one source, the sharpest main-line railroad curve in the United States at that time.

Stillaguamish River Mines

Continuing along the Mountain Loop Highway, cross over Red Bridge at mile 18 and look closely at the hillside adjacent to the intersection of the highway and the first road leading off to the left immediately after Red Bridge. If you look carefully, you can see an old mine adit: This is the Black Chief Prospect, rated at A-1, that penetrates the mountain for about 80 feet but failed to strike any ore. It was worked from about 1900 until 1926 by Alvah "Alf" and Alton Eldredge. The tunnel is unshored but blasted into solid rock and presents little danger from cave-in. However, if you're over 5 feet tall, watch your head because the ceiling is quite low, as is typical of many mine prospects from that time. It is worth taking a minute or two to examine this tunnel. No appreciable minerals are present.

Our next stop is just up the road at mile 19. You will know it when you are forced to slow or stop where the road dips badly and continuously requires repaving. The "sinkhole" has caused problems for road builders ever since the railroad construction crews first crossed it in 1893, and it remains an engineering nightmare today. Pull over to the right side of the road and park at the far, or east, end of

---

[40] A far more interesting story is that a locomotive and several Chinese men were buried in the tunnel collapse. This could never have happened because locomotives were never allowed in unfinished tunnels and Chinese never worked on the construction of the Monte Cristo Railroad. For more information on this incident, see *Monte Cristo* by Philip R. Woodhouse (The Mountaineers)

[41] A shoo-fly is a temporary detour around an obstruction.

[42] The degree of a railroad curve represents the change in heading, or direction, of the tracks for every 100 feet of travel. Thus, a 25° curve changes its heading by 25° for every 100 feet that the track travels.

the sinkhole. Walk toward the river far enough to peer down the near shore and note the old log railroad pile bridge protruding out into the river. This pile bridge extended for 630 feet in a losing attempt to win stability over the constantly changing landscape. At mile 20.5, you cross Martin Creek where, if you wish, you can park and hike the steep bulldozer-and-foot trail up, up, and up the Martin Creek Trail to some lofty silver, gold, and asbestos adits that are now caved. Some ore samples can be found, and the view of the valley and surrounding peaks can be very rewarding.

Just a few hundred feet farther up the Mountain Loop Highway from Martin Creek Trailhead, look carefully back against the hill across the marshy area. Somewhat hidden by brush and trees, and rated at A-1, are the Lucky Strike adits—two short tunnels, one 65 feet long and partly flooded and the other 15 feet long, with neither striking paying ore. Continue along the highway to mile 21, and stop at the Sperry Iverson Mine, rated at A-1, on the left side of the road. The adit is blocked by a grating, as it should be, and a good stream of water flows from its depths. This mine was one of several in the valley owned by A. D. Dick Sperry and Andrew Iverson of Silverton. Sperry was a friendly, well-liked man who could tell tales and visit by the hours, but it's said that he wasn't above "salting mines."[43] On several occasions he was reported to have asked for high-grade ore under false pretenses from the owners of the St. Louis and Jackson Mine for this purpose. The mine has a small mineralized area not too far into the tunnel on the footwall, but it does not appear to be of much value—the mine is only 119 feet long. A short trail off to the right of the portal leads up the hill to the cabin site above the mine.

Two of Silverton's well-known characters pose on a town street. On the left is Dick Sperry, and on the right, Frank Kazenski.

45 Mine

Although this mine's ore bunker was just up the Mountain Loop Highway from the Sperry-Iverson Mine, it is rated at D-5 or E-5 when it is accessed from the Sultan Basin, in which it is actually located. This rating varies depending on how far you are able to drive up Williamson Creek when approaching the mine. The 45 Mine was actually in the Wallace Mining District, but we describe it here because the main trail to the outside world during the early days ended nearby at Silverton and the 3-mile tramway from the mines ended here.

---

[43] "Salting" means loading high-grade ore into shotgun shells and firing it onto the bare rock of the mine to make it appear that the tunnel contains rich ore. Often the purchaser of such a mine didn't discover the deception until after he had "signed on the dotted line."

45 Mine
(isometric projection)

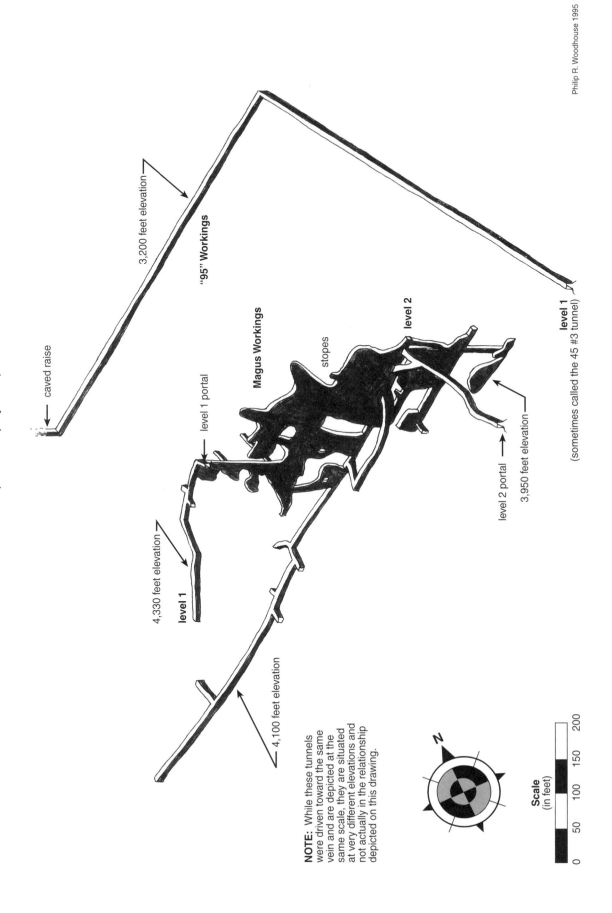

caved raise

3,200 feet elevation

"95" Workings

Magus Workings

stopes

level 2

level 1 portal

level 1

4,330 feet elevation

4,100 feet elevation

level 2 portal

3,950 feet elevation

level 1
(sometimes called the 45 #3 tunnel)

NOTE: While these tunnels were driven toward the same vein and are depicted at the same scale, they are situated at very different elevations and not actually in the relationship depicted on this drawing.

N

Scale
(in feet)

0   50   100   150   200

Philip R. Woodhouse 1995

The first four claims were discovered in 1891, at almost the same time, by three separate groups of prospectors. The first group located the Mountain Ram claim, while the second group located the Sarah (later renamed the Magus). A third group, consisting of brothers James and Ambrose Deupree, located the Deupree Brothers and Hard to Beat claims. Later, while setting their corners on their Hard to Beat claim, the Deuprees, along with a man named Swinnerton, encountered a prospector named Livingston who was working the ridge on the opposite side of the mountain from them. The two factions battled over claim boundaries, with each side charging the other with overlapping onto the other's claim. This fight went on for some time and at one point, in typical Old West fashion, with guns blazing. The feud was finally settled when both sides agreed to let a third party mediate. William F. Brown, who had recently become a co-owner of the Sarah claim, suggested that each party relocate their claims. As a result, each party took a different side of the divide, with Livingston on the Silver Gulch (Silverton) side and the Deuprees on the Sultan Basin side. This plan worked out well for both parties. Not much work was done on the properties during the next few years. In 1896, the Magus claim merged with the newly formed 45 Mining Company, which got its name from the 45-caliber rifle kept at the mine over the winter of 1895-96 to ward off claim jumpers. In 1897, many other claims were absorbed into the new company, including the Mountain Ram, Hard to Beat, and Deupree Brothers, bringing to 25 the total number of claims that the 45 Mining Company held. To reflect these additions, the company's name was changed to The 45 Consolidated Mining Company.

In 1896, the first aerial tramway was constructed from tunnel #1 on the Magus claim down to the lower camp near the base of the mountain. This tram used manilla rope to carry the ore buckets, instead of the steel cable most often used in this type of operation. The tram was gravity-powered, with the loaded buckets descending the hill being used to pull the empty buckets back up to the mine. At the lower end of the tram, an ore bunker was constructed and the ore was hauled to the railroad at Sultan by horse—a 23-mile trip over a rough pack trail until a trail over Marble Pass was completed later that year. The ore was then moved via the Monte Cristo Railroad.

Structures at one of the adits of the 45 Mine. Notice the ore car between the two upright logs just to the right of center. It appears that many of the crew emerged to pose for this shot. (Snohomish County Historical Society)

In the summer of 1897, a new tramway from tunnel #2 down to the camp was constructed, and a 5,000-foot-capacity sawmill was hauled in for the construction of new camp buildings and mine shoring. By July, a contract had been let for an aerial tramway extending from the lower ore bunkers at the main camp, over Marble Pass, and down to ore bunkers at the Monte Cristo Railroad. This covered a distance of $2^1/_2$ miles. This tram would also use manilla rope to carry the buckets and would be capable of moving 20 tons of ore per day.[44] Construction was started soon after the contract was let, but even though the tramway was completed, no ore was carried over it until July 11, 1900 because in November 1897, after heavy snow had fallen in the mountains for some time, the area experienced a warm Chinook wind that drove a massive amount of rain before it. In this "100-year storm,"[45] the railroad was badly washed out, and it was not rebuilt until 1900. With the closest rail line wiped out, the mine went back to hauling ore by pack train to Sultan at the rate of about 1 ton per day. When the Monte Cristo line was finally rebuilt, the long tram over Marble Pass was immediately put into operation and promptly broke the big bull wheel at the mine end. When that was replaced some weeks later, two pulleys up on the pass twisted and broke, delaying shipments once again. Again the ore had to be packed out by beast of burden, but this time over Marble Pass.

After the merger of the various mines into the 45 Consolidated Mining Company, William F. Brown took charge of the mine, which was now heavily mortgaged to the Pinkham family of Massachusetts. The Pinkhams continued to pour money into Brown's hands for mine development. Brown, in turn, put massive amounts of that money into the main camp building where he was living, while ignoring the needs of the mine. Brown finally left the company, but it was rumored that for quite some time he was behind a lot of the turmoil that continued between company officers and the mine's trustees. These internal problems were remedied somewhat when the Pinkham family foreclosed on the mortgages on November 12, 1903, and a "sheriff's sale" followed on January 4, 1904. The Pinkhams gained control of the company for $102,088—the total amount owed to them by the company. With the mine under its control, the family made changes that allowed the company affairs to flow a little more smoothly, although some officers and stockholders of the company claimed that a conspiracy existed involving some of the officers and the Pinkhams. They felt that this had brought about the foreclosure and reorganization. Nothing came of their protest, however.

This fuzzy picture is the only photo we could find of the 45 Mine buildings. The mine was located "over your right shoulder" high up the mountainside. The ore was brought down to these buildings by aerial tramway and then transferred to another, longer aerial tram for the trip over Marble Pass to the Monte Cristo Railroad on the Stillaguamish River. (The Coast magazine, circa 1900)

In the spring of 1905, the mine was leased to S. G. Wightman, and the company was renamed Magus Mining Company. The new firm went right to work repairing the road to Sultan and making mine improvements. But on July 6, 1907, the Pinkhams were forced to foreclose on Wightman and to look for serious buyers or lessees with enough money to carry on operations at the mine and allow the Pinkhams to concentrate on the family medicine business.

---

[44] This aerial tramway was later replaced with a Hallidie Patent tram, which was capable of transporting 120 tons per day.

[45] Often called a "Chinook" or "Pineapple Express" in this part of the country, the winds out of the southwest carry in warm, moist air and heavy rain off the Pacific Ocean, which is released on the mountains. This results in massive flooding and storm damage. The term "100-year storm" refers only to a high probability that such an event will occur only once every 100 years, but it can happen at any time.

Not much more happened at the mine until the spring of 1913, when snow slides destroyed the upper camp buildings. Since the mines were idle at that time, no one was injured.[46] In July, Mrs. Pinkham and family arrived in Sultan in a private Pullman car for a look at the mines and camp. The next day they were outfitted in appropriate clothing for the journey and were loaded on buckboard wagons and horses. They made the trip from Sultan to a point on Williamson Creek the first day. The second day, they completed the trip to the mine on sleds because much snow remained on the ground. They found the mine in operation, although the upper camp was still in ruins and there were problems with the compressor. But despite the problems, everyone enjoyed the visit and departed very satisfied. On December 9, 1913, patents were approved for all 25 claims. On March 30, 1914, the Pinkhams reincorporated the mines as 45 Mines Inc. All mining from that time on was done in the #3 tunnel 1,000 feet below the #2 tunnel as they continued pushing this long crosscut tunnel deep under the upper workings with the intent of encountering the vein at depth.

On November 10, 1915, Mrs. Pinkham and family again visited the property, and they found things going well with two shifts working 1,600 feet back in the #3 tunnel. Up to this point, $400,000 had been spent on the mine and 125 carloads of ore had been shipped. This amounted to 3,185 tons with a value of about $100,000, all taken from over 1 mile of mine workings. In 1916 and 1917, both good and bad ore was found in the #3 tunnel. Every year that the mine operated, the road had to be rebuilt, along with some of the bridges to the property and the long compressor pipe from the compressor house to the mine. This expense, combined with the United States' entry into World War I and the resulting lack of men and machinery, forced the mine to shut down again.

Over the next 10 years, mining was only sporadic. In 1925 and 1926, as an incentive to prospective buyers, a new road, 32 bridges, hydraulic and water pipes, 3,000 feet of 3-inch compressor pipe, several thousand feet of 2-inch air pipe, and a ventilation fan in #3 tunnel were installed. Rails, tools, air drills, and other equipment were brought to the mine, and a 24-by-40-foot storehouse was built at Olney Creek. In 1928, a large pump, dynamo, and gas engine were taken to the #2 adit and a shed was built to house the engine and men. The winze and lower workings were then dewatered with the pump for viewing by prospective buyers, who passed on the sale even though the ore showing in the winze and tunnel looked promising.

In the spring of 1946, the construction of a mine-to-market road was started but wasn't finished until late October 1947, and then only to within 3/4 mile of the lower camp. It was located on the wrong side of the valley to protect it from washout and storm damage that would demand almost constant repair. All this investment was to no avail. This once-proud mine that had shown so much promise finally fell victim for the last time to bad management and bad luck. When the railroad was running the tram wasn't, and when the tram was running the railroad wasn't. The mine-to-market road was built in a poor location. In 1953-54, the road was extended to the headquarters camp, and all the timber and metal on the property was sold for $10,000 and removed for scrap and lumber. So ends the story of the 45 Mine.

To get there, follow Highway 2 to the town of Sultan. Just east of the business district, turn left on the Sultan Basin Road and proceed about 14 miles to Olney Pass. Go left at the junction of three roads just past the information booth at the pass summit, continue over the dam, and turn right at an intersection roughly 1 mile from the dam. Continue above the lake shore (watching out for logging trucks on this twisting, hilly road) and up Williamson Creek Road to where it crosses over to the west side of the creek. At that point, drive straight ahead on a lesser road as far as possible and continue by foot or bike to Copper Creek. The old road switchbacks up along the creek bed. As of this writing, an

---

[46] An article in the *Everett Herald* on March 1, 1913, indicated that much of the lower or main camp also had been destroyed, including the three-story bunkhouse, the headquarters building, the sawmill, and the powerhouse.

old railroad flatcar bed serves as a bridge at one of the creek crossings. Continue switchbacking up the road until, with careful observation, you spot the ruins of the headquarters camp. Some rotted timbers and ore samples that have dropped from the bunkers give the location away. The road, very overgrown by this point, continues upward to the right of the camp. Eventually you will arrive at a yawning chasm. The road originally crossed this chasm on a suspension bridge.

> **Warning** The descent into, and the climb out of, this canyon can be treacherous. Wear good climbing boots with sturdy lug soles if you plan to attempt this feat. A pair of thick gloves also can be helpful because you will be hanging onto rusted wire cable to guide your descent. If you are not comfortable with the prospect of traversing this canyon, turn back now.

Locate a set of the old cables that once supported the bridge, and use them to assist your descent into the canyon. Once at the bottom, notice how steep the sides are. You are now standing in the very vein of ore that the miners were mining! The ore material is much softer than the surrounding rock, so it has weathered away at a more rapid rate, leaving this defile in the mountainside. Ascend the opposite side of the canyon by using the mountain azaleas as hand-holds. Once out of the canyon, do an ascending traverse of the mountainside, trying to follow the old road. Eventually you should encounter the 2-inch air pipe from the compressor house. Follow this directly up to the #3 tunnel.

The tunnel is all in firm rock and should not present a problem if you wish to explore. Remember, entry is your choice. Read the applicable sections at the front of this book if you are inclined to enter the tunnel.

> **Warning** There is a winze toward the back of this mine that is usually filled with water; don't step into it.

Leaving the #3 tunnel, climb directly upward over the logged-off mountainside until you reach a small trail running horizontally to the left and right. Follow this to the left. When you have almost reached the chasm that you crossed far below, you will come upon the ruins of the headhouse and upper tram terminal of the #2 tunnel. As of this writing, the great bull wheel of the aerial tram is still intact and resting amid the ruins. If you are planning to explore this tunnel, read all the sections at the beginning of this book and take heed. We have not probed to the back of this tunnel, so we cannot say whether it is safe to explore. The tunnel quickly opens into a large stope, where the floor drops steeply away and the ceiling climbs out of flashlight reach. The view from here is astounding—an unobstructed view into the Sultan Basin and beyond. Halls Peak rises to your left, and Big Four Mountain beyond that. There is another, short tunnel above the #2. Climb the cliffs above the #2 adit, staying near the gulch until you reach it. This is *very* steep country, so climb here only if you are properly equipped and experienced. The return is basically the opposite of your ascent. Be careful in the chasm.

The metals at the mine were silver, lead, gold, zinc, and copper, which were derived from the ore minerals galena, sphalerite, ruby silver, chalcopyrite, arsenopyrite, pyrite, pyrrhotite, marcasite, scheelite, and tetrahedrite. The gangue consisted of quartz and calcite.

Silverton

The old mining camp of Silverton dates back to the summer of 1891, when Abe Gordon and Fred Harrington located the Hoodoo Ledge of pyritic ore on the right side of Hoodoo Gulch between Big Four Mountain and Halls Peak. A few days later, William and James Hanset located the Independent in a small gulch between Anacortes Gulch and Silver Gulch. At about the same time, the Anacortes ledge was discovered by George Hall and W. M. Moleque, and on Deer Creek the Bonanza Queen ledge was located by J. F. Bender, Z. W. Lockwood, and J. O. Marsh. These new mineral discoveries brought a small rush of miners and prospectors, and the new mining town of Camp Independence located on a flat at the base of Silver Gulch next to the Stillaguamish River became a bustling little mining center. On August 26, 1891, the Stillaguamish Mining District was organized at a meeting of the miners, and the name of the camp was changed from Camp Independence to Silverton. In May 1892, the miners met and drew up rules and regulations for the new district and voted to "allow no Chinamen in that section of the county."[47]

Downtown Silverton circa 1902. Silverton also had a Monte Cristo Hotel, which was located just past the street lamp. This town reportedly had more saloons than it had churches.

In 1893, the railroad passed through on its way to Monte Cristo. The town site was platted and filed on May 5. It was a typical mining camp of the time, with a rowdy crowd of mountain men. It's said that Five-Finger Lewie, the toughest one of all, could punish barrels of whiskey and played as stiff a game of poker as anyone in camp. There was also Billy the Packer, who took no back seat to smashing a man in the face or making a tenderfoot take to the woods. By 1897, the town boasted six hotels, five saloons, four general stores, two meat markets, two lumberyards, two carpenter shops, one shoe repair store, one assayer, two restaurants, two laundries, two barbershops, a newspaper (the *Silverton Miner*), and a cigar and stationery store.

Silverton is at mile 22 from Granite Falls. Slow to 35 mph (the speed limit) and enjoy the old houses that line the road on the left. Turn right and cross the bridge; all the property in the town site is privately owned and, as of this writing, some of the streets in the town which were once county roads and open to the public have now been vacated. This means that some of the streets in the town site may

---

[47] Why this prejudicial law was enacted is unknown because the camp prided itself on the fact that all nations of the world were represented there except China. This was even stranger in light of the fact that Snohomish County then had a law that excluded Chinese people from its soil. We can only speculate that the miners feared large masses of Chinese would descend on the rivers and streams and remove all the placer gold before whites got it.

now belong to the property owners that abut them. Remember, it's your responsibiity to check the status of all properties you may need to cross to get to a mine. Do not turn after the bridge crossing; instead, follow Whitton Avenue straight ahead and note the old, unpainted house on the left. This is the old Reiley place, which is said to still have bullet holes in the ceiling from wild poker games in days long past. During Prohibition, it is said, a still was in operation here to fulfill the needs of the locals, and when news that the revenuers were on their way to search for moonshine, the still was disassembled and taken up the street to the preacher's house (the red farm house up the road on the right) and hidden. According to the story, the Feds searched every building in town but the preacher's house and left without finding a thing. The still was then moved back to the Reiley place and put back in business.

Independent Mine

Rated at B-2 to C-5. The most extensively worked mine in the district was the Independent (also known as the Copper Independent and the Virginia Agenda). This mine tapped one of the first ore deposits found in the area, and the town took its original name, Camp Independence, from this claim. This mine and the old Eclipse tunnels were worked off and on into the 1940s by several different companies. While the area is noted mostly for copper and silver mines, the Independent was, for the most part, a gold producer. In September 1902, construction of a 300-ton-capacity concentrating and cyanide mill was begun on the flat just west of the town site. A 4-by-6-foot wooden flume 5,600 feet long was also in the works that was to provide a 54-foot head of water from the Stillaguamish River 1 mile above town to the mill. This would supply ample water power to run the mill and a 10-drill air compressor. It would also provide lights, not only for the mill but also for the town. The mill was housed in a nine-story building, one of the tallest in the county. By December 1, 1903, the mill and flume were sufficiently completed that a carload of concentrates was shipped to the smelter. Some finishing touches remained to be completed, but the Independent was in business. The compressed air for running the drills was piped from the mill through a 4-inch-diameter pipe to the portal of the #3 adit, where a receiver tank was located. From there it was distributed throughout the mine via 2-inch pipes to the big air drills that bored the holes for the giant powder.

Cross the bridge at Silverton, and then proceed along Whitton Avenue to what looks like the end of the street. Continue along a lesser road that resembles a driveway. Continue past a large house on the right, until you reach the intersection of another road, Third Avenue. From here you have two options. The first option, which requires that you have prior permission to cross the private property, involves parking out of the way on the side of the intersection and hiking to the right (west) for about 100 feet. The old puncheon road leading off to the left goes to the mine. It is on private property, so you must get permission before using it. The second option, if you do not get permission, is to continue driving straight ahead on Whitton Avenue, ignoring the intersection and parking at the very end of the road. Begin walking to the right (west) through the brush for about 50 feet on Fourth Avenue to the old puncheon road. This route allows you to remain on public land all the way. Turn left on the road and follow it as it eventually turns into a creek bed. Watch closely for a trail that crosses the creek bed just after the road (stream bed) turns left; climb the trail up the right bank. (The left trail leads to the old Imperial Mines). Notice that you are still on an old puncheon road. From the creek bed, walk a couple hundred feet to a point where you can look left up a wide cut in the trees for quite a distance.

You now have a choice: If you prefer a mellow walk, follow the road up the switchback. For a more vigorous trek, take the shorter but steeper route up the open swath. This swath was cut up the hillside as a path for the compressor pipe to the mine from the powerhouse at the town site. Either way, you end up at the end of the road, where a large silver log points the way to Independence Gulch and the mines. Scamper up the tailing pile and turn to the left toward the gulch. The #3 adit is just to the right of the gulch. This was the main working and haulage tunnel for the mine and is connected underground, by a series of raises, with the other four main and three intermediate levels above.

> **Warning** Abandoned underground mine workings and related surface structures are NEVER safe! Please stay back from them; breathe in the history, take pictures, and then walk away. These mines are old, poorly shored, and in some cases collapsed.

After peering into the dank darkness of the mine, trace your way back along the flat from the mouth of the mine to the point where the trail drops down the tailing pile. Instead of descending the tailing pile, continue along the flat to its end and climb down the brushy slope to the next flat. This was the site of the blacksmith shop, machine shop, and ore bunkers: Look around at some of the old pieces of equipment and tools left by the miners. (You might have to dig through the brush and tall grass to see much of it.)

The metals mined here were gold and silver, derived from the ore minerals pyrite and arsenopyrite. The gangue consisted of sheared granite and quartz.

A typical pack train prepares to head into the hills to supply the miners. This scene is in front of the Price Hotel in Silverton. (The Coast *magazine, October 1907)*

Other smaller mines and prospects can be found up Silver Gulch by finding the trail leading away from the shop area in a westerly direction (away from the gulch) and following it as it climbs up the side of the mountain and into Silver Gulch. Look carefully above and below the trail for mine workings and structures. Many are located near the top of the mountain, including the Winter Coon, Summer Coon, and Cleveland claims. If you choose not to continue up the gulch, drop down to the switchback road and descend to the point where the wide cut in the trees meets the lower part of the road—in other words, to the point where, on the hike up, you made your decision to continue up the road or turn up the hill. At this point, you can continue across the road and down the hill at roughly a 45-degree angle to your left until you reach the creek. Once there, look across the creek for a large oak tree on the hill about 150 feet up on the opposite bank. Once you find it you have also found the entrance to the #2 adit, which is about 500 feet long but failed to strike anything worth mining. Upon returning to the road, walk down to where the road enters the creek bed again and, if you have time, instead of turning left and heading to the car, cross the creek bed and walk the trail for about 300 feet (note the old puncheons in the trail) to the base of a large tailing pile. At the top is an old cabin believed to be built by Sheridan McElroy, a well-known engineer and carpenter, in later years. Just behind this cabin is the lower adit of the old Imperial Mine,[48] now caved at the portal.

Imperial Mine

Rated at A-1. The Imperial was for the most part a silver and copper prospect with lesser amounts of lead and arsenic. The Independent Mine just a few hundred feet away produced higher values in gold. The ore mined at the Imperial was chalcopyrite, arsenopyrite, and galena. This is one of the better areas around Silverton to find ore samples of showcase quality, and you should search the tailing piles outside the mines for specimens, but be sure to get the permission of the owner before collecting samples.

The mine is 640 feet long with a 60-foot raise to the surface that opens in a short snub tunnel 80 feet above and to the right of the adit. It also contains a 26-foot winze and two small stopes. The 600-foot adit #2, which is partly flooded and has minor stoping, is 140 feet above the lower tunnel. Another 140 feet above this is tunnel #3, which is about 410 feet long and also partly flooded. In the large gulch to the left of this adit and 780 feet above the upper tunnel is the Pieere (Pierre?) tunnel, a 375-foot crosscut. These mines, along with several short adits on the old property, total more than 2,000 feet of underground workings.

> **Warning** None of these tunnels is shored, and the rock is shattered and in danger of collapse. KEEP OUT FOR YOUR OWN SAFETY. THIS MINE IS IN A SERIOUS STATE OF DETERIORATION.

As you drive back toward the old auto bridge (now a foot bridge), park off the road at the intersection just before the Stillaguamish Bridge at Silverton. Walk across the foot bridge to the left and follow it as it swings left past several summer cabins to a three-way intersection with a road that comes in from the right. Turn and follow this road about 250 feet and note a trail drifting off to the left. (This is now private property, and access should be by permission only.) This crosses what appears to be an old, narrow road bed at about 75 feet from the point at which you left the road. This is not a road but the remains of the old water flume from the river to the Independent Mill. Cross the flume and continue a short distance to a couple of brick structures. These are the remains of old mercury retorts[49] built to process mercury found in the incline shaft a short distance away. Cross the small, dry stream bed and proceed toward the base of the mountain, where you will find two adits.

> **Warning** Near the entrance to the shorter of these tunnels is the mouth of the incline shaft. Watch your step and stay clear. It might be obscured by brush or debris.

The long, flooded mine is the old Eclipse Mine, which later became known as tunnel #1 of the Copper Independent Company. This adit contains about 300 feet of workings and is VERY DANGEROUS AND IN A STATE OF COLLAPSE. The other, shorter portal was put in later, possibly by Ore

---

[48] This was located as the Anacortes Ledge and was one of the first claims filed in the area during the summer of 1891. It was incorporated into the Imperial Mining Company in 1897.

[49] A retort works like a moonshine still; the mercury ore (cinnabar) is heated in the kiln until the mercury vaporizes. As the vapors rise, they enter cooling coils, called condensers, where as the vapors cool they liquefy and drain into 80-pound flasks.

Recoveries Inc. in 1938 or by Lambda Chemical Products Company between 1939 and 1942. The latter were the last operators to ship ore from the mine before it was shut down by a federal law that closed all mines that were not producing large amounts of war-essential minerals.[50] The incline was a two-compartment shaft 5-by-8 feet in cross-section and descended 240 feet to access horizontal drifts at the 120-foot and 200-foot levels, which comprised another 300 feet of underground workings. The rock collector won't find much here, although some of the mercury extracted from the mines was said to be native mercury. More adits can be found along the base and on the sides of the mountain (known as Huckleberry Ridge) here.

Nemo Tunnel

Rated at A-2. In 1897, five claims were held here by C. H. Packard, A. W. Hawks, and D. C. Johnson of Everett. They had driven a 175-foot tunnel in hopes of tapping the riches there. This tunnel is now about 300 feet long and rather uninteresting. A difficult climb up the cliff will bring you to a higher tunnel that is only about 30 feet long. This can be a dangerous climb, and the reward is not worth the effort or the risk. While we found no evidence of rich ore in the tunnels, we did find one large boulder of arsenopyrite near the road, and a chip from it was assayed. The value in gold registered at 1.25 ounces per ton, a very rich amount. If only one could determine from where the boulder originated!

Drive about ¹/₂ mile east from Silverton, and locate an old road on your left, leading into the forest. If you reach the Deer Creek Bridge, you've gone too far. Park on the shoulder of the Mountain Loop Highway, and walk up this road for about ¹/₃ mile. Listen carefully for the sound of gurgling water to your left. When you hear the water, turn left and locate the lowest tunnel that we have discovered, a short distance above the road on the cliffside.

Deer Creek Mines

Rated at D-2. Drive through Silverton on the Mountain Loop Highway for 1 mile to Deer Creek Road, and then turn left. This was the site of the Bonanza Spur on the Everett and Monte Cristo Railroad, where cars that serviced the mines along Deer Creek could be left to be loaded and unloaded. It is now a popular winter destination for Nordic skiers, snowshoers, and snowmobilers. Drive up this narrow dirt road 1 mile and watch for a wide spot on the right with the remains of an old logging road leading off into the brush. This road is now impassable by vehicle, but you can walk to near its end, where a trail takes off to Devil's Lakes and the area of the Double Eagle Mines. These consist of a series of short adits that you can seek out for yourself. These mines were said to contain free-milling gold.[51] One adit is known to be near the falls at the first switchback and another along the trail to the lake, but we have not visited either of them.

Bonanza Queen Mine

Rated at B-2 through D-5. The Bonanza Queen Mine dates back to the summer of 1891, when John Bender, Z. W. Lockwood, and J. O. Marsh located the Bonanza Queen Ledge. Over the next two and a half decades, the mine changed hands several times. Soon after the turn of the century, the claims were patented. By 1918, about 830 tons of ore averaging 3.5 percent copper had been produced. The

---

[50] Although copper, silver, lead, and mercury were found in this mine, they were not found in sufficient quantities to comply with federal law, so the mine had to be closed.

[51] Free-milling gold can be seen with the naked eye and is therefore cheaper to mine because no complicated and expensive milling operation is necessary to free it from the country rock.

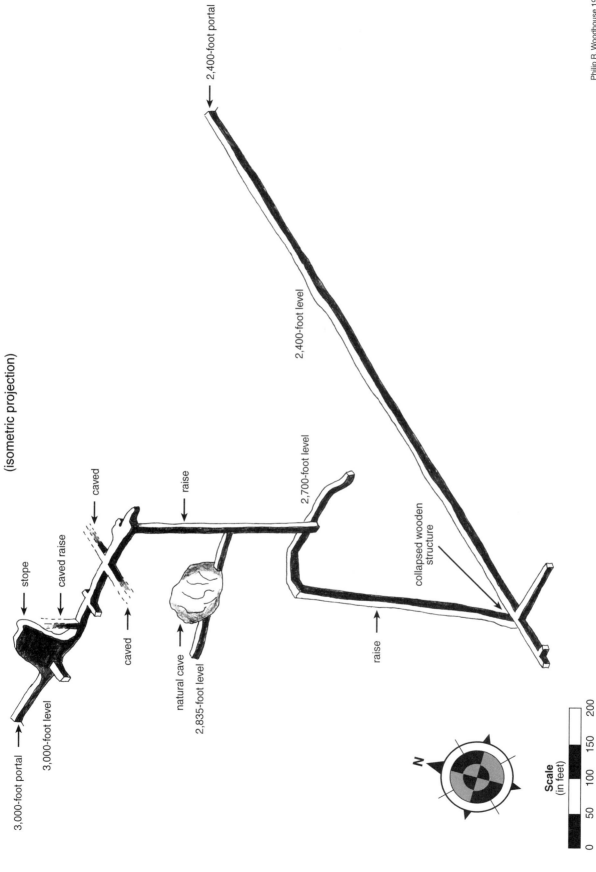

Bonanza Queen Mine
(isometric projection)

3,000-foot portal

stope

caved raise

caved

caved

3,000-foot level

raise

natural cave

2,835-foot level

2,700-foot level

2,400-foot level

2,400-foot portal

collapsed wooden structure

raise

N

Scale
(in feet)

0   50   100   150   200

Philip R. Woodhouse 1995

mine had produced off and on from the turn of the century, but it was handicapped by the sporadic washouts of the railroad. On October 18, 1924, Snohomish County took title to the property because the owners failed to pay their taxes. Since 1926, the mining claims have been back in the hands of private interests, but only occasional attempts at mining have been made. No ore has been shipped since that time, and most work has been put into an effort to repair the raise from the main haulage level to the 2,700-foot level.

This is a patented mine that you cannot access without written permission from the owners. From the Mountain Loop Highway, take a left onto Deer Creek Road and at about 2 miles begin looking for a small, badly deteriorated road descending to the left. Park and walk down to the creek and, assuming you have the permission of the owners to proceed, cross the creek and take the left-hand road (trail) at the fork just above the creek. Follow it to the end and find a trail leading straight ahead across a small seasonal creek. You will come face to face with a large rock. Take the trail that leads above the rock, and ascend the steep switchback trail to some old mine debris at an elevation of about 2,400 feet; turn right and find the haulage tunnel 25 feet beyond. This long crosscut tunnel was driven 1,100 feet into granite to cut the ore deposit at depth and to facilitate a raise to the upper main workings in Glacier Gulch at an elevation of 3,000 feet. At 1,000 feet from the entrance of this haulage tunnel is a crosscut tunnel where the remains of the collapsed raise is located. This ascended at an 81-degree angle to the 2,700-foot intermediate level, and from there another raise climbed an additional 300 feet to the 3,000-foot level.

> **Warning** The upper levels ARE NOT on the same side of the hill as the haulage tunnel and must be accessed up Glacier Gulch. Do not attempt to climb above the haulage tunnel because the hill becomes very steep and dangerous.

Getting to the upper workings is tricky and dangerous and should not be attempted. However, if you feel it is worth putting your life at risk, all that can be said is that you reach the upper levels by finding a route up the cliff where the gulch and a small waterfall are clearly visible to the right of where you parked. After you reach the top of the cliff, ascend the gulch to your immediate left. (This gulch is not visible from the road where you parked.) The intermediate level (2,700 feet) is caved at the portal, and the upper level is open at an elevation of 3,000 feet and is about 800 feet long with various raises and stopes.

> **Warning** Do not enter this mine! The dangers include the top of the raise that accesses the 2,700-foot level. This raise is wide open and presents a 300-foot sheer drop.

Some nice samples of ore have been found on the tailing pile just outside the mine adits, including the lower haulage tunnel. The ore mined was pyrite, chalcopyrite, pyrrhotite, arsenopyrite, sylvanite, and realgar, and the gangue consisted of quartz, calcite, and altered diorite.

St. Louis and Jackson Mine

Rated at B-2. This mine dates back to the early 1890s, when pioneer prospectors John (Jack) Jackson and Louis (St. Louis) Lundlin worked the upper reaches of Deer Creek and made locations along its banks. At the base of the lower waterfall there were once three power drills with a compressor run by a Pelton wheel. With this equipment, the lower crosscut tunnel was driven to the vein. Although the mine held promise of a rich future, the vein, while high in assay value, was too narrow to be worked profitably. Operations ceased after Jackson shipped at least one carload of high-grade ore on a large sled over frozen ground from the mine to the rail head at Bonanza Spur.

Take Deer Creek Road past the sharp switchback to the right and watch for milepost 4. Continue to the next turn to the left, pull over, and park at the wide spot in the road on the right side. Locate a steep trail down the hillside (bring your camera) and follow it as it turns right and parallels the road above. When the trail enters a small creek, look to the right and see the upper tunnel. Just over 100 feet long, this tunnel was probably the first adit and was an exploratory tunnel intended to define the upper limits of the ore body. L. K. Hodges, in *Mining in the Pacific Northwest*, a complete review of the mineral resources of Washington and British Columbia (Seattle Post-Intelligencer, 1897), reported that a winze was sunk from this tunnel to a lower one (which you will visit next), but no winze is visible now. One old map does show the winze about halfway back in the tunnel, so be careful—or better yet, stay out of the mine. Continue down the trail to Deer Creek, stop at the log crossing and look upstream at the picturesque little waterfall and pond. Then walk over to the base of the falls. There, to your left, out of sight from the trail, is the second adit and possibly the original mineral location.

Warning Near the mouth of this portal is a partly collapsed and flooded winze of unknown depth: Be careful not to step near it—IT MIGHT COLLAPSE FURTHER.

You can find some mineral samples around this short tunnel, but the scenery is by far the best part. Now proceed very carefully across the log, or wade the creek and locate the trail on the other end of the log. From this point, walk down to the building ruins.[52] You can find the remains of one of the original cabins by walking along the old puncheon road behind this ruin for about 150 feet. (At one time, this was the main road up Deer Creek and was used by many mines in the area). Back at the first cabin ruins, locate the trail down through the brush to the creek again. (This trail might be brushed over; it's near the treeline on your left.) Turn upstream to view the large waterfall as it cascades over the high, steep cliff. This view, by itself, is well worth the short walk from the car. The main mine workings are just to the right of the falls and consist of a 120-foot crosscut tunnel that strikes the ledge 105 feet from the entrance, at which point a drift runs along the vein for 250 feet and cuts a beautiful but narrow ore deposit.

Warning Near the end of the left drift are two flooded winzes of unknown depth that are covered by large planks. These should not be considered safe to cross. These winzes are NOT CLEARLY VISIBLE, so you should avoid the interior of these mines.

The metals mined here were copper, gold, silver, and tungsten, and the ore consisted of chalcopyrite, pyrite, scheelite, and possibly tetrahedrite. The gangue was sheared granite quartz.

---

[52] This lean-to was built in later years by recent owners—Carl Martin and his son Carl, Jr.—but it is on the location of one of the old mine cabins.

Great Helena Group

Rated at D-4. These claims were located in 1894 by John (Jack) Jackson, Louis (St. Louis) Lundlin, and Thomas Johnson.[53] These mines caused great excitement in the Silverton area, and plans were made for a new town at Bonanza Spur that would accommodate a huge influx of people and supplies into this fabulously rich strike, as well as large shipments of ore on their way to the smelter. Plans were also made to run a tram or a long ore chute to the wagon road 1,500 feet below the mine. But only a few small shipments of ore—totaling only about 150 tons—were made from the mine before the railroad washed out and the mines were abandoned.

Drive up Deer Creek Road and park at the Lake Kelcema trailhead near the end of the road. Walk up the road about 50 feet to find the trail, which plunges into the brush toward the ridge to the north and heads up to Deer Creek Pass near the base of Helena Peak. Just before you reach the high point, look for a lesser trail leading off to the right in the direction of the peak, and follow it to the mines. This faint track will leave the main trail about 100 feet short of the Deer Creek Pass summit. Before leaving the trail to the pass, notice that the portion of the trail that approaches the summit is wider than the previous part of the trail. This is the upper end of a pack road built by the original owners of the Helena Mines.

Once you find the old mine trail, the track is fairly easy to follow for about 1/4 mile. It gains some altitude, but it mostly contours along the northern side of the ridge that connects Helena Peak to the pass area. You will have to climb over large trees that have fallen across the trail, and in some places the brush might obscure the meager pathway. Good routefinding skills are needed here.

> **Warning** This trail will become steeper and narrower the farther you travel. It is best to leave your sneakers at home and wear a good pair of hiking boots with lug soles to aid your traction.

The trail continues its lazy contour for about 0.8 miles, and you can watch as the ridge above you becomes ever more formidable. There is no sign of mineralization on the cliffs above, and you might begin to wonder why the prospectors came this way at all. After the contouring, the trail heads abruptly upward, switchbacking up almost 1,000 feet of elevation in a very short time. Part of this ascent is across an open rock slide with virtually no trace of the trail. Make a steady climbing traverse here, and look for a few small rock cairns near the opposite edge of the rock field. These will help you find the trail again as it reenters the forest. Continue the punishing climb until the trail finally, mercifully, returns to a more gentle, almost contouring grade. At this point, however, the way is narrow and indistinct, and you will have to watch carefully to keep on the path.

Within 1/8 mile, you will arrive at the southern tunnel of the Helena Mine,[54] which is at an elevation of 4,640 feet. You'll see evidence of a considerable amount of modern-day camping in the immediate area of the adit, with sheets of decaying plastic scattered and stashed everywhere. Just to the south and up the rock slope about 150 feet is the crushed remains of a 55-gallon drum. Other evidence around this area suggests that prospecting was done here in modern times, with at least some of the access achieved by aircraft. Few old artifacts are left. If you decide, on your own, to enter the 125-foot tunnel, you will find it relatively uninteresting except for a few highlights. One is the blue stain along the right wall of the tunnel just inside the portal. Another is near the end of the tunnel, about 90

---

[53] The Helena claims were originally intended to be called the "Helma" after Jack Jackson's daughter, but during the recording process it was probably inadvertently filed as "Helena."

[54] This might be one of the upper tunnels alluded to by L. K. Hodges in *Mining in the Pacific Northwest.*

feet in, where you'll find a good showing of the vein along the right wall as you face into the tunnel. A good rock hammer and some perseverance can yield excellent samples of ore. Good samples of ore also litter the dump in front of the mine.

If you have the energy and you crave adventure and more vertical territory, climb above this tunnel up the edge of the forest to the right of the tunnel as you face Helena Peak. The previously mentioned 55-gallon drum will be in the rocks to your right. About 60 feet of elevation above this, you will come to an excellent trail, probably built in the 1890s, across the rock slide to your right. It appears to have been wide enough at one time to allow wagon travel. Follow this trail to your left across a small wooded area and into the next major rock slide. Climb this rock slide and you will encounter many rust-stained rocks, some quite large. Carefully make your way to the base of the cliffs above.

Warning This is steep country. If you don't feel comfortable here, don't attempt the climb.

When you reach the cliffs, at an elevation of about 4,900 feet, the reason for the prospectors' interest in this area becomes evident. The rocks, which rise steeply above you to the summit of Helena Peak, are stained with magnificent, intense gossan coatings. From the other side of the valley, this area must light up like a neon sign when the sun is at the proper angle. It would appear to be the mother lode of the area.

Carefully traverse the steep slope to the south (your right as you face up the peak), and you will come upon two snub tunnels, one 15 feet deep and the other 10 feet deep, plus several surface workings. By examining the tunnels, you can see why this area turned from boom to bust so quickly. The surface ore that defines the vein is spectacular. Almost every boulder that has been removed glitters with sulfide ore, and these are solid chunks, not just surface stains! However, if you dig just 10 feet into the vein, it vanishes! The rock at the back of the snub tunnels and test pits appears to be totally barren of mineralization. The tunnel that you visited earlier, now 200 feet of elevation below you, also revealed a surface deposit only.

As you scramble about the area, notice all of the $^3/_4$-inch plastic tubing scattered about the rock slides. (We'll explain in a moment.) Now descend to the lower tunnel that you first encountered on the trail. Along the rock slides above this bore, we discovered a claim notice with the date of October 1, 1976, on it. A test pit was also dug about 100 feet of elevation above this tunnel. When you return to the original tunnel, probe to the north at the base of the mine dump, and realize that the trail continues on across the next rock slide. Follow this distinct track, and you will find yourself walking next to more of that plastic pipe. The trail, and the pipe, will lead you into the woods on the far side of the rock slide, and to the main cabin site of the mine. Here you can find artifacts from the 1890s: broken pottery, pieces of a cast iron stove, and other odds and ends. The cabin appears to have been about 15 by 35 feet, and it commanded a spectacular view of the valley below and beyond. The plastic pipe stops here.

Climb directly above the cabin site and discover the main tunnel of the mine complex, which is 720 feet below the summit of Helena Peak. If you enter this adit, you will find a tunnel roughly the same length as the previous one, about 124 feet. About 80 feet beyond the portal, this tunnel turns abruptly to the left, and then it divides to the left and right, drifting about 20 feet left and 60 feet right. While there are ample blue and green stains of azurite and malachite from the decaying chalcopyrite in the vein, no good sample sites were located in the bore. There is also a test pit/snub tunnel just uphill from this tunnel to the north (left as you face uphill). At the main adit, we discovered yet another claim paper from modern times that was dated February 14, 1965. One wonders what the snow was like in the area at that time of the year.

Mountain Loop Highway

When you descend once again to the cabin site, you can contemplate, as we did, the purpose of the plastic pipe. We determined that it was used as water pipe to supply water to a portable, gasoline powered, hollow-core drilling machine that might have been helicoptered into the area. A portable pump must also have been transported to the site. The diamond bits of the coring machine require water to lubricate them, or they burn up very quickly. We found many core samples in the area, as well as pipes that had been driven into the loose soil in the direction of the veins, apparently to guide the drill until it could encounter solid rock below.

The metals mined here were copper, gold, and silver, and the ore mined was pyrite and chalcopyrite. The gangue consisted of sheared granite and quartz.

For the Rockhound

The rock piles outside the tunnels, especially the snub tunnels at the base of the cliffs, yield high-quality samples of chalcopyrite and pyrite.

The Big Four Inn in the late spring or early summer of 1931. The Hartford Eastern (formerly Monte Cristo) Railway ran just behind the row of cabins along the front of the inn. The ice caves are in the permanent snow field at the base of the cliffs. The snow is replenished by avalanches that carry new snow down the side of Big Four Mountain. (John A. Juleen photo)

Hoodoo Mine

Rated at D-3. The Hoodoo Mine was the first known mineral discovery in the Silverton area. The easiest approach is to park at the Big Four Ice Caves Trailhead (at mile 25.5 from Granite Falls along the Mountain Loop Highway). The old fireplace is still standing from the once lively resort built by the Rucker Brothers in 1920. Take the trail as if you are going to the caves and, after crossing the creek on the footbridge, step off the trail and onto the creek bed next to the Stillaguamish River. Proceed downstream while watching for a small creek entering the river about ⅓ mile from the bridge. Turn up this little stream and follow it until you stop at a large waterfall. Turn and make your way up the hillside to the right through the brush and trees.

After gaining several hundred feet of elevation, turn left (this might involve working around some cliffs, so watch your step), and proceed up the hillside above the creek. Remember, do not climb back down into the creek bed below, but slowly continue to gain elevation. You are looking for the old surface tram road, which now looks like a long-forgotten logging road. Once you are on the surface tram road and out of the logged-off area, simply follow it to the gulch and note the adit on the other side. This tunnel is about 400 feet long.

The minerals mined were copper, gold, and silver. The ore was chalcopyrite, pyrite, pyrrhotite, and stannite. The gangue consisted of quartz, calcite, and country rock.

Stop here and backtrack to the car or, if you prefer, hike to the Ice Caves about 1 mile from the footbridge and peer in. But be safe and stay out; these caves can be very dangerous. They are worth the walk to see, and in the extreme heat of summer, a cool breeze can be felt for hundreds of feet in front of them. This makes for a nice spot to stop for a lunch break on a hot day.

A Big Four ice cave in the 1930s. Notice the person standing on the snowfield far above the cave entrance. The caves today are in smaller snowfields and, with snow avalanching from above and the caves subject to collapse, are dangerous to enter. Enjoy them from a distance. (John A. Juleen photo)

Our last stop is the Sunrise Mine Trail. Turn right onto the Mountain Loop Highway and, just ahead, look over to majestic Big Four Mountain on your right, in all its snow-capped beauty. You might wonder why it was named Big Four, when five peaks are clearly visible. The mountain was not named for the peaks but for the snowbed on the eastern flank of the mountain. In mid to late summer, this snowfield melts to form almost a perfect number four as seen from the upper mines at Monte Cristo. Continue up the road to mile 28.8 and turn right on the Sunrise Mine Road. Follow this road to its end at 2.8 miles (the distance varies with road conditions) and note the spectacular view of Sperry, Morning Star, Lewis, and Vesper peaks. Eldredge Basin is straight ahead, and the large, hanging basin across the valley is Wirtz Basin. Several prospect adits and shafts dot the valley, including the Manley and Eldredge prospects, but none was reported to have shipped ore. No large-scale underground work was ever done. The Sunrise Mines are on the other side of Headlee Pass in the valley of the North Fork of the Sultan River. They are more closely tied to the Bren Mac exploratory work of the 1960s on the Sultan side, so the Sunrise Mine is covered in the Sultan Basin chapter. See that chapter for detailed hiking directions.

The Manley family, shown here, worked several claims up the Sunrise Mine trail at the headwaters of the South Fork of the Stillaquamish River. They later built a stout cabin about a mile up the trail from the end of the present-day logging road, where its remnants can still be seen. Mrs. Manley was a common sight along the railroad; she would ride her flanged-wheel rail-tricycle down to Silverton and pedal along the grade back to the mine with groceries.

The mines and prospects between Granite Falls and Barlow Pass number in the hundreds, if not thousands. Most of them are small, unnamed diggings. Few have outlasted nature's vengeance; many are caved, washed away, or covered with brush and downed timber. Their locations range from lofty mountain peaks to just across the highway from the Youth on Age Interpretive Site parking lot that is seldom noticed by travelers on the Mountain Loop Highway above. And, naturally, there are as many stories as mines. We have brought you the stories of the better known ones.

Barlow Pass in the 1920s. The gas car, or galloping goose, is headed toward Monte Cristo, 4 miles away. The small building in the background is the Forest Service ranger station. The building in the foreground is the warehouse of the Penn Mining Company at Goat Lake. Sheep Mountain presides over the scene. (John A. Juleen photo)

Sultan Basin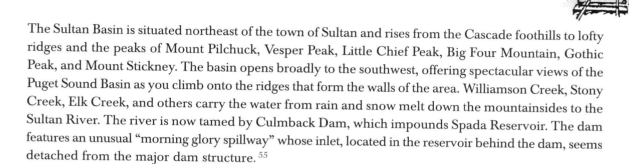

The Sultan Basin is situated northeast of the town of Sultan and rises from the Cascade foothills to lofty ridges and the peaks of Mount Pilchuck, Vesper Peak, Little Chief Peak, Big Four Mountain, Gothic Peak, and Mount Stickney. The basin opens broadly to the southwest, offering spectacular views of the Puget Sound Basin as you climb onto the ridges that form the walls of the area. Williamson Creek, Stony Creek, Elk Creek, and others carry the water from rain and snow melt down the mountainsides to the Sultan River. The river is now tamed by Culmback Dam, which impounds Spada Reservoir. The dam features an unusual "morning glory spillway" whose inlet, located in the reservoir behind the dam, seems detached from the major dam structure. [55]

> **Caution** The Spada Reservoir provides water to the city of Everett. When you are in the valley, respect the fact that any contamination you cause might have a serious detrimental effect on many people. Leave the area at least as clean as you found it.

Below the dam is the famous horseshoe bend of the Sultan River. Many placer-mining claims were located here in the past. The Sultan then joins the Skykomish River at the town of Sultan.

> **Warning** Do not enter the bed of the Sultan River anywhere below the dam. The release of water from the structure can occur at any time, without warning. The innocent trickle of the river can turn to a raging torrent in seconds. People have been caught off guard here—don't become one of them.

History

Placer mining in the Sultan Basin began in 1868, when Thomas Lockwood and James Harris began extracting $30 worth of ore per day from the river sediments. The area quickly gained a reputation as the richest placer district in the Cascades, until other discoveries in the early 1890s dwarfed the deposits there. The earliest major lode gold operation in the basin was established by the Stillaguamish and Sultan Mining Company at its mine on the eight Little Chief claims high on the side of Little Chief Mountain above Williamson Creek. It is described by L. K. Hodges in *Mining in the Pacific Northwest* (Seattle Post-Intelligencer, 1897) as being an entire cliff of chalcopyrite about 300 feet high and 120 feet wide. By 1897, a great deal of tunneling had already been done at the mine, with a large ore body blocked out. The first mine to ship ore from the basin, however, was the 45 Mine across the valley from the Little Chief. (The 45 Mine is covered in the Mountain Loop Highway chapter.)

---

[55] The dam is now also equipped with a generating station far down the river so that the water does double duty, for human consumption and for power generation, as it leaves the reservoir.

Sultan Mining Area

Lockwood Mine

Kromona Mine

Little Chief Mine

45 Mine

Bren-Mac Prospect

48-55 Claim

Iowa Mine

Florence Rae Mine

Sultan Queen Mine

Pilchuck River

an River

Gate (closed)

Olney Pass

Spada Lake

Olney Creek

Bald Mountain

Everett Creek

Gilbert Creek

Williamson Creek

Stony Creek

Greider Creek

Greider Lakes

Boulder Creek

Boulder Lake

South Fork Sultan River

Lake Stickney

Mount Stickney

Elk Creek

Kelly Creek

Vesper Creek

Red Mountain

Little Chief Peak

Copper Lake

Marble Peak

Marble Pass

Halls Peak

Big Four Mountain

Vesper Peak

Sperry Peak

Foggy Pass

Del Camp Peak

Gothic Peak

Foggy Lake

Salmon Creek

N

Scale
(in miles)

1   1/2   0   1   2   3

By 1896, the Horse Shoe Bend Mining Company was exploiting the placer deposits along a stretch of the Sultan River and had sold the Horse Shoe Bend portion of that property to the Sultan River Mining Company. To facilitate the mining operation, the Sultan River Mining Company reduced the river's flow by blasting a tunnel 800 feet long between the two end loops of the horseshoe bend. This short-circuited the river and virtually dried up the riverbed in the horseshoe.[56] Many other claims were staked and mines established, such as the Lockwood, Florence Rae, Calumet, Sultan King, Iowa, Sunrise, Kromona, and, most recently, the Bren Mac. Early in the 1890s, the main line of the Great Northern Railway was constructed through the towns of Sultan and Index, thus opening the region to exploitation on a large scale.

What to See

This river basin is a scenic wonder, with its snow-capped peaks rising above deep, narrow valleys cut by rushing creeks. Access to the area is limited due to its classification as a watershed. As a result, the area is in a more primitive state than it would be otherwise, so don't expect to drive to too many places in the basin. Hiking and some mountain biking are the best means of getting around. Hiking or biking to the Bren Mac, Iowa, or Florence Rae mines will take you into a valley in which the roads are closed to vehicular traffic. Many mountain climbs begin in this area, and the ascent of Mount Stickney or Vesper Peak will reward you with some of the most breathtaking views around.

For the Rockhound

The area of the Little Chief and 48-55 claims high on the ridge between Little Chief Mountain and Vesper Peak contain some fine specimens of very large quartz crystals. Also to be found are garnet and other crystal-forming minerals. These locations are difficult to reach, and caution should be exercised.

> **Caution** A few of the claims along this ridge are patented property, and you must obtain permission from the owners before entering.

Getting There

To reach the Sultan Basin, drive east on Highway 2 from the town of Monroe through the town of Sultan. Just as the speed limit picks up upon leaving the town, turn left onto the Sultan Basin Road. Drive about 11 miles up Olney Creek to Olney Pass. You must sign in at this point, because here you are entering the watershed. Notice and obey the rules posted. The valley is patrolled. To reach the other side of Spada Reservoir, to visit Culmback Dam, or to reach the 45 and Little Chief mines, take the left-hand road after Olney Pass and switch tightly back to cross the dam. To remain on the eastern side of the river and to reach the Florence Rae, Iowa, and Bren Mac mines, take the road straight ahead. To head up the South Fork of the Sultan River toward the Kromona Mine, take the right-hand road (which is now gated and closed to vehicular traffic). It is exactly 5 miles from the gate to the Kromona mill site.

---

[56] The project had varied success because the tunnel became clogged with debris every time the river went on a rampage. Many attempts were made to keep it clear. Some worked, some did not. Today the tunnel is plugged at the upper end.

Geology

In some ways, the geology of the Sultan Basin can be thought of as a southern extension of the geology described for the Silverton area in the Mountain Loop Highway chapter. The intrusive Tertiary dunite along which most of the major mines in the Silverton area are situated extends to the south into this valley and provides the lodes of the Little Chief, the 45, and the 48-55 garnet prospect on Vesper Peak. This intrusive body contacts Upper Jurassic/Lower Cretaceous layers consisting of mostly sedimentary and some volcanic rocks on the west. On the east, it contacts low-grade, pre–Upper Jurassic metamorphic rocks characterized by breccias and greenschists. The lower portion of the Sultan Basin, along the horseshoe bend region, is composed of Tertiary/Cretaceous basic intrusive rocks consisting of diorite and gabbro. Intruded into this are small bodies of Tertiary/Cretaceous rocks consisting of granite, granodiorite, and quartz diorite. Up the South Fork of the Sultan River, the Upper Jurassic/Lower Cretaceous rocks abut Tertiary granitic rocks. It is along this latter contact that the Kromona Copper Mine is located. All told, many contact zones exist for the formation of ore deposits in this region, and Mother Earth does not disappoint.

The Bear Cave, a natural cavern on a vein adjacent to that of the Kromona Mine. To reach this cave, you must climb over the ridge from the mine's adit and descend the opposite side of the ridge. (Sky Valley Historical Society Collection)

The Mines

Little Chief Mine

Rated at D-4. This mine, which is located on several patented claims with two mill sites, lies on the side of Little Chief Peak across the creek from the 45 Mine (in Section 5, T29N, R10E). The first claims were staked in 1891 by Archie Williamson and A. Gordon. The claims were then patented by the Stillaguamish and Sultan Mining Company.

Reaching this mine requires good route-finding skills and mountaineering experience. After you locate the area of the mine on a USGS map, drive up Williamson Creek as far as you can, park, and continue on foot until, according to the map, you find an appropriate route up the right side of the valley as you face upstream. Ascend until you approach 3,000 feet elevation. You should be able to see the red stains on the wall of the gully in which the mine is located.

> **Warning** Proceed with caution. This is steep, unforgiving country.

Two tunnels are situated on the Little Chief claim, both lying in a steep gully. One is at 3,000 feet elevation, and the other is 800 feet farther to the east and is 700 feet higher in elevation. Both are bored into the northeast wall of the canyon. The lower tunnel was drifted about 410 feet to the east, and no veins were intersected, with the only mineralization being a small amount of iron sulfide. Apparently, the miners were building the lower tunnel in an attempt to reach a vein that outcropped near the upper tunnel, but they never located it. The upper tunnel branches only 30 feet inside the adit and cuts two fracture zones containing some mineralization.

The gangue materials encountered at the Little Chief were quartz and calcite. The metals mined were primarily gold and silver, with some cobalt and nickel. The ore minerals consisted of chalcopyrite, arsenopyrite, and pyrrhotite.

Alpha and Beta Placers

Rated at D-2. Along Williamson Creek, between the 45 Mine and the Little Chief, are the Alpha and Beta Placers. No evidence of workings on these patented properties can be seen today, and no production records remain to indicate what, if anything, was once produced there. Northwest Underground Explorations hasn't been able to locate these properties.

> **Note** Due to the abandonment of the North Fork Road, the ratings for the following mines are taken from the Greider Lakes Trailhead.

Sultan King Prospect

Rated at E-4. Also known as the Sultan Queen, or the Hicks property, this mine is located at the headwaters of the North Fork of the Sultan River. This places it in the south 1/2 of Section 36, T29N, R10E, and the north 1/2 of Section 1, T28N, R10E at elevations ranging from 3,300 feet to more than 5,000 feet. It can be accessed by 3 miles of trail beyond the end of the Sultan Basin Road. The prospect consists of 16 claims, 8 of which are patented. One adit on the property allows entry to 1,200 feet of underground workings, while other small adits and open cuts complete the attempts at mining. The metals taken from the Sultan King were gold, silver, copper, and molybdenum. Forty-two tons of ore were reportedly shipped to the Tacoma Smelter in 1920. The ore was valued at $42 per ton.

The mine is blasted into the western flanks of Crested Buttes approximately 3 miles southeast of the Florence Rae bunkhouse, which is at the very end of the North Fork Sultan River Road. From the bunkhouse, a very overgrown caterpillar track road leads southeast up the valley. Then a badly deteriorated foot trail continues on to the workings.

Florence Rae Mine

Rated at E-4. At the end of the old road is the old Rudebeck Cabin (elevation 2,500 feet)—if it is still standing. Several trails lead up the hillside to a number of different workings. At one time, a two-cable, gravity-operated tramway about 4,500 feet long connected a bunker on the road with the Florence Rae Mine, at an elevation of 4,450 feet. Looking up Red Mountain from the old cabin, the Florence Rae adit is at the head of the talus slope.

Also known as the Rudebeck Mine, this mine consists of 14 unpatented claims in Sections 26 and 27, T29N, R10E, at elevations between 4,000 and 5,000 feet. Drive as far as possible, walk or bike to the end of the North Fork Sultan River Road,[57] and then proceed by trail to the mine. A total of 606 tons of ore were shipped to the Tacoma Smelter in 1918 and 1919 and between 1938 and 1941. The ore produced about 12.6 percent copper and 4.2 ounces of silver per ton, with some gold also being extracted. Also part of the Florence Rae group are the Moshier Mine, with an estimated 1,400 feet of underground workings, and the Junie Mine, which is said to have a 170-foot drift on the property. Metals assayed were gold, silver, copper, zinc, and nickel.

An adit of the Marguerite Moshier Mine in Sultan Basin. (Mining Truth magazine, September 1, 1928)

Iowa Mine

Rated at D-3 for the lower adit and D-4 for the upper adit. This mine, also known as the Mint Mine, was originally staked by George S. Moshier in 1901 (in the northwest 1/4 of Section 27, T29N, R10E). The North Coast Copper Company developed the mine, but it became idle until it was again worked in 1914, when the Iowa Mining Company was formed by M. W. Stotreon, Frank Curtis, and others. In 1915, 104 tons of excellent-grade copper ore were produced. The property again became idle until 1930, when the Sultan Basin Mining Company did considerable exploratory work on the Calumet claim (one of the Iowa group of claims) and also shipped about 96 tons of ore from the old Iowa Mine workings. When we visited, one of the original two mine buildings was still standing in the valley but in an advanced state of disrepair. A two-cable, gravity-operated aerial tram 1,000 feet long once connected the mine (at 2,550 to 2,895 feet of elevation) with the camp in the valley below,[58] while a single-cable

---

[57] This road may be difficult to bike because of the removal of a critical bridge, which makes it very dangerous to reattain the right of way on the other side of the gulch that this bridge once spanned. Getting yourself across will be challenge enough. You might want to try going up-river and crossing as best you can. Then you can regain the track of the road by heading cross-country toward the valley wall.

[58] Parts of the lower aerial tramway can be found just upstream from the cabin.

aerial tram connected the lower workings with the Calumet claim 2,000 feet up the side of the mountain. Remnants of these trams can be found on the property today.

Drive and hike the North Fork Road for 6 miles beyond the Greider Lakes Trailhead. Look for the cabin (still standing in 1994) on the right side of the road. From the old cabin, the mine dump of the lower tunnel can be seen several hundred feet above the creek. An old switchback road climbs to the portal of the lower tunnel. From here, a very steep (and dangerous) climb up a rock outcropping to the right of the lower adit will bring you to the mine dump of the upper (now caved) workings. On the knob above these workings are the glory holes.

The Iowa property has three adits, which total about 1,000 feet of underground workings. Tunnel #1 is at an elevation of 2,550 feet, tunnel #2 is at 2,850 feet, and tunnel #3 is at 2,895 feet. Stoping is evident in all three of the tunnels, but tunnel #3, now caved at the portal, is perhaps the most interesting because it stopes to the surface in a glory hole. A crosscut in this tunnel also penetrates the mountain, exiting in a steep gully and providing it with two adits. A 110-foot tunnel was driven southward on the Calumet claim. This is most easily accessed by trail from the Florence Rae property farther up the valley.

The metals mined here were copper, gold, and silver, derived from the ore minerals chalcopyrite, scheelite, powellite, molybdenite, sphalerite, bornite, and malachite. The gangue was quartz, calcite, and chlorite.

A certificate representing 1,008 shares of Sunrise Mine stock. This mine, located high on the side of Vesper Peak in the Sultan Basin, tapped the same lode as the present-day Bren Mac prospect. (Collection of the authors)

Sunrise Mine

Rated at E-5 from the Sultan River and D-5 from the Stillaguamish River. This mine is located on the north boundary of Section 15, T29N, R10E, high on the side of Vesper Peak at an elevation of 4,400 to 4,600 feet. The first claims here were filed in 1897 by F. M. and T. E. Headlee (who became mayor of Everett in 1903) and G. E. Humes. The property is mostly a breccia pipe containing copper and molybdenum ores. There are four tunnels on the property, with the upper three being the original workings. In the 1960s, a Canadian firm, the Bren Mac Company, bored an exploratory crosscut tunnel over 7,000 feet into the breccia pipe.

Hike or bike to the old Bren Mac cabin at Vesper Creek on the North Fork Road. Then hike to the Bren Mac access road just before the cabin 4 miles from the Greider Lakes Trailhead, and climb past the Bren Mac tunnel and up the bulldozer road to the right. At the upper exploratory tunnel of the Bren Mac, make your way up across brush to open scree and boulders to a trail that traverses the open rock field between Headlee Pass and the mine. Head left on this trail until you reach the mine.

Another way to access this mine is from the Mountain Loop Highway. Drive the highway east and south up-river from the town of Silverton. Pass the Big Four Ice Caves and the Mount Dickerman

Trailhead, and cross Buck Creek. Shortly thereafter, turn right on the Sunrise Mine Road, going from pavement to gravel. Drive about 2 miles to the end of this road and park in a logged-off area.

> **Caution** This area, along with other areas in the vicinity of Barlow Pass, are well known to car prowlers. Break-ins occur often, especially to cars that have been parked overnight. Do not leave any valuables in your vehicle.

Start hiking (mountain bikes will not work here!), and cover the first mile of the trail in rough, muddy, up-and-down fashion. The trail will split, with the ruins of a cabin located to the left. Turn right at this point and cross the stream descending from Del Campo Peak. There's no bridge here—cross the best way that you can. This is much easier in the fall, after most of the snow has melted. Find the trail again and begin switchbacking sharply upward. (This was a miners' trail; steepness was not a concern for them.) You will enter a spectacular hanging valley where the grooves cut by its forming glacier can be clearly seen on the wall of the canyon opposite the trail. You are entering Wirtz Canyon.

Continue to follow the trail as it ascends the right-hand wall of the canyon, and note the grand vistas behind you as you gain elevation. You will climb many steep, small switchbacks through a stand of ancient, virgin timber and then cross a rock field where care must be taken to maintain contact with the track, as the shifting rocks have partially obliterated it.[59] You are heading toward a V-shaped gap in the rear wall of Wirtz Canyon. Can this be Headlee Pass, which you are seeking to cross? No, and the trail seems to end abruptly below this defile. Look carefully, however, and you will see that the trail turns sharply to the right. At this point, look up the side of the canyon, and in the left-hand gully you will see the upper switchbacks of your trail immediately below Headlee Pass at the top of this chute.

Head upward once again to Headlee Pass, at an elevation of 4,600 feet. Stop here and cool your feet. Take in the view of the Sultan Basin, which lies on the opposite side of the pass. Continue along the trail, over the rock field immediately ahead of you, toward Vesper Peak, the white pyramid beyond. The mine lies at the end of the trail.

To vary your trip, leave the trail at the waterfall just before reaching the mine, and climb upward along the stream to the arm of Vesper Peak to the 6,200-foot summit. The views from this mountain will take your breath away, but watch your step: Vesper Peak is a matterhorn, and the north face drops 3,000 feet to beautiful, green Copper Lake. Beyond Copper Lake is the site of the 45 Mine. Along one of the ridges above the western side of the lake lie the 48-55 and Little Chief properties. Brick-red Big Four Mountain rising on the east side of Copper Lake affords a stunning contrast in colors, especially with an azure-blue sky serving as the backdrop.

> **Warning** If you have climbed over Headlee Pass from the Stillaguamish River Valley to reach this area, remember to *cross back across the pass* when returning to your vehicle. Failure to do so will place you in the Sultan Basin, a long way from where you began.

---

[59] People often leave rock cairns along this part of the trail to mark it. Look for them, but don't be too disappointed if you don't find any. Once you have located the way, a nice gesture is to build a few rock cairns of your own to give those who follow a route.

The metals found at this mine were copper, gold, silver, and molbdenum, with the ore minerals being chalcopyrite, molybdenite, pyrrhotite, and bornite. The gangue consisted of quartz, siderite, and brecciated metamorphic rock. This is reported to be a good crystal hunting area.

Bren Mac Mine

Rated at C-3. The story of the Bren Mac demonstrates the difficulty of attempting to mine in the Cascade Mountains in the 20th century. In 1972, the Bren Mac Company tried to undercut the three old Sunrise tunnels by driving over a mile of crosscut tunneling to block out the ore body within Vesper Peak. The ore that they blocked out reportedly consisted of 40 million tons of low-grade copper/molybdenum ore as well as significant values of tungsten and some gold. Their exploration revealed that the ore body appeared to continue far below the tunnels and could be tapped at a lower level, thus accessing a greater amount of ore. To this end, Bren Mac proposed boring a haulage tunnel from the Williamson Creek Valley, near the Alpha and Beta claims, beneath the Little Chief, and into Vesper Peak. Because of the sensitivity of this area as a watershed, the City of Everett threatened to sue Bren Mac, reasoning that any large-scale mining operation would degrade the city's water supply. Bren Mac protested that their water would be recycled at the mine and would not pollute the environment, but to avoid the possibility of protracted litigation, Bren Mac put forth another, more ambitious, proposal: instead of accessing the ore body from the Sultan Basin, they would reach it from the valley of the Stillaguamish.

The operation that Bren Mac proposed would have located the adit below the hanging valley of Wirtz Canyon near the Sunrise Mine Trailhead at the end of the Sunrise Mine Road. A large headhouse was to be built there, along with a concentration mill and other support facilities. The tunnel would have been a 12-by-20-foot, double-track haulage crosscut 2 miles long to cut the ore body at depth. This would not have tapped the lode as deeply as a tunnel driven from the Sultan Basin, but it would have been lower in elevation than the exploratory work already done. According to the proposal, the waste water and tailings from the milling and mining process would be piped down the Stillaguamish River Valley as a slurry, all the way to a pumping station at Boardman Creek far down-valley from Silverton. The water would then be pumped up the mountainside to a tailing settling pond that would be built in the Bear Flats area. After settling, the water would be returned to the mine site via a gravity line to a point near Silverton, where a pumping station would return the water to the Wirtz Canyon site under pressure. This operation was to produce 5,000 tons of concentrates per day, running three shifts, 24 hours a day, seven days a week at the mill. The supporting mining operation was to produce 6,800 tons of ore per day by working five days a week and two shifts a day. All tailings from the milling operation would be piped as a slurry down the pipeline to Bear Flats. Again, because of the environmental sensitivity of the area, the responses to the proposal were mostly negative, and the project was never undertaken.

Finally, an agreement was reached in the early 1970s, in which the company would run a long crosscut into Vesper Peak from the North Fork Sultan River side. About 7,000 feet of crosscut and drifts weave their way through the massive breccia pipe deep in the core of the mountain.

We visited this tunnel in about 1986 and 1990 and discovered, among other things, that the mine has reduced oxygen in the tunnel. At that time, the adit was in a state of collapse and very nearly caved. We determined that the tunnel was completely exploratory in nature, because there is no evidence of stoping or any other effort to remove ore other than for assay purposes.[60]

---

[60] The authorities were not pleased when the Bren Mac was abandoned without the requisite cleanup work being performed on it. Attempts to enforce the cleanup have, as yet, come to naught.

Warning Today, the tunnel is probably completely caved, but even if it is not, due to the conditions noted above, entry is highly discouraged. Explore the area, enjoy the beauty around you, and live to visit again on another day.

In addition to the adit just described, the Bren Mac Company also ran a cat road up the mountainside to the right of the tunnel toward the old Sunrise Mine's lower workings. Along this road, the company drifted two exploratory tunnels on different levels toward the lode of ore to help define its boundaries. These bores are in the vicinity of the lower Sunrise Mine tunnels and might even be extensions of them.

Drive, hike, or bike on the North Fork Sultan River Road for about 4 miles beyond the Greider Lakes Trailhead. Just before crossing Vesper Creek, find a bulldozer road that ascends the hillside by switchbacking steeply to your left as you face up-road. Follow this steep road for about $^2/_3$ mile to the adit. The bulldozer road continues upward to the short exploratory tunnels located higher on the mountainside. Farther up the side of the mountain is the Sunrise Mine property.

The metals and minerals at this prospect are the same as for the Sunrise Mine mentioned earlier.

Lockwood Mine

Rated at B-2. Also known as the Lockwood Pyrite, this property is on the southern side of Blue Mountain where the Sultan River enters a narrow canyon. It is in the northeast $^1/_4$ of Section 36, T29N, R8E, between the elevations of 1,700 and 2,350 feet. In 1934 and 1937, the mine was investigated by the state of Washington under the Civil Works Administration, which provided jobs to the unemployed. Two adits are on the property, one about 210 feet long and the other about 15 feet long. The investigations determined that 3.5 million tons of ore to a depth of 500 feet were available at the site. The metals in this ore are iron, sulfur, gold, and silver. In 1994, the property was leased from the state, and assaying and core drilling were done.

Take Olney Creek Road until about a mile before Culmback Dam, and turn left onto an old logging road. Drive about $^1/_4$ mile until it dead-ends, and then travel by trail as it ascends along a forgotten, brush-covered road to an elevation of 2,100 feet. Locate a steep gulch below this trail at that elevation. The main workings are on the east side of the gulch, 100 vertical feet below.

Kromona Mine

Rated at E-4. Also called the Scriber-Jones Prospect, this mine is situated near the center of Section 13, T28N, R9E, at an elevation of 2,000 to 5,000 feet. Prior to 1992, a good road led directly to the Kromona. The road has since been closed and is probably water-barred, requiring a 5-mile walk from Olney Pass. You park at Olney Pass and hike or bike along the road, which leaves the pass area to the right, heading uphill and then left at the fork. The property was located around 1900 and originally consisted of eight claims and five mill sites. The prospect was abandoned and was later relocated by Joe Krom in 1940. He had a 1,700-foot aerial tramway constructed from the mine to the mill site along the river below. The buildings at the adit, which is located 900 feet up the mountainside from the road, consisted of a headhouse, tramway terminal, bunkhouse, cookhouse, and toolshed. In 1952 and 1953, a flotation mill was built near the lower tram terminal to produce a copper and molybdenum concentrate from the Kromona ore. The mine operated off and on until the late 1960s, when all mining at the site ceased.

Joe Krom in the early years of the Kromona Mine, which bears his name. (Sky Valley Historical Society Collection)

An early headhouse and cookhouse at the Kromona Mine. The cable represents an early, rudimentary aerial tram, which was powered from the lower terminal. In later years, a new upper terminal was built, new aerial cables were strung, and the tramway was powered from the mine adit area. (Sky Valley Historical Society Collection)

Sultan Basin

The workings consist of several thousand feet of tunneling on three main levels and several sub-levels connected by raises and ore chutes. Other workings on the property include a short but now caved adit called the Wheelbarrow Tunnel[61] and a short adit in the gulch to the right and above the main workings, known as the Water Tunnel, which was dammed and used as the water supply for the upper camp and mine.

An interesting feature of the property is a natural cavern called the Bear Cave, located on the opposite side of the ridge. To reach it, you climb 900 feet elevation to the ridgetop above the main workings and then descend 300 feet down the opposite side. From this point, locate two talus slopes on your right as you face downhill. Traverse toward the talus slopes until you reach the first one. You will see the cave above you to your right.[62]

---

[61] This tunnel is connected just inside the main portal by a raise.

[62] Some interesting samples of bornite (peacock ore), malachite, and other copper-bearing ores have been found at this site.

In the main tunnel, a large amount of stope work exists between the lower tunnel and the upper levels. During the mid-1980s, Northwest Underground Explorations acquired the mineral rights to this site and spent several years doing assessment work and obtaining assays from the mine. One assay from the intermediate level showed 1.225 ounces of gold per ton. Rumor has it that around 1969 or 1970, a helicopter carried some people to the mine adit, where they loaded a large amount of tools and property into one of the tram cars and sent them plummeting down the cable, hoping to retrieve them later via the road. Instead, the tram car, without restraint, rocketed down the cable and struck the lower terminal, demolishing it. The contents of the car were scattered into the stream bed below. No mining has been attempted since.

The metals located here were copper, gold, silver, tungsten, and molybdenum, derived from the ore minerals chalcopyrite, pyrite, pyrrhotite, molybdenite, scheelite, powellite, marcasite, bornite, and malachite. The gangue was quartz, calcite, and shattered wall rock.

The lower aerial tramway terminal and ore bunker at the Kromona Mine. The bucket is about to enter the structure. This photograph was taken in the late 1950s. The rugged slopes of Mount Stickney can be seen in the background. (Sky Valley Historical Society Collection)

Silver Creek to Silver Lake

In 1898, former Washington State geologist Henry Landes described the hardships of prospecting in the western Cascades:

> *Anyone making his way through the mining districts of this area would be surprised at the large amount of development done, but he would be even more surprised that the bodies of ore had been discovered in the first place because of the inaccessibility of the regions and the almost impenetrable mass of vegetation everywhere present. Few places in the world present a denser growth of vegetation than does the western slope of the Cascade Mountains. In many places it is a jungle through which one can see but a few rods ahead of him. Prospecting in such a country is done under the most adverse circumstance.*

Anyone who has ventured off the road up the Silver Creek Valley can surely attest to Landes's statement. Not only heavy brush, but downed logs, steep cliffs, slick rocks, and stream beds make the 8½-mile-long canyon, stretching from the mouth of Silver Creek to the head of the hanging valley below Silver Lake, one of the hardest areas in the state to explore.[63]

Elevations in the area range from 1,100 feet to 6,140-foot Silvertip Peak. Other prominent peaks bordering the valley are Mineral Butte (5,255 feet), Crested Buttes (5,338 and 5,318 feet), Sheep Gap Mountain (5,819 feet), National Peak (5,630 feet), Hubbart Peak (5,936 feet), and Scott Peak (5,288 feet). The valley floor rises from 1,100 feet at the mouth of Silver Creek to 4,000 feet at the head of the hanging valley. Great amounts of snow often remain in various areas of the valley into mid-June, and avalanches are a frequent threat during the winter and spring months, especially in the lower, narrower region of the valley between Mineral City and Galena.

> **Warning** If you hike this area, even on the old road, be extremely careful where you step. Steep and overhanging cliffs are as common as trees in this canyon, especially in the lower portion. It would be very easy to step over one or have the overhang you are standing on give way while you are enjoying the fantastic scenery. So be careful and live to enjoy it.

---

[63] Although the mining boom started in the Silver City (Mineral City) area in about 1874, only a foot trail existed up Silver Creek until the Wilmans brothers completed a horse trail in 1890 to supply their camps at Monte Cristo. This was in spite of the fact that large mineral discoveries had been made in the Silver Creek area. These facts say plenty about the rough topography and vegetation of the canyon.

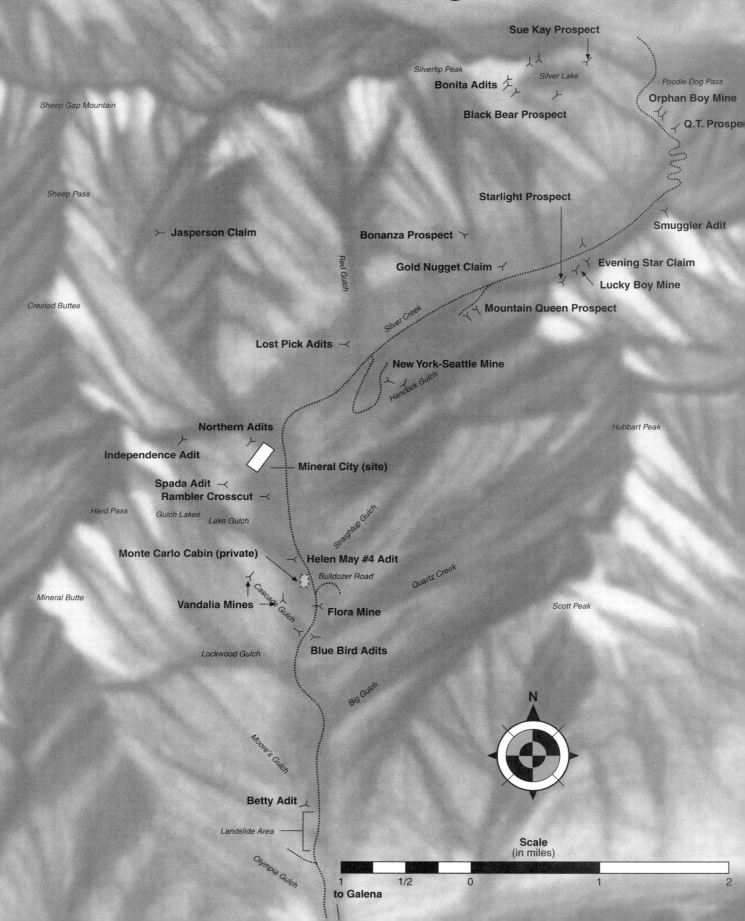

Silver Creek Mining Area

Sue Kay Prospect

Silvertip Peak

Bonita Adits

Silver Lake

Poodle Dog Pass

Orphan Boy Mine

Black Bear Prospect

Q.T. Prospe

Sheep Gap Mountain

Starlight Prospect

Smuggler Adit

Sheep Pass

Bonanza Prospect

Jasperson Claim

Evening Star Claim

Gold Nugget Claim

Lucky Boy Mine

Red Gulch

Crested Buttes

Mountain Queen Prospect

Silver Creek

Lost Pick Adits

New York-Seattle Mine

Hancock Gulch

Hubbart Peak

Northern Adits

Independence Adit

Mineral City (site)

Spada Adit

Rambler Crosscut

Hard Pass

Gulch Lakes

Lake Gulch

Straightup Gulch

Monte Carlo Cabin (private)

Helen May #4 Adit

Quartz Creek

Bulldozer Road

Mineral Butte

Vandalia Mines

Cascade Gulch

Scott Peak

Flora Mine

Lockwood Gulch

Blue Bird Adits

Big Gulch

N

Moore's Gulch

Betty Adit

Landslide Area

Scale
(in miles)

Olympia Gulch

1/2   0   1   2

to Galena

History

The history of this mining district predates that of any other district in the western Cascades of Washington State, with the first known mineral discoveries by white Americans made in 1871. George White and Hill Tyler located eight claims there that year. The following year, a small gold rush developed along Silver Creek after Joseph Prunette made his way from the Sultan Basin over the divide by way of either Hard Pass (aptly named) or Sheep Gap and located several claims on the Silver Creek side. One of the hopeful prospectors who followed the gold rush was Theron Ferguson (a member of the prominent Ferguson family of Snohomish), who in 1873 cut a foot trail from Gold Bar up the North Fork of the Skykomish River and terminated it somewhere along Silver Creek, possibly at the junction of the north and west forks of the creek. That same year, he founded the town site of Silver City at the junction of the two forks, which became the first vestige of civilization in the upper Silver Creek country.

There had been prospecting activity along Sliver Creek for some years, culminating in 1874 when Hans Hansen located the Norwegian Claim (the first recorded claim in the area) by carving the name and date on a tree 500 feet above the fork in the creek. By 1874, however, activity had died down in the Silver Creek Valley, and until 1880 Silver City was almost a ghost town,[64] with the only remaining inhabitants being George White, John Cochran, and L. T. Ireland. Later, a man by the name of Johnson discovered an outcropping of iron pyrites (fool's gold) on the bank of the creek, and, mistaking it for gold, located the Anna Claim. When news reached Snohomish City, a new (but minor) gold rush began.

In about 1880, E. C. and Theron Ferguson, along with Lot Wilbur and W. M. Whitfield, spent two or three thousand dollars to construct an arrastra at Silver City. This was a 28-foot-diameter, 24-ton ore-crushing wheel run by water power. The project failed,[65] and things quieted down again. Then, in 1882, Elisha H. Hubbart rebuilt the trail through to Galena and up Silver Creek, where he relocated the old Anna Claim along with the Trade Dollar Claim and Morning Star Claim. Discoveries continued at a rapid pace in the area through the 1880s, with most activity confined to assessment work, locating new claims, establishing claim boundaries, and building cabins.[66]

A typical scene of a miner posing with the cabin that he most likely built with his own hands. Although the cabin looks crude, a pot-bellied stove and adequate firewood would have made this a snug and toasty place in which to spend the savage mountain winters. This cabin was located near Mineral City in the Silver Creek district. (Enid Nordlund Collection)

[64] Prospectors of the 1870s bypassed the iron-capped sulphide ores of the lower Silver Creek Valley, which were said to be too low in grade and refractory. Their main interest centered on silver-lead ores and stories of free-milling gold found in the upper reaches of the district. This, coupled with the almost complete lack of transportation, distracted them from the Silver City/Galena areas.

[65] Two stories conflict here. Hodges's *Mining in the Pacific Northwest* says that a piece of amalgam about the size of a goose egg was produced and stolen by one of the employees, while the Seattle newspapers said that the gold was not free milling and therefore was incompatible with the arrastra. In either case, the project was soon scrapped. The purpose of an arrastra is to grind the country rock to the consistency of sugar to allow the free-milling gold (gold that can be seen with the unaided eye, such as nuggets or flake or placer gold) to be more easily separated. However, the gold found in the Silver Creek area was lode gold (too fine to see with the unaided eye). Thus an arrastra would be useless there.

[66] Actual ore shipments were not yet made, primarily because of transportation difficulties. The Great Northern Railroad had not yet passed the town of Index, and the connecting roads were no more than glorified trails.

In 1890, the Wilmans brothers, having located the major claims at Monte Cristo, began building a pack trail from Scott's Camp to 76 Gulch north of Silver Creek, where their mines were located. This was the first horse trail up Silver Creek, and it allowed more development of the claims in the valley. Also that year, the Silver Recovery Act was passed into law, and this, along with the big Monte Cristo strike in 1889, opened the floodgates for miners searching for silver, a mineral quite abundant (it appeared) in the district. Henry Hewitt, the "Father of Everett," let it be known that the Everett and Monte Cristo Railroad would either make its way up Silver Creek and over (or through) the divide to Monte Cristo or that a spur line would be built from Monte Cristo to Silver Creek.

The hotel at the town of Galena in 1911. Galena was situated at the confluence of Silver Creek and the North Fork of the Skykomish River, and it served as the gateway to the mines of the Silver Creek area. (Garda Fogg Collection)

Rumors of a large smelter to be located at Galena hit the newspapers, and on November 30, 1891, the plat for the town of Galena City, formerly called Scott's Camp, was filed by John N. Scott. The plat contained 30 blocks, and the town was situated at the confluence of Silver Creek and the North Fork of the Skykomish River. The lots were 25 by 100 feet, with the streets 60 feet wide and the alleys 16 feet wide. This roaring little mining town also boasted its own weekly newspaper, the *InterCascade Miner,* which was launched on April 1, 1892, after the installation of a complete printing plant. This plant was taken by rail and wagon as far as the town of Index and then hauled by pack horses the rest of the way to Galena. The first edition appeared on April 10 of that year. However, in August of the following year, due to a lack of appreciation for the paper, the editor printed a brief but sarcastic valedictory, packed up his printing outfit, and left town over the mountain trail.

On June 20, 1892, the old Silver City town site was refounded and filed as Mineral City, and it included 15 blocks. The town was located on the old Anna Claim at the confluence of the north and west forks of Silver Creek.[67] By 1894, a puncheon wagon road had been built along the west side of the North Fork of the Skykomish River from Index to Galena, partly by the miners and partly by the county.[68] (The present road runs along the east side of the river.)

As fast as the silver promise came, it faded with the repeal of the Silver Recovery Act in 1893 and with the completion of the Everett and Monte Cristo Railroad up the South Fork of the Stillaguamish River, which never passed near Silver Creek. In addition, the puncheon road under construction was badly washed out in the famous November 1892 storm,[69] leaving Silver Creek and the rest of the area

---

[67]   This town was typical of the western Washington gold camps of the time: The buildings were one-story and two-story log construction or canvas tents. They housed the usual general stores, blacksmith shops, hotels, saloons, and of course a stable or two. The streets were dirt (or mud), unleveled, and full of stumps.

[68]   This road was soon extended to Mineral City.

[69]   This was the same storm that wreaked havoc on the 3 S Railroad and the Monte Cristo Line.

isolated. Later, the Alaska Gold Rush iced the already doomed rush for wealth in the valley. Allan May, a retired *Everett Herald* columnist, might have summed it up best when he wrote, "It is doubtful that anyone got rich mining in Silver Creek. But at least they had a beautiful place to be poor."

The Mineral Hotel at Mineral City in 1900. This establishment was typical of the small hotels throughout the mining camps. One did not rent a room. A person would be lucky to get a bed indoors, out of the elements. (Josiah E. Spurr photo, University of Wyoming American Heritage Center)

A visitor to Mineral City in 1896 would have found a clutter of buildings and tents reminiscent of other early mining camps. The buildings included two stores, two saloons, two hotels,[70] and several other buildings. The photograph above shows the name as "Mineral City Hoetl," and the hotel's front window sill is loaded with mineral samples, which were likely collected by local prospectors. For the prospector, the following insight into the mineral character of the district is in order: From the upper reaches of the valley just below Silver Lake, the ore values are mostly in copper and iron sulphides carrying gold and silver. But as you descend toward the lower portions of the district below Mineral City, silver-bearing galena becomes prominent, while gold and copper values decline. Below Cascade Gulch, where the Vandalia Mine is located, to the mouth of Silver Creek, gold and copper become the minerals of interest, and silver and galena values decline.

In the late 1950s, major companies began exploring for porphyry copper deposits in the area, and in 1967 and 1968, Seacrest Oil Company explored a copper deposit using geophysical methods and subsequently drilled eight holes. Cities Services Company staked claims and drilled several holes from 1976 to 1979. In 1980, Exxon Minerals Company drilled a deep hole in a porphyry system. Other companies that explored the area included Duval Corp., Bear Creek Mining Company, Texasgulf, Inc., Nord Resources, Burlington Northern, Inc., Bren Mac Mines, Ltd., and Bethex Corp.

What to See

This valley offers breathtaking scenery, many old, short mining tunnels and prospects, and, in the upper reaches of Silver Creek, sublime alpine meadows and mountain peaks. This is definitely not whitewater rafting country, nor is it a good place to fish due to the difficulty of reaching the creek. The sides of the valley are precipitous and in many areas extremely dangerous. Where the cliffs meet the creek at the bottom of the chasm, tiny waterfalls scintillate into the churning waters below—a stunning scene,

---

[70]   Hotels in these remote mining camps seldom resembled the Old West buildings seen in your favorite John Wayne movies but instead were large, crude log cabins. Patrons did not rent a room—only a bed in the open upstairs bay, next to other travelers.

especially when the sun is at just the right angle. Watch your step when you strain to catch a glimpse of these from the roadway as you walk along; one misstep can be fatal. The roar of Silver Creek will accompany you on your trip to Mineral City and will be your constant companion as you climb into the meadows at its head. The alpine scenery at the upper stretches of the valley is the jewel in the crown of this area, with their rushing freshets and broad views of the surrounding locale.

Getting There

Silver Creek is about 8 miles northeast of Index on the Index-Galena Road. Just past the Howard Creek Bridge, turn left and cross the bridge over the North Fork of the Skykomish. After a few hundred feet, turn right at the fork in the road and proceed. You are now within the city limits of the old mining and supply camp of Galena. (Most of this area is privately owned, so take this into account if you go exploring.) When you can drive no farther (it will be obvious), park and continue on foot as the Silver Creek Road quickly deteriorates into a narrow trail that crosses a massive collapse area where the roadway has slid into Silver Creek. Past the slide, the grade of the road resumes.

Geology

The macro geology of the Silver Creek area is relatively simple, with the majority of the country rock in the valley consisting of Paleocene and Cretaceous nonmarine rocks of cross-bedded arkose and interbedded conglomerate and siltstone. The ore deposits occur largely in thin stringers and cracks in this material. As if to offer some variety to the geologic scene, the upper valley, in the vicinity of Mineral City, also has some Tertiary granitic bodies consisting of granite, quartz monzonite, and quartz diorite. These form contact zones with the predominantly nonmarine rocks, providing excellent conditions for the formation of ore bodies containing valuable minerals. These veins are substantially larger and more fully mineralized than those farther downstream. Farther up the valley, underlying the alpine meadows and extending onto the surrounding lofty peaks, are Lower Tertiary volcanic rocks characterized by ancient flows of andesite and flow breccia, along with basalt flows and some rhyolitic rocks. Occasional sedimentary rocks are also included in this group. This provides a complex mixture with ore occurring along every fissure and crack in the rock. At the valley's upper end, in the region dominated by Silver Lake, you are at the divide that separates the Silver Creek Valley from the Monte Cristo Valley to the north. Read the Geology section of the Monte Cristo chapter to learn more about this interesting pattern of geologic structure.

The Mines

The ratings were determined from the present road, or from the road's end at the washout on Silver Creek (as of 1994). Mines located before the landslide area (not shown on map) are referenced from the first fork in the road after you cross the bridge over the Skykomish River. The mines above the landslide area (see map) are referenced from the downstream side of the slide area. As of this writing, the road ends 1.3 miles from the junction of the Silver Creek Road and the Salmon Creek Road.

Several adits populate the lower stretches of Silver Creek in the Galena area, such as the Everett, Morning Glory, and Ione prospects on the east side and the Lucky Friday on the west. However, due to space limitations, we'll explore only the more prominent and notable ones. At 1 mile from the beginning of Silver Creek Road is a small gulch that crosses the road.[71] Another 1/4 mile up this gulch is the first of the mines in this chapter. We'll describe the mines in the sequence in which you'll probably want to explore them, continuing from one location to the next.

---

[71] This gulch has been known as both Pole Gulch and Olympia Gulch.

A typical prospect adit along the road above Galena. The wheelbarrow and a few hand tools are all the miners had to work with in their attempt to wrest their fortunes from the mountains. (Special Collections, University of Washington Libraries, Neg. #7022)

Silver Strip Mines

Rated at A-2. You'll find two (now caved) adits, one 10-foot tunnel, and a large pit. The lower adit, known as the "Ye Old Snowshoe Adit", is 235 feet long. A narrow but highly mineralized vein of pyrite in quartz can be found in the creek near the mouth of the tunnel. A narrow, mineralized fault is also exposed in the creek at the portal of the upper workings. Just ¹/₈ mile farther up the road, it crosses a very small but steep (and dangerous) gulch. Behind the rock slide on the left of the road is the Magnusen Adit.

Magnusen Adit of the Broken Ridge Copper Mine

Rated at A-1. The tunnel here is 575 feet long, with several small snub tunnels. The plan was probably to run this drift about 3,000 feet to intersect the Bonanza No. 1 vein (discussed a little later) above this adit. If so, another 2,400 feet of tunneling would have been necessary. This, of course, would have been a highly speculative venture at best. The adit follows a narrow, sparsely mineralized fault in fractured and jointed hornfels. Some ore was said to have been shipped in 1934.

The metals mined here were copper, gold, zinc, and silver. The ores were chalcopyrite, bornite, and sphalerite. The gangue was limestone and quartzite.

> **Warning** This mine is very unstable, so DO NOT enter it! Several rockfalls in the tunnel attest to the danger of more collapses. Merely climbing over a rockfall or brushing against the wall could cause tons of rock to fall on you.

Bonanza Mine

Rated at C-2. Continue around the bend in the road, past the Magnusen Adit, and to the fork in the road. Go up the steep switchback for about a mile to the prospect. The workings are several hundred feet up the steep hillside from the road. They consist of two open cuts and an 86-foot crosscut adit. Disseminated pyrite, arsenopyrite, galena, sphalerite, chalcopyrite, and bornite are found here. Several road cuts found below the workings expose iron-stained, course-grained quartzite breccia containing black tourmaline. A small test shipment from the lower cut was made in 1957.

Silver Creek to Silver Lake

At the side area, note the tree-covered rock outcropping on the near side of the creek below. This is reported to be the location of the Last Chance Mine.

Last Chance Mine

Rated at A-3. A 39-foot adit, driven in dark hornfels, exposes several narrow mineralized fractures less than 1.1 feet wide that contain quartz, pyrrhotite, and chalcopyrite. A sample taken from the face of the adit assayed 0.05 percent copper, nil gold, and 0.12 ounces of silver per ton. A small amount of ore was reported to have been shipped from the mine, but considering the above assay, the shipment might have been from another adit owned by the same people and reported as coming from the Last Chance Mine. We have not yet visited this adit.

Just beyond the rock slide on the Silver Creek Road, 1.6 miles from its start, is the portal of the Betty Adit.

Betty Adit

Rated at B-1. The workings consist of a 206-foot-long drift along a sparsely mineralized fault consisting of quartz-feldspar-sericite hornfels, which in turn contains sparsely disseminated chalcopyrite and pyrite. Two assays by the USBM averaged 0.09 percent copper, a trace of gold, and 0.18 ounces of silver per ton. They suggest that this adit was driven to intersect the Troly No. 2 vein, which lies some 250 feet ahead of the face of this adit.

Jeff Schempp, a member of Northwest Underground Explorations, peers from a snub tunnel a short distance up the road from the Betty Adit on Silver Creek. This tunnel is typical of the many short mine entrances in the Silver Creek area. (Phil Woodhouse photo)

Troly No. 2 Adit

Rated at B-2. Just past the portal of the Betty is Moore's Gulch. On the opposite side of the gulch is an obscure switchback trail to the old Skrinde Cabin. From this cabin, the trail continues northwest about 1,000 feet to the portal of a 23-foot adit on the south bank of a small stream. Here pyrite, pyrrhotite, arsenopyrite, chalcopyrite, and bornite in tonalite are found, and USBM assays have shown 1.24 percent copper, 0.16 ounces of gold, and 1.24 ounces of silver per ton.

Back on Moore's Gulch at higher elevations are the Schley, Troly (meant to be "trolley"), and Troly No. 1 adits, all rated at C-4. Arsenopyrite, pyrite, and chalcopyrite are the gangue, carrying zero to trace amounts of copper and only minor amounts of gold and silver.[72] The adits range in length from 60 to 330 feet.

Lockwood Prospect

Estimated rating at C-4. These claims are located on Lockwood Gulch 2.2 miles from the start of Silver Creek Road and were named for Thomas Lockwood, a well-known prospector in the area. The claims extend westward up the gulch and hillside, where assays of $23 to $97 per ton of gold, silver, and lead were reported by state geologist Broughton in 1942. Broughton also reported development of a 90-foot adit, two 10-foot adits, a 30-foot adit, and another one of unknown length. The ore was galena and pyrite.

Continuing up the road, you'll pass the upper adit of the Cascade Prospect.

Cascade Prospect

Rated at D-1. There is not much here to talk about. Below, on the creek, is reported to be the lower adit of the Cascade Prospect and the Drednot Prospect.

Drednot Prospect

Rated at D-5. The three adits (the upper and lower Cascade and the Drednot), which total 90 feet of underground workings, contain trace amounts of gold and small quantities of silver. These could be the Blue Bird Adits described on the next page.

Vandalia Mines

Rated at D-3. This property is located on Cascade Gulch, 2.4 miles from the start of Silver Creek Road. Although only a small amount of ore was shipped, these mines were considered to be among the more promising prospects in the Silver Creek District.[73] They were also among the oldest, having been located on September 17, 1888, and were owned by Frank Leslie, Edward Blewtt, William Evans, and L. S. J. Hunt.[74] They were among the few mines in the area where silver was the chief value. The property consists of three tunnels and a vertical shaft that is reported to be 75 feet deep. From the shaft, two levels were reportedly run 80 and 90 feet to open air on the side of the gulch.

About 700 feet up the gulch from the road, at an elevation of 1,825 feet, is a 330-foot crosscut tunnel that fails to strike the ledge of ore. Above this adit and upstream at an elevation of 1,915 feet is the upper crosscut (77 feet long), while around the corner in a steep, ascending side gulch is the upper adit at 1,955 feet elevation. This adit is caved, but it is reported to be 220 feet long and is said to access the vertical shaft at some point.

Silver Creek to Silver Lake

---

[72] We are now leaving the predominately copper and gold country and entering the silver and lead territory.

[73] In 1894, 200 tons of ore from the mine dump were reportedly washed down the creek by a flood.

[74] Blewtt and Hunt later became active in the development of the great Monte Cristo Mines.

> **Warning** In addition to being private property, this is very rugged and dangerous country and should not be explored by anyone untrained in rock climbing and off-trail travel. You must obtain permission from the owners before exploring here, and you should never go alone.

Blue Bird Adits

Rated at D-2. Just downstream from the mouth of Cascade Gulch, on opposite sides of and immediately above Silver Creek, are the Blue Bird Adits. These are 19 and 30 feet long. The country rock here is hornfels and gray porphyry. Assays taken across the two faults where the prospects are located indicated about 5 percent zinc with only trace amounts of copper, gold, and silver. These tunnels might be the same as the Drednot and lower Cascade prospects mentioned earlier.

> **Warning** Silver Creek in high water is very dangerous and can carry a person away in a flash! Do not try to cross it or climb to the mouth of the east side adit. It is only 30 feet long and not worth the time or trouble, and it is certainly not worth the risk of death.

Returning to the bridge over Cascade Gulch, continue up the road and around the bend. The flat area just below the road to your right was the location of the mill site, storehouse, and boarding house for the Vandalia Mines. Walk about 200 yards on the trail past a bus belonging to the Vandalia Mine owners (it is not abandoned), and off to the right locate a small gulch just opposite a drain pipe that runs beneath the road. The gulch drops steeply to the creek some 150 feet below. Near the base of this gulch, just above the creek, is the caved portal of the Flora Mine.

Flora Mine

Rated at D-2. This adit is 608 feet long and was likely intended to strike the ore body of the Salome Workings (described on the next page).

Young Ryan Taylor, son of Northwest Underground Explorations member Jeff Taylor, wears chest waders in preparation for the flooded conditions inside the Flora Mine adit. The timber cross-member indicates the height of the mine's ceiling. (Phil Woodhouse photo)

Coils of unraveling flexible ventilation piping fill this ore cart in the flooded adit of the Flora Mine. Debris, mud, and rocks partially block the entrance, causing the flooded conditions. (Phil Woodhouse photo)

Salome Workings

Rated at D-3. These workings are located at about 450 feet of elevation above the portal of the Flora Mine and on a bearing of about N 70° W. Only sporadic mineralization of arsenopyrite, pyrite, chalcopyrite, and galena occurs in hornfels along a fault that is exposed in the three adits of the Flora and Salome Mines. Although assays were poor, you can find some nice pyrite and galena samples around the tunnels, including at the caved portal of the Flora Adit. Several tons of high-grade ore were shipped from these mines. At 3 miles from the start of Silver Creek Road is the old Devenny (Monte Carlo) cabin, about 75 feet west of the road. This is private property. In the area of this cabin, on both sides of the creek, are well over a dozen small prospects, including the Monte Carlo Adits. (We have not visited these mines; the following information is taken from USBM reports.)

All the workings around the cabin contained zero to poor mineral value, but most were considered to have "potential for resources" by the USBM.[75]

Monte Carlo Adits

Rated at D-2. There are at least three adits here of varying lengths. The three adits are said to be located on the steep hillside above the Monte Carlo cabin between the steep gulch to the left of the cabin and a point just inside the timber line to the right of the cabin.

Gray Copper No. 2 Adits

Rated at D-2. The three adits here are 30 to 180 feet long. The three known Gray Copper #2 Adits are located about 1,000 feet southwest of the Monte Carlo cabin, on the hillside. The lower adit, 120 feet long, is at an elevation of 2,100 feet. The next is 30 feet long and is located above this one and slightly to the right at an elevation of 2,300 feet. The third is located above and slightly to the right of the second at an elevation of 2,400 feet. This adit is 180 feet long. A fourth adit is said to exist, but no documentation or location is available.

---

[75] Environmental concerns combined with the close proximity of the Henry M. Jackson Wilderness Area make mining here highly unlikely.

Silver Creek to Silver Lake

Helen May Adits

The eight claims here are rated at D-1 through D-4. Not all of the claims have adits on them. The adits range in length from 7 feet to 90 feet. The two Helen May #1 Adits, one 7 feet long and one 8 feet long, are located in the gulch due east of the Monte Carlo cabin across Silver Creek. The elevation of these adits is unknown.

The two Helen May #6 Adits, which are 23 and 70 feet long, can be reached by continuing up the Silver Creek Road about $^1/_{10}$ mile beyond the Monte Carlo cabin to an old bulldozer road that descends to the creek. Cross the creek if water conditions allow, and follow it south for 300 feet, where it turns east up the mountainside to an abrupt end against a steep slope where the two adits can be seen on either side of a stream channel.

Crown Point Prospects

Rated at D-2. There are two adits, which are 42 and 88 feet long. To reach them, travel about 600 feet up Silver Creek Road beyond Lakes Gulch, descend to and cross Silver Creek, and then climb the gulch several hundred feet to the portals.

Blue Canyon Prospects

Rated at D-2. The two adits are 30 and 32 feet long. They are a short distance above the Crown Point adits in the same ravine. USBM samples from this prospect assayed from 0.072 to 0.542 ounces of gold per ton—not bad at all.

Kotzebue Prospect

Rated at D-2. The single adit is 490 feet long. It is located above and at a much higher altitude than the Blue Canyon and is in the same gulch.

Siberia Prospect

Rated at D-2. This single adit is 59 feet long, including crosscuts. It is adjacent to the Kotzebue Adit.

Helen May #4 Prospect

Rated at D-1. This is the adit that you pass on the road beyond the Monte Carlo cabin just before the Lakes Gulch bridge. This adit was driven 90 feet and exposes a series of weak, sparsely mineralized joints with a maximum individual width of 0.1 feet. These joints contain pyrite, arsenopyrite, and chalcopyrite. Here again, assays were poor, with the highest coming from silver at just over $^1/_2$ ounce per ton. At 3.7 miles from the start of Silver Creek Road is a small, boulder-strewn gulch that gently ascends the mountain to the left. Look up the right side of the gulch as far as the eye can follow it from the road. This is the tailing pile of the Rambler Crosscut. It might be difficult to recognize due to the lack of mineralization in the rock.

Rambler Crosscut

Rated at D-2. This 570-foot-long crosscut (at an elevation of 2,163 feet) was likely intended to strike the Spada structure at a depth of about 700 feet. The Rambler intersects numerous minor faults and fractures containing pyrite and chalcopyrite, but none appear to be the Spada Fault.

Spada Adit

Rated at D-3. The Spada Adit is located above and to the right of the Rambler Crosscut some 700 feet higher at an elevation of 2,860 feet. This 230-foot drift is much better mineralized than the lower workings, with the best showings of sphalerite, galena, and pyrite occurring from a point 80 feet from the portal to the face. USBM assays show gold at 0.16 to 0.22 ounces per ton, silver at 12.92 to 13.46 ounces per ton, no copper, lead at 3.84 to 5.78 percent, and zinc at 10.4 to 12.1 percent.

Continuing up the road from the Rambler Gulch a short distance, you'll come to an old clearcut and a large expanded area on the road that was used as a landing pad for a more recent helicopter logging operation. In the early 1960s, the old Ben Butler Adit could be found in the logged-off area just above the road.

Ben Butler Adit

Rated at D-1. The landing pad mentioned above might have wiped out the old portal. But if you are able to find this adit, be extremely careful.[76] About 60 feet from the portal is a flooded 22-foot-deep winze. WATCH YOUR STEP! This adit, which dates to the early days of the district, also contains 145 feet of horizontal workings. Abundant arsenopyrite and minor amounts of pyrite and chalcopyrite are found along the fault in country rock in the vicinity of the winze. But assays by the USBM show only minor amounts of copper, gold, and silver.

Up the road 0.2 mile from the Ben Butler Adit is the old town site of Mineral City, which was platted at the confluence of the north and west forks of Silver Creek. The plat map shows one main street (Pine Street) running southwest to northeast, with five cross streets (Prospect, Granite, Mill, Post, and Keystone) running southeast to northwest. But the business district was actually up in the area of the present-day road, just before the point where it crosses the west fork.

Apart from the occasional gold or silver strike, the most notable event in Mineral City was the arrival in 1891 of a "fat Parisian lady," who came on horseback and took an apartment next to the hotel. With the intention of offering the fruits of the world's oldest profession, she soon found the community not in the best of humor and certainly not in a financial position to partake of her wares. According to an account in the *Seattle Times,* after a few days she mounted another pony and was last seen "humming blithely and bon-jouring the poor but tolerant citizens as she rode off down the gulch." That same year, Edward D. Cowen of the *Seattle Press-Times* wrote of Mineral City:

> *The first house you meet on entering this future great is a two-story shack without a window. If you step into it and stay long enough to get on terms of ocular familiarity with the furnishings, you will see that they consist entirely of a bar. In the prospective streets of Mineral City the chipmunks amuse themselves with an abandon, which shows they are still unconscious of the civilization that has dropped in on their habitation with an axe in one hand and a whiskey bottle in the other. The*

[76] As always, we do not recommend that you enter any mine for any reason. But should you do so on your own, please remember to watch your step and examine the roof of the mine for impending danger. Remember that danger can come at any time from any direction.

Silver Creek to Silver Lake

healthiest symptom about the place is a legal controversy over the site.... A dozen shacks and tents are scattered over the rough ground, and at the upper end of town a Frenchman has put in a hotel that meets all the requirements of the place.

Standing at the creek crossing and looking up the west fork, the prominent peaks in the distance are Crested Buttes (5,338 and 5,318 feet). To the east at 5,558 feet is the north summit of Hubbart Peak.[77] To the north, the pyramid-shaped mountain is 5,630-foot National Peak, and to its right are the flanks of 6,140-foot Silvertip Peak. Just up the west fork of Silver Creek from Mineral City (lower Trade Dollar Gulch), look for a large boulder in the stream near the left bank. On the bank beside the rock, 20 feet above the creek, are the Northern Adits.

Northern Adits

Rated at D-2. These two interconnecting adits provide a pretty good example of early exploratory hard rock mining. We do not recommend that you enter old mines, but if you choose to do so on your own, this might be one of the more interesting ones to explore. Behind the framework of the hoisting block, in a short drift, is a flooded incline winze of unknown depth. Watch where you step! If you enter the downstream adit, the first drift to the left shows a perfect example of how early miners drifted along faults looking for precious minerals. The tunnel was hand-drilled with a "single jack" and was only large enough for one man to work in at a time. This small, cramped drift suggests (as we know for certain today) that many men were smaller in those days. This mine consists of about 300 feet of workings on the main level, with no stopes or raises. The incline winze might or might not access lower workings.

Pyrite and chalcopyrite are the chief ores here, bearing minor amounts of silver and trace amounts of copper and gold. Continuing up the west fork of Silver Creek, just before the next creek junction, is the Daniel Webster Adit.

Daniel Webster Adit

Rated at D-2. Also located on the left bank, this is a relocation of the old Trade Dollar Claim and was one of the first claims located in the Silver Creek area. The adit pierces the hillside for about 150 feet, following a small stringer of pyrite. It is now partially filled with rock and debris that has been washed in by heavy runoff from the raging west fork of Silver Creek. Some nice pyrite crystals have been found on the outcropping at the portal. Chalcopyrite and bornite were the ores mined, and copper was the chief mineral. We have not thoroughly explored the area above the Daniel Webster Adit. Most of the information here has been gleaned from early maps and accounts. Above the Daniel Webster, the creek splits to the right and left. On the gulch to the left, you can gaze up, up, up, toward Hard Pan Pass (not to be confused with Hard Pass). Several prospects can be found between here and the pass. Some of the small but notable ones are the Alice, Katie, and Hard Pan. Above and around the left corner from the Daniel Webster Adit is the Independence Adit.

Independence Adit

Rated at D-2. We have not yet explored this mine, which is listed as a sparsely mineralized 600-foot tunnel. One of our members visited in 1994 and reported that the portal was open but contained about a foot of water at the entrance.

---

[77] This was likely the peak that Joseph Pearsall scaled as he followed a mineral outcropping up the mountain, which led to his discovery of the great Monte Cristo strike.

Much evidence of the earliest history of the Mineral City area lies in the gulch to the right just across from the Daniel Webster Adit, in upper Trade Dollar Gulch. Mines and prospects are numerous here and include the Jasperson Group, Union Group, Dewey No. 1 and No. 2, Copper King, Copper Queen, Champion, Alta, and Ethel. Near the turn of the century, the above-mentioned mines were owned by the Commonwealth Consolidated Mining Company, which did most of the development work on the claims. (The most extensive work was done on the Jasperson Claim.) Because of transportation difficulties, they fell idle until about 1919, when they were taken over by a Mr. McCombs. After that time, the properties became known as the Clara Thompson Mining Property. You reach the mines by climbing the right side of the gulch, on the right fork of the west fork of Silver Creek, and finding an old and poorly maintained trail leading up the gulch.[78]

Dewey No. 2 Claim

Rated at E-undetermined. This claim is on the eastern slope of Crested Buttes and extends over Sheep Gap some 300 feet on the Sultan Basin side. It has a 35-foot lower tunnel and a 25-foot upper adit that is 80 feet above the lower. The owner reportedly hand-picked specimens of ore running $200 per ton, with averages of $6 to $35 per ton (probably copper, silver, lead, and maybe some gold). This was prior to 1928, however, and today's values would be much higher. It was on this property that a crosscut haulage tunnel was planned by the owners of the Hicks Property (also known as the Sultan Queen or Sultan King) on the opposite side of the divide. This crosscut was to run an estimated 2,000 feet to a portal on the Union #2 Claim, and then an aerial tramway would deliver the ore to the mouth of Trade Dollar Gulch. From there, it could be trucked to the railroad at Index and on to the smelter.

Union No. 3 Claim

Rated at E-undetermined. This claim is located on the south slope of Mineral Mountain[79] at an elevation of about 3,400 feet. The claim is said to be covered with a huge talus slide containing low-grade milling ore of copper, gold, silver, and lead. The claim has a 200-foot tunnel running northeast in granodiorite on a vein 2$\frac{1}{2}$ to 4 feet wide between vertical walls of heavy sulfides. There is reportedly a 3-inch to 4-inch talc seam on each wall and a streak in the middle of the vein that is said to run high in vanadium. The claim also has a caved shaft, one caved tunnel believed to run 200 to 300 feet, and another 735-foot tunnel that trends in a northeasterly direction but is also caved at a point about 100 feet from the portal.

Jasperson Claim

Rated at E-undetermined. The Jasperson Claim is located near the head of a small, deep, and narrow ravine called, appropriately enough, Jasperson Gulch, which scars the western flanks of Mineral Mountain about 3,000 feet north of the junction where the two forks of the west fork join in Trade Dollar Gulch. The adit is at nearly 4,000 feet elevation. The tunnel runs east from the portal a distance of 750 feet and contains five short crosscuts and drifts as it follows a finely developed vein between vertical walls that pinch and widen from 2 feet to 6 feet or more in width. The vein carries gold, silver, lead, and copper.

---

[78] This description is based on old mining company maps and should be used only as a general reference. The trail varies from about 200 feet to 500 feet from the west fork of Silver Creek. Its elevation above the creek also varies. The trail is almost nonexistent in many places, and we suggest that you use your own judgment in traversing the hillside. Mines on both sides of Trade Dollar Gulch should be accessed from this side.

[79] Mineral Mountain forms the north side of the west fork of Silver Creek, just above Mineral City, and should not be confused with Mineral Butte, which is located southwest of Mineral City.

Jasperson Tunnel and Mill Site Claim

Rated at E-2. Although this "fraction claim" covers only about 6 acres, it was the location of a proposed main haulage tunnel that was to intersect all the known veins in the Clara Thompson Group. The tunnel is now about 35 feet long and is adjacent to the Mineral City town site on the south slope of Mineral Mountain. It is at an elevation of about 50 feet above the west fork of Silver Creek and about 100 feet northeast of the creek. The tunnel was to run N 31° W for about 4,900 feet. Plans for development included a concentrating mill on the flat just below the portal of the tunnel for processing the ore from the various mines in the group. Water for milling and power would be brought from the west fork to the mill by way of a flume. The concentrates would then be loaded onto wagons and delivered to the railroad at Index. On the claims owned by the Commonwealth Mining Company, the gangue was mainly quartz and the metals were gold, silver, lead, copper, mercury, and vanadium. The ore mined was cinnabar, pyrite, arsenopyrite, chalcopyrite, galena, sphalerite, stibnite, and vanadinite.

Cross the west fork of Silver Creek at Mineral City, and continue northeast a short distance to a bridge across the north fork of Silver Creek. Just before this bridge, find an overgrown trail off to the left. Take it about 2,000 feet to the mouth of Red Gulch. Follow the old cat road or stream bed as it quickly enters the steep chasm of the gulch. The gulch floor is an excellent place to find several mineral varieties in float (mixed with the talus), as well as quartz crystals. The high, red-stained walls of the gulch are impressive enough to excite any rock or mineral hound, and the ice-cold water from the snow-fed stream has its own rewards after the long hike on a hot summer day. About ¼ mile from the mouth of this colossal canyon, on the west side, are the Lost Pick Adits.

Lost Pick Adits

Rated at E-3. These consist of two tunnels, 67 and 60 feet long. The lower one is said to be blocked at the portal by boulders. Minerals found here are pyrite and chalcopyrite, with some bornite and sphalerite.[80] A USBM grab sample from a zone 1,000 feet downhill from the adits assayed 0.11 percent copper, with no gold or silver.

From the old town site of Mineral City, scan across the valley to the east. The hillside you see is the base of the 5,558-foot north extension of Hubbart Peak.[81] It is also said to be the lofty perch from which Joseph Pearsall made his fabulous discovery of the famous "Broad Bold Ledge of Gold"[82] that started the great Monte Cristo gold rush. As you gaze across to the lower flanks of the mountain, note the remains of a long-forgotten logging road drifting first left to right and then switchbacking sharply left in a gentle climb at the edge of a nearly vertical gulch. Notice that as it parallels back to the left, it soon crosses another smaller gulch, Hancock Gulch. In this gulch is the well-known upper New York–Seattle Mine.

---

[80] A story in *Gold Magazine* in 1971 tells of a group of Tacoma, Washington, prospectors who, in 1955-56, prospected for uranium in the gulch, and while doing so uncovered the workings here. The article's author insisted that this was the famous "lost Shaky Bill Mine." (Who was Shaky Bill?) They also claimed to have found a very rich vein of pitchblende (uranium ore) in the gulch. To our knowledge, this has never been substantiated. (No pitchblende mining has been undertaken by the Tacoma businessmen or anyone else.)

[81] This peak was named for Elisha H. Hubbart, an early prospector credited with building the first real trail into the area in 1882. The spelling is occasionally changed to Hubbard by modern authors.

[82] "A Broad Bold Ledge of Gold," a 40-page booklet by Rosemary Wilkie, was one of the first attempts to document the history of Monte Cristo.

New York–Seattle Mine

Rated at E-3. Just past Hancock Gulch and above the road, the trees turn from evergreens to an alder variety in a small patch. This was the area of the lower adit (now caved).

> **Warning** While following the old logging road, do not cross the gulch on the remains of the bridge! It is not only unnecessary and a longer route, but it is extremely dangerous. Instead, at the lower crossing, turn sharply up the bank and climb through the trees to the road level above.

Follow the road from Mineral City across the west fork and to the bridge that crosses the north fork of Silver Creek. Just across this bridge, take a hard left into the trees and move upstream a short distance, looking for old metal remnants. This was the site of the mine's mill (with a 100-ton-per-day capacity), sawmill, cookhouse, air compressor, and a couple of dwellings for the mine manager and mill crew. Ore from the mine was sent down from the lower portal (haulage tunnel) to the mill on a small aerial tramway.

Climb the moderate hillside to the road above, and find the point where the above-mentioned old logging road takes off from this road. Continue along it to the bridge remains. DON'T CROSS HERE!! Turn left and ascend the hillside to the road level above. It is best not to attempt climbing in the gulch during times of high water, but instead make your way up the left side of the gulch on the hillside above and continue past the second road level. A properly set altimeter would come in handy here, as the portal of the upper adit is at an elevation of 2,700 feet above sea level and about 80 vertical feet above the creek.

This adit pierces the mountain for a distance of 288 feet. The tunnel is driven along a vertical fault in a mineralized quartz vein, carrying pyrite and chalcopyrite. Just below the lip of this upper adit is the portal of a 185-foot, 38-degree incline shaft. This descends to the top of the vertical shaft, connecting it with the lower (now caved) workings.

> **Warning** Stay away from the incline shaft. If you slip, there is little chance that your mangled body parts can be recovered.

On the hill, well above these workings, is another short snub tunnel and caved vertical shaft, both of little interest. Descend the mountainside in a slightly northwesterly direction, and you will come to another brushed-over road with wood and metal mine debris scattered about on the road and over the bank below it. This was the site (find it or guess its exact portal location for yourself) of the lower main workings and haulage tunnel, now caved. These lower workings consisted of 1,724 feet of cross-cuts and drifts.

Twenty-seven samples from the New York–Seattle Mine were assayed by the USBM during the Glacier Peak RARE II study[83] in the late 1970s and early 1980s. Fifteen samples assayed from 0.08 to 0.082 ounces of gold per ton, four assayed from 0.4 to 1.4 ounces of silver per ton, and 20 assayed from 0.10 to 6.10 percent copper per ton. Although no shipping records are available for this mine, we know that shipments of ore were made to the smelter in late 1907.

---

[83] A RARE II (Roadless Area Review and Evaluation) study includes a mineral study conducted in a roadless area before it can be declared a wilderness area or park. In this case, the RARE II study was conducted in the Mt. Baker–Snoqualmie National Forest in the area that became the Henry M. Jackson Wilderness.

Silver Creek to Silver Lake

New York–Seattle Mine

(isometric projection)

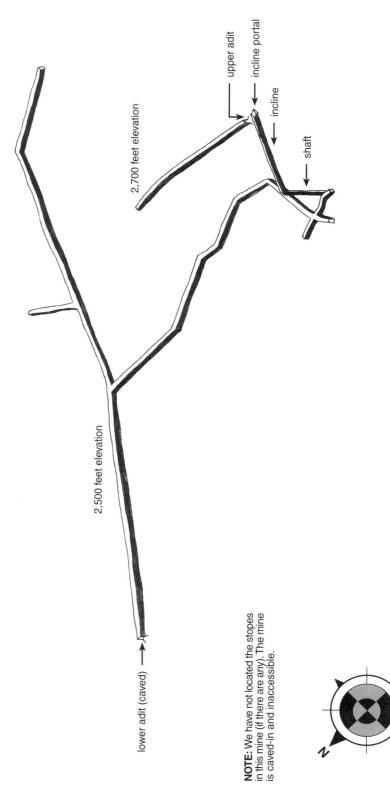

upper adit

incline portal

incline

shaft

2,700 feet elevation

2,500 feet elevation

lower adit (caved)

NOTE: We have not located the stopes in this mine (if there are any). The mine is caved-in and inaccessible.

N

Scale
(in feet)

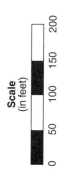

0   50   100   150   200

Philip R. Woodhouse 1995

Mountain Queen Prospect

Rated at E-2. To reach the Mountain Queen Prospect, also known as the Cheecko Prospect, travel 1.3 miles north from Mineral City along the main road up Silver Creek. At that point, two secondary roads switch back to the right and climb the hillside in a southerly direction.[84] The main portal is on the upper road, about 450 feet from the junction. Although it's only a few feet above the road, it is almost impossible to see from the right-of-way. Instead of looking for an adit, look for a small but steep bank or cliff that is somewhat wet and has a ledge about 10 to 12 feet above road level. This tunnel is 256 feet long, including a short drift near the face. This adit was driven to explore the disseminated iron and copper sulfide mineralization along a gradational granodiorite-conglomerate contact.

This contact zone ranges up to 20 feet in width and strikes east-west, with an apparently vertical dip. Pyrite, pyrrhotite, arsenopyrite, and chalcopyrite are disseminated in the contact zone. Minor amounts of bornite, limonite, and molybdenite, with manganese oxide staining, are also present. This was primarily a copper and silver prospect, with a trace of gold found by the USBM.

From this portal, about 380 feet in a direction of S 70° E and 218 feet higher, is the second adit, which is about 30 feet long. Although this prospect is also on the same contact zone, only trace amounts of copper, gold, and silver were found. A roadcut described by the USBM as being a few feet south of Molybdenum Creek at the north end of the claim exposed a narrow, mineralized fault in which they took assay samples. These samples assayed 1.02 percent copper, a whopping 1.44 ounces of gold per ton, and 2.72 ounces of silver per ton. However, the fault could be traced only a few feet on the surface and does not appear to have any extensions.[85]

Stop at Moly Gulch for a rest, and scan the hillside across Silver Creek. Just a little higher up the mountain, at an elevation of 3,025 feet, you will see a large tailing pile with two small, black holes at the top of the pile. At the bottom left is an old cabin (still standing in 1994). This is the famous Bonanza Prospect.

Bonanza Prospect

Rated at E-3. This mine is also known as the Mineral Center, Edison, Louise, and Washington-Iowa. The long main tunnel, which is the source of the large tailing pile, consists of 2,430 feet of horizontal workings and a flooded winze of unknown depth. This, along with the upper tunnel, 418 feet long and 800 feet higher, and another short adit about 100 feet long are the principal workings of the property.

Locate and follow a bulldozer road that drops sharply from Silver Creek Road just on the other (north) side of Moly Gulch. Cross Silver Creek at a point that will allow you to regain the road on the other side. (The bridge is gone.) Make your way up the road or trail to the cabin. These mine claims are patented, so as always make sure you have the permission of the owner before going exploring. Behind the cabin, a steep trail climbs to the top of the mine tailings and the main adit.

> **Warning** The flooded winze is at the junction of the first crosscut. Vertical shafts are like rattlesnakes: They can be anywhere. But unlike with rattlesnakes, there is seldom any warning of their presence.

---

[84] Do not confuse this road with a badly brushed-over road not far above the New York–Seattle mill site. The road you want is located just before the main road dips into a small gulch (Moly Gulch) and crosses a creek.

[85] For many mines in production today, 1.44 ounces of gold would be exceptional; some make a profit from as little as 0.5 ounce per ton. But the prospect apparently had too little ore to make mining efforts worthwhile.

The main tunnel was driven 1,977 feet into the mountain, and it intersects several sparsely mineralized northeast-trending faults of varying dips. The most favorable mineralization in the main tunnel is reported to be in the conglomerate of two faults, 110 and 400 feet from the portal, respectively. Mineralization consists of pyrite, arsenopyrite, pyrrhotite, and chalcopyrite. Azurite, malachite, galena, sphalerite, and molybdenite are also found here. Silver is the chief mineral value of the mine. The 418-foot adit exposes several sparsely mineralized faults that are not readily correlated with the faults exposed in the main tunnel, according to the USBM.

In 1946, five buildings were standing on the property, including a sawmill, blacksmith shop, and compressor house. No production was ever recorded from these workings. In addition to the three tunnels mentioned, several short tunnels were run on Louise Creek and Edison Creek, southwest of the main adit. Little development work was ever completed on any of them.

> **Note** Only a few of the following mines have been explored by Northwest Underground Explorations. The text is primarily a compilation of written information from our library and from trail hikes made by our members.

Gold Nugget Claim

Rated at E-2. Continue up Silver Creek Road from Moly Gulch to the point where the road crosses the creek, about 1.7 miles above Mineral City. The adit is about 300 feet downstream on the northwest side of the creek and about 30 feet above it. The tunnel is said to be 330 feet long, but it is caved at the portal so badly that its location can be determined only by close examination of the ground contour. The mine dump is nearly barren of minerals except for an occasional pyrite and chalcopyrite showing. The creek bed, however, contains some highly mineralized rocks and boulders. U.S. Government Patent Survey Plat #932 shows a 210-foot adit bearing N 23° E, 1,100 feet from the 330-foot portal.

Lucky Boy Mine

Rated at E-2. This tunnel is on the south bank of Silver Creek just upstream from the crossing, 1.7 miles north of Mineral City and upstream from the caved adit of the Gold Nugget Claim.[86] The portal is caved but is estimated by the USBM to be about 1,000 feet long; it was meant to develop the Starlight, Evening Star, Good Hope, and Smuggler deposits (described later). The adit was apparently not driven on any geologic structure and therefore was barren of any mineral except possible trace amounts of leached sulfides.

Starlight Prospect

Rated at E-undetermined. This prospect is higher up the hill, above the Lucky Boy Mine, and is defined by an 8-foot-long adit and one open cut. Twelve samples assayed by the USBM were reported as 0.012 to 0.142 ounces of gold per ton, 0.5 to 18.3 ounces of silver per ton, and 0.09 to 0.78 percent

---

[86] If you seek this adit, you'll have to look very closely into the brush because it is well hidden from view if you are standing in the streambed.

copper per ton, along with 0.19 to 5.50 percent lead and 0.88 to 0.89 percent zinc. Also, a minor amount of arsenic (as usual) was indicated. The steep topography limited the areas that could be sampled.

Good Hope Group

Rated at E-3. The main adit of this group is the Lucky Boy tunnel described above. The Good Hope group of patented claims consists of the Good Hope, Good Hope Extension, Starlight, Starlight Extension, Prince, Queen, Lucky Boy, Evening Star, 41144, 41144 Fraction, and the Minnehaha. Total underground workings in the group are said to be about 2,000 feet, most of it believed to be in the caved Lucky Boy tunnel. One carload of ore was reportedly shipped in 1909 to the Tacoma Smelter.

The upper adits of the Evening Star Claim are on either side of this waterfall. The right-hand tunnel is in shadow, while the left-hand adit can be seen immediately to the right of Daryl Jacobson, who is standing at the left of the photograph. (Vic Pisoni photo)

Evening Star Claim

Rated at E-4. This claim, mentioned earlier, is part of the Good Hope Group and is located about 1,000 feet upstream from the Lucky Boy tunnel. The workings are on both sides of Silver Creek, near the foot of a small waterfall. On the north bank are a small open cut, a 14-foot adit,[87] and a 98-foot adit. On the south bank is a 140-foot crosscut with 100 feet of drifts. In the 98-foot tunnel, two mineralized faults were drifted along for 48 feet. The andesite rock contains sparsely disseminated arsenopyrite, pyrite, and chalcopyrite. Between 29 and 36 feet from the portal, the walls of the tunnel are covered with iron oxide, and the country rock contains abundant arsenopyrite, pyrite, and chalcopyrite. The 14-foot tunnel exposes a fault varying from 1 to 2 feet in width, containing appreciable but spotty occurrences of galena, sphalerite, and chalcopyrite. The best showings on this side of the creek are in lead (4.37 percent) and silver (9.96 ounces per ton).

The crosscut on the south bank cuts two faults that are not correlated with those on the north bank. Pyrite and arsenopyrite are abundant along the faults and in the altered andesite adjoining them. A USBM report notes that "a very interesting feature of the deposit is a conglomerate exposed in both adits. It is from 1.5 to 2.0 feet in width and contains altered, bleached, well-rounded fragments of andesite and granitic pebbles." Because of the narrowness of the gulch, this trip should be attempted only late in the year, when the water in Silver Creek is at its lowest and the rocks are somewhat dry. Note the highly mineralized boulders in the streambed.

---

[87]   This appears to be an incline and is flooded. STAY OUT.

Daryl Jacobson, exploring the partially flooded south tunnel of the Evening Star Claim, works his way along the 140-foot crosscut adit in September 1995. (Vic Pisoni photo)

Smuggler Adit

Rated at E-undetermined. Travel to the end of the Silver Creek Road, and then go north along the north bank of Silver Creek for about $1/2$ mile to an indistinct path that leads across Silver Creek and continues for about $1/4$ mile to the portal of the main adit. The underground workings connected to the main adit account for 834 feet of crosscut and drifts.

> **Warning**   The tunnel map indicates that the first 100-plus feet are in overburden. This indicates that the tunnel is shored. Stay out of the mine and explore the area around it. The danger of cave-ins is much greater in the absence of solid rock.

In the tunnel, 460 to 470 feet from the portal, is a gradational contact from a dark, fine-grained hornfels to a light-colored, medium-grained andesite. The andesite near the face of the adit contains as much disseminated pyrite as any rock observed in the Silver Creek area by the USBM. Iron oxides are abundant on the walls wherever the rock is fractured. The adit intersects two mineralized vertical faults striking east-west that average about 1 foot in width. Assay samples taken from the mine show very poor returns in all valuable minerals sampled.

From the end of the Silver Creek Road, find a foot trail leading off from the left bank of the turnaround in the logged-off area. Follow this trail northeast as it ventures toward the roar of the creek. Note the high, beautiful falls upstream. This is Minnehaha Falls. On the left side of the lower of the two falls is the Minnehaha Mine.

Minnehaha Mine

Rated at E-undetermined. This 61-foot adit crosses a poorly exposed vein, which assays from 0.032 to 0.156 ounces per ton of gold, while averaging 0.072 ounces per ton. Silver assays from 0.5 to 5.9 ounces per ton, while copper assays from 0.23 to 0.40 percent. (The Hiawatha Mine, reported by Hodges to be a 40-foot tunnel, is said to be on the other side of the falls.)

After the trail crosses Silver Creek downstream from the falls, it turns and climbs steeply up the hillside to a switchback trail. Follow this trail as it climbs upward and ascend to the mouth of the hanging valley (elevation 3,880 feet).[88] Just inside the mouth of the valley, the trail splits.[89] The upper trail continues along the hillside above the valley floor and passes near the portal of the Q. T. Prospect.

Q. T. Prospect

Rated at E-4. Watch for the portal above the upper trail. The workings here consist of one 96-foot-long tunnel on a sulfide-bearing quartz vein that averages 0.3 feet thick and is exposed for 85 feet in andesite. Near the head of the valley, at the base of the hill on the right side, is the large mine dump of the lower portal of the Orphan Boy Mine.

Orphan Boy Mine

Rated at E-3 to E-4. This mine has two adits. The lower adit and upper adit (located 125 feet higher, just above the upper trail) are both partially flooded. The tailing piles of these workings are very evident at the end of the hanging valley. The two adits contain a total of 513 feet of underground workings (304 feet in the lower tunnel and 209 feet in the upper tunnel). These mines, once owned by pioneer prospector Elisha H. Hubbart, have by far the best assays of any mines in the area. (Remember that these adits are patented and are on private property.) USBM assays taken during the Glacier Peak RARE II study indicated that 8 samples assayed from 0.182 to 2.582 ounces of gold per ton, 10 assayed from 0.6 to 14.1 ounces of silver, and 12 showed from 0.26 to 21.2 percent zinc. Copper showings were minor, while arsenic peaked at 8.69 percent. Across the creek, on the west side, the Stockton Claim climbs the hillside.

At creek level is another, nearly-collapsed adit of unknown length. (This could be the Lower Stockton Adit, which is reported to be 30 feet long.) Above this prospect, in an old burn, is the caved portal of the main Stockton tunnel, which is believed to be over 120 feet long. Ascend the head of the hanging valley toward Silver Lake. On the east side of the ravine as you approach the Poodle Dog Pass area below Silver Lake, at the base of a cliff, is the 117-foot-long Seattle-Aurora Prospect.

Seattle-Aurora Prospect

Rated at E-undetermined. The ore showings here are nothing to write home about. As you continue your climb, the topography begins to level out, and the splendor of the rock-and-snow-covered Silvertip Peak looms into view, while the tall evergreens begin to give way to meadows of dark green mountain heather and stunted alpine trees. A meandering brook sparkles in the sun and begins its steep descent to the hanging valley below, where it joins with Silver Creek to create the spectacle of Minnehaha Falls.

This Nordic meadow was once the location of the well-known El Dorado Mine cabin, built near the turn of the century. As you ascend to the upper meadow area, the scenery changes even more, and the overwhelming beauty of Silver Lake (elevation 4,260 feet), tucked snugly in the cradle of stunning Silvertip Peak (elevation 6,140 feet), comes into view. Gazing around this pristine alpine lake you will

Silver Creek to Silver Lake

---

[88] This trail is in great shape in places and extremely hard to follow in others.

[89] The junction of the trails might be hard to see at certain times of the year, and snow can remain in the valley until late in the summer. If you miss the junction, stay in the valley and keep an eye out for the upper trail on the right hillside, 75 to 100 feet above the valley floor.

see the ugly scars of mining from a century ago.[90] On the south side of the lake, and 175 feet above it, is the Black Bear Prospect.

Partially frozen Silver Lake nestles beneath Silvertip Peak at the extreme head of Silver Creek. The last mines mentioned in this chapter are located in this area. (Phil Woodhouse photo)

Black Bear Prospect

Rated at E-4. The tailing pile of the Black Bear Prospect (also known as the F. E. Davis Prospect) can be seen tumbling nearly to the lakeshore. This property consists of a 160-foot, partly-caved adit (the source of the tailings you see), one 7-foot adit, and an open cut 160 feet above the caved portal. The caved tunnel crosscuts about 30 feet to a N 40° E trending, 70° NW dipping sulfide-bearing shear zone, averaging 2 feet thick and exposed for 100 feet in andesite. Assay samples from the open cut and mine dump indicate that the chief values here were in gold and zinc.

Attracted by garbage, bears were frequent visitors to some of the mines. Such a visitor might have given the Black Bear Prospect its name. (Sky Valley Historical Society Collection)

---

[90] Although this book is about mining and its history, we believe that mining and breathtaking scenery can coexist. Some areas of spectacular beauty in the mountains have been somewhat spoiled by old mine dumps. This is one of them.

If you didn't bother to visit the Black Bear Prospect and are standing on the trail overlooking the lake on the east side, get out your field glasses. High on the lesser peak (to your left) of Silvertip are the Bonita Adits.

> **Note** None of the following mines has been visited by Northwest Underground Explorations. Source information is from the USBM.

Bonita Adits

Rated at E-5 to impossible. Of the four adits, only three can be seen from the east side of Silver Lake. All are high on the face of the mountain, and the ones visible from the east side of the lake can be seen only when the sun is in the correct position to shine on them. One of the four is completely inaccessible and was not examined by the USBM. However, the Glacier Peak RARE II report indicates that the three adits visited are 4, 37, and 50 feet long. The best assays here were in gold, with one showing 0.57 ounces per ton, the average being only 0.10 ounces per ton. Just above the lake, far below the Bonita Mines, is the Cheryl Lee Prospect.

Cheryl Lee Prospect

Rated at E-4. This prospect has a 43-foot adit and four open cuts. The steep topography limited the areas that could be sampled here. But one assay showed 0.17 ounces of gold per ton, and four assays showed 0.1 to 0.3 ounces of silver per ton. On the northwest corner of the lake, and 200 feet above it, is the W. Danseau Prospect.

W. Danseau Prospect

Rated at E-undetermined. Also known as the Outlook Prospect, this prospect consists of a 17-foot adit with a 10-foot connecting open cut, and one 19-foot adit with a 12-foot connecting open cut. The workings expose a mineralized fault that is 0.5 feet wide in the lower (17-foot) tunnel and 1.5 feet wide near the portal of the upper (19-foot) tunnel, 50 feet higher. The fault contains pyrite, chalcopyrite, and arsenopyrite, while the country rock is andesite. Only minor amounts of gold and silver were found, but there is a potential for resources. The final stop in the Silver Lake region is the Sue Kay Prospect.

Sue Kay Prospect

Rated at E-undetermined. This caved adit is estimated to be 50 to 75 feet long and is located in a small draw on the north side of the lake. Samples collected here contained no appreciable mineral value.

Index

The Index area, located within an hour's drive of Everett in Snohomish County, offers countless opportunities for anyone who enjoys outdoor activities, from adrenaline-pumping whitewater sports to mountain climbing, camping, fishing, and hiking. Majestic Mount Index, looming high and proud against the sky, is always an invitation to artists and photographers. In addition to 5,991-foot Mount Index, other peaks in the area are Gunn Peak at 6,240 feet, Spire Mountain at 6,213 feet, and Mount Index's faithful neighbor Mount Persis at 5,464 feet. The lowest elevation in the district is near the confluence of the North and South Forks of the Skykomish River, which lies at a 500-foot elevation. The valley floor is blanketed with evergreens, while steep cliffs and snowfields are common at higher elevations. Summer temperatures are mild, while winters are cool and wet in the lower elevations. Snow usually blankets the higher ground by mid-December.

The bustling mountain town of Index in the heady days of mining. In the 1890s, Index was a stop on the Great Northern Railway's main line between Chicago and the West Coast and a busy staging point for the trek to the area's mines. This view looks northeast along Main Street (now Avenue A) from a point just beyond the bridge into town. (Pickett Museum)

History

The human story of the area began with the Native Americans who passed through from one side of the Cascades to the other via Cady Pass. They were followed by fur trappers who set their traps along the many streams cascading down the mountainsides. But it was the early prospectors who opened up this ruggedly beautiful area of the Cascade Mountains and attracted businesses and tradespeople to the early mining camps. They, in turn, soon summoned their families, who were followed by the schoolteachers, mule skinners, lawmen, and the lawless once the rush was on.

Nobody knows for sure who made the first mineral strike in the area or when the early claims were filed with local recorders. A recorder could have been anyone from a local homesteader to a circuit judge, and over the years many of these records were lost or destroyed. [91] The first claim filed with the

---

[91] It was not until 1888 that the territorial legislature enacted a law that required all mining claims to be recorded with the county recorder.

Index Mining Area

Good Luck Prospect

Lower Howard Creek Mines

Spire Mountain

Conglomerate Point

Upper Howard Creek Mines

Shamrock Prospect

Non Pareil Mine

Galena (site)

South Fork Trout Creek

Howard Creek

Kittaning Mine

Iron Mountain

Sunset Mine

Lake Simms

Merchant Mine

Merchant Peak

Eagle Lake

Eagle Creek

Trout Creek

Calumet Mine

Gunn Peak

Barclay Lake

Baring Mountain

Gunn Lake

Bitter Creek Adits

Bitter Creek

Uncle Sam Mine

Grotto Mountain

Canyon Creek Mines

Lewis Creek

Grotto

Ethyl Mines

Index Bornite Mine

Excelsior Creek

North Fork Skykomish River

Snowslide Gulch

Baring

North Star Creek

Barclay Creek

Index Creek

U.S. Highway 2

N

South Fork Skykomish River

Lake Isabel

Buckeye Mine

Red Cross Mine

Copper Belle Powerhouse (site)

Jumbo Adit

Copper Belle Mine

Deer Creek

Philadelphia Mountain

Index

Bridalveil Falls

Mount Index

Lake Serene

Honeymoon Prospect

Lake Serene Mine

May Creek

Anderson Creek

Mount Persis

Scale
(in miles)

1   1/2   0   1   2

county recorder was filed by George White on August 24, 1871, for a discovery he had made on Lost Creek. Later that day, five other claims were recorded, also on Lost Creek. In 1874, a large number of claims were filed on Silver Creek and adjoining creeks. In all, about 50 claims were recorded.

On October 15, 1874, a meeting of miners was held at Silver Creek, and the laws and boundaries were drawn up for the newly formed Skykomish Mining District. Interest waned during the 1880s because lack of transportation for supplies, equipment, and ore prevented any large-scale operations.[92] But in 1890, James J. Hill began pushing his Great Northern Railway over Stevens Pass, and surveyors and engineers worked in the area while locating the route for the Iron Horse. This promise of new transportation rekindled the search for valuable minerals around Index. In 1891, Amos Gunn, who ran a small roadhouse on the present site of Index, found it necessary to construct an addition to his hostelry to accommodate the large influx of prospectors and railroad people. This spot had been used by the local Skykomish people as a fishing camp. By 1892, two stages ran every week from Snohomish to Index and on to Galena at the mouth of Silver Creek. In 1893, Gunn had the town site platted. The plat was filed on April 25, 1893.

What to See

When you enter this area on Highway 2, the rugged, massive mountains are sure to impress. In addition to the scenery, this area also possesses an historic gem worth visiting. As you cross the bridge into the town of Index, take a right immediately after entering the town and look for 510 Avenue A (old Main Street). This was the home of Lee Pickett, the official photographer of the Great Northern Railway. It now contains the Pickett Museum, which has a fine display on mining, although space is a problem in this tiny building.[93] One block straight ahead is the Bush House, built in 1897 as a hotel and still in use today as a restaurant and hotel. Down the street to the right is the Redmen's Hall, built in 1903, which belonged to a fraternal order.

Getting There

To reach this area, drive east from Everett, Snohomish, or Monroe on Highway 2, passing through the towns of Sultan, Startup, and Gold Bar. As you leave Gold Bar, you will enter the Index area. Continue driving, and several miles past the Reiter Road turnoff the highway will begin to twist and turn as it follows the Skykomish River into the mountains. Eventually, the highway will cross the river from south to north via a through-span steel bridge at milepost 35. Just before this crossing is a road to the right that leads toward some of the mines detailed in this chapter. This is the Index River Road. Just beyond the river crossing, on your left, is the turnoff to the town of Index, the heart of this area. About a mile after taking this turnoff onto the Index-Galena Road, you can see the town across the river, and you can reach it by crossing the bridge just beyond the railroad overpass.

Geology

The Index area has a relatively simple geologic structure. For some reason, the major metal of value found in this locale was copper, which led to the designation of "copper belt" for this region of the Cascade Mountains. The rocks consist mostly of granitics from the Tertiary era that intruded into a mix of Upper Jurassic–Lower Cretaceous sedimentary and volcanic rocks. This intrusion occurred when

---

[92] In 1882, a trail was built from Index to the mining camp of Galena at the mouth of Silver Creek, and many claims were staked on silver, gold, and lead deposits that year; but no actual ore shipments were made.

[93] This little museum is a volunteer project of the Index Historical Society and is open only from noon until 3 p.m. on Saturdays and Sundays, Memorial Day through Labor Day. Special viewings can be arranged on holidays.

the area was deep below the earth's surface. The contact between these two disparate structures defines the western edge of the copper belt. Mines associated with this contact are the Copper Belle, Index Independent, and Honeymoon prospects. Other mines in the area appear to be located on fissure veins within the intrusive Tertiary rocks. The copper belt extends east-west from the Beckler River to Reiter Road, and north-south from Evergreen Mountain to Mount Index.

The Mines

Copper Belle Mine

Rated at A-1. This mine, also known as the Bunker Hill Mine, was one of the major mines in the Index area. It dates back to January 12, 1897, when C. H. and L. W. Gray located the Copper Belle and South Copper Belle mining claims. On May 5 of that year, the Copper Belle Mining Company was formed, and seven more claims were added. From 1902 to 1905, it was better known as the Bunker Hill Mining Company after it was sold to the Metropolitan Life Insurance Company. In 1905, a 50-ton-per-day concentrator was constructed near the mouth of the main haulage tunnel,[94] and a 15-to-20-ton reverberatory smelter was built at the base of the mountain and connected with the concentrator by a flume that carried the concentrates from the mill to the smelter. However, the mine closed in 1908 or 1909 because there was not sufficient ore for profitable mining. After that time, efforts at mining were sporadic.

Explorers prepare to investigate the workings of the Copper Belle Mine. Several can be seen holding souvenirs that were most likely taken from the buildings. The main adit is located behind the far structure. This photo was taken during the mine's dormancy, possibly in the 1910s or 1920s. Notice that the fellow in the front row, third from the left, is holding a folding Kodak camera. Many geologist's hammers can also be seen. (Special Collections, University of Washington Libraries, Neg. #17626)

Caution This trip should be attempted only in a high-clearance vehicle with a paint job you're not worried about.

To get there, travel east from Gold Bar along Highway 2. After 1 mile, turn left on Reiter Road and follow it up the hill and across the flat to a sharp bend to the left. Continue straight ahead on the gravel road to the Reiter Pit area (a popular staging area for motorcyclists and off-roaders). Turn left again on a lesser road at the far end of the pits just before the main road starts its descent. Follow this road through the woods and under the power lines.

---

94 The mill's capacity was later increased to 100 tons per day, and the smelter's capacity was increased to 50 tons per day.

Water spews from the tailrace of the 10-foot-diameter water wheel at the Copper Belle Mine's powerhouse on May Creek. This wheel powered a pair of double-acting air compressor pistons that supplied compressed air to the mine, a half mile away, via a 4-inch pipeline and receiver tank. Today the building is gone, reduced to a few rotting timbers on the forest floor. The wheel, with its attendant air compressor cylinders, remains on its concrete foundation pedestals, a monument to the miners who toiled here.

Warning This area is used by many off-road vehicles, so use extreme caution. A large number of trails enter the road from both sides, so you might have no warning as an offroader emerges.

Turn right at the fork in the road just past the stand of trees on the far side of the power lines. Stay to the left as you follow the gradual climb up the hill. After the road makes a sharp switchback to the left and climbs another $^3/_4$ mile, it divides. Take the right (and steeper) road to the top; continue as far as possible (about 400 feet), watching for a partly collapsed adit on the left. Park at the portal of the second tunnel.

Warning In addition to being flooded, this mine has a winze of unknown depth and an incline shaft you don't want to step into. Also, at a rockfall just beyond the winze, the air becomes *oxygen deficient!* If you linger in the area, you will use up the already depleted oxygen supply and stand a very good chance of suffocating or losing control of your mind or your body. This can happen in a very short time and without your awareness. Because of the extreme danger, and because this mine is on private property, please stay out.

The adit where you are now standing is the K level, which was the main haulage tunnel extending about 2,450 feet into the mountain. Inside, 600 feet from the portal, a drift branches right and left. The right branch dead-ends within a couple of hundred feet while the left one enters a large room known as the "hoist room," where the Belle Vein, or main ledge of ore, is encountered. Here an incline shaft descends about 200 feet (now under water) and accesses three short sublevels 50, 125, and 175 feet below; they are the L, M, and N levels, respectively. From the hoist room, this incline continues as a raise bored upward another 160 feet to level H. From this level, another 140 feet was raised to level D, where the vein outcrops at the surface. From the hoist room, two drifts branch out a short distance, but these exit the vein boundaries and show no ore. The main tunnel continues back several hundred feet to the vertical winze—a very large, flooded, and dangerous hole. If you have actually come this far, stop here and make no attempt to continue because crossing the winze can be hazardous, and just beyond the next "rockfall" (collapse) the air becomes dangerously bad. There is little to see, anyway, except more rockfalls and an empty tunnel with very little mineralization.

The smelter of the Copper Belle Mine. The facility was at a lower elevation than the mine's haulage tunnel to allow a gravity feed of the ore to the plant. Ore was introduced to the mill through the "cupola" via the elevated tramway at the upper right of the building. Notice the tall flue stack at the left of the picture.

From where your vehicle is parked, you can walk up the steep old cat road beyond the mine and locate a foot trail leading up the bank to the left about 200 feet. You'll reach the collapsed portal of level H, and 140 feet of elevation above it the portal to level D (now "glory holed," or stoped, to the surface). Peer into the abyss, but don't stand too close—it is an almost sheer drop of 20 feet or more to the bottom, and a sure trip to the hospital, or worse, if you slip. This is where the cool breeze comes from on a warm day when you stand in front of the main tunnel below. Climb slowly back down to the old cat road and turn left, making your way up the road to its end at the Jumbo rock pile. Find a foot trail that leads into the massive rocks and bends to the left as you hop and climb from rock to rock. The trail ends in a smaller boulder pile and area of downed logs. Turn right and climb to the base of the cliffs and parallel them up the valley while looking for a partly caved mine adit in a small gulch at the head of a talus slope. These are the workings of the Jumbo Mine, which is rated at C-3.

The ore concentrator at the Copper Belle Mine. The surface tram that conducted the ore from the mine to the concentrator is at the far upper left of this picture. In addition, an aerial tramway was used to carry ore down from a higher tunnel. The two trees joined by ladder rungs, visible at the top-center left, formed the lowest support tower of the aerial tramway. (Index Historical Society)

> **Warning** Don't enter the Jumbo Mine! Fifty feet from the entrance (and under water) is a large winze 45 feet deep that takes up nearly the entire floor of the mine.

The tunnel is only about 250 feet long, with three short drifts and a 45-foot-deep winze that accesses two short sublevels.[95] The ore from this mine, coming mostly from the winze, was carried down to the mill on a small gravity tram with probably about a 10-ton-per-day capacity. Power and compressed air for running the mines and the mill were furnished by a small power plant on May Creek, to which a 240-foot flume and a 1,400-foot pipe carried water from a point farther up the creek. The water turned two Pelton wheels, one 3 feet in diameter and the other 10 feet in diameter. These Peltons furnished power to drive two air compressors that ran 12 drills at the mine, a 90-horsepower dynamo, and an electric light plant that was used to light both the mine and the mill. The nearby Red Cross Mine purchased power from this plant for their operations.

The tailrace stream at the powerhouse for the Copper Belle Mine is shown spectacularly in this photo. The water was tapped from May Creek, seen in the distance, far above the site of the plant. (Special Collections, University of Washington Libraries, Neg. #17629)

To get to the powerhouse ruins, find a trail in the trees right before the nearly caved portal you passed (just before the main adit, a ways back down the road). Follow the trail up the hill for quite some distance. As you ascend the trail roughly ⅓ mile from the mine, watch for the old iron tank down the hill below you. This is a large air receiver that stored compressed air for the mine. You can descend from the trail and examine this artifact. It is rather unimpressive, but you can locate the rusted remnant of a 4-inch pipe that comes toward the receiver from the direction of May Creek and follow it to the wreckage of the old powerhouse. Much of the equipment is still on its concrete footings!

The largest single piece of equipment is the giant 10-foot-diameter Pelton wheel that was connected to two air compressor cylinders. The cylinder nearest the creek is a Leyner low-pressure duplex unit; the cylinder farthest from the creek is an Ingersoll-Sergeant duplex unit. The two were hooked up to compress in parallel and combine their output through the 4-inch pipe that you saw from the trail. Also on the property are the remains of a Westinghouse 90-horsepower dynamo that was dismantled and stripped of its copper windings. You can find the frame, pole pieces, bearings, and rotor, although not in one place. A 1907 report on the plant described two water wheels in use, one of them 10 feet in diameter and the other 3 feet in diameter. When we visited the site, we saw the 10-foot wheel still in place, but we found no trace of the other machine. Instead, we found the remains of another 10-foot wheel scattered about the area! Perhaps the 3-foot unit was replaced by a 10-footer, or perhaps

---

[95] When we explored the mine in 1987, it was flooded. Only prior knowledge of the winze from earlier studies kept one of us from stepping into the nearly invisible shaft.

the original large wheel was broken and replaced with the current one. The wheel that is now in place was constructed by the Sumner Iron Works of Everett, as were the frames that attached the cylinders to the rest of the assembly.

The 10-foot-diameter air compressor Pelton wheel of the Copper Belle Mine powerhouse serves as a backdrop for members of Northwest Underground Explorations in 1995. On the concrete pier, from the left, are Jeff Schempp, Bill Petersen, Steve Reeves, Scooter (upper), and Ryan Taylor (lower), with Terry peering through the wheel. Standing on the ground, from the left, are Mike Culp, Vic Pisoni, Phil Woodhouse, Daryl Jacobson, Jeff Taylor, and Doug White. (Phil Woodhouse photo)

The water wheels were driven by the water of May Creek, which was diverted through a flume high above the plant and then funneled into a 24-inch-diameter wood-stave penstock that conducted it to the area of the powerhouse. Just above the water wheels, the penstock necked down to a 16-inch pipe, also of wooden construction. Just before the plant, the pipe transitioned to a steel "y" splitter, where it divided into a 12-inch and an 8-inch line. The 12-inch line conducted the water to the big 10-foot wheel while the 8-inch transitioned back to a wood-stave line that now vanishes into the debris of the plant's timbers. It most likely ran the 3-foot wheel or the other 10-foot wheel, whichever was actually present. Traces of other machinery, which we could not identify, also litter the site. The big wheel makes a spectacular sight, rising as it does from the dank, mossy forest floor.

The trail continues past, or over, decayed pilings and to a road that leads to the old Red Cross Mines, which are rated at D-3. These mines consist of several small adits and open cuts. Follow the road as it climbs and then switchbacks to the mine cabin. You can find the Red Cross workings by following the old road that goes to the left just before the cabin. They consist of a couple of old open cuts that are now flooded. This mine was in operation at the same time as the Copper Belle and bought its power from the Copper Belle powerhouse.

At the Copper Belle, the metals were copper, gold, silver, and tungsten, derived from the ore minerals chalcopyrite, pyrite, bornite, magnetite, and hematite; the gangue was quartz, calcite, and crushed and altered granodiorite. At the Red Cross Mines, the minerals were copper, gold, and silver, derived from the ores chalcopyrite, bornite, and pyrite; the gangue was quartz.

Lake Serene Mine

Rated at A-1. Also known as the Wilber Index, Pride of Index, and Index Independent Mine. (This is not the Honeymoon Prospect. It will be described later in this section.) The mine dates to 1898 and was relocated and patented in 1906. Four carloads of ore were reportedly mined here prior to 1901, and a small amount was shipped to the Tacoma Smelter in 1949.

Travel east from Monroe on Highway 2 to the Index River Road, located just before the steel through-span bridge that crosses south to north over the Skykomish River at milepost 35. Follow this road about 2 miles to a small store, and then turn right. Follow the switchbacks upward until the road splits just before the Bonneville Power Administration (BPA) power lines. Take the lower road to the right under the power lines and continue for several miles until it goes up the hill. At the top, continue left as far as possible.[96] Find a large clearing at the end of the road near the base of the mountain. (We will refer to this place from here on as the "parking lot" because it is still used as one by four-wheel-drive vehicles.)

The adits are in the gulch straight ahead. This mine has three tunnels. The lowest is a crosscut tunnel consisting of 535 feet of horizontal workings and several hundred feet of raises and stopes, including a winze.

Warning In the second drift back, and only a few feet from the start of this drift, is a vertical winze that is sometimes partly covered with boards. If you choose to enter this mine, and we do not recommend that you do, watch out! This winze is in hard rock, and the water level varies with the water table from a few feet to completely full. Anyone falling into this shaft when it is half full would stand a very poor chance of surviving.[97]

In the lower tunnel, throughout the side drifts, you can find many narrow stringers of high-grade bornite (also referred to as "peacock ore" by collectors) and malachite, especially on the roof of the tunnels. At the junction of the second drift from the portal, the stringers completely cross the main crosscut. You can find nice samples here. REMEMBER TO WATCH OUT FOR THE WINZE. The next level is 180 feet above the lower. You can reach it from the parking lot by following the bulldozer path past the short trail to the lower adit and continuing a few hundred feet upward to a small (maybe brushed-over) path leading up and back toward the gulch again. Follow this trail to the ledge in the gulch.

Warning Before you step onto the ledge, look it over closely and look down the gulch. If the rock is wet, it's likely to be slick. One misstep could send you over the cliff to the rocks below. BE SURE YOU WANT TO PROCEED BEFORE YOU STEP ONTO THE LEDGE.

The second adit is under the small waterfall on the ledge and consists of a single tunnel running 180 feet straight back into the mountain with a 35-foot-high stope and raise near the end. Nice samples of peacock ore have been found on the floor of the tunnel under the stope. We have not visited the upper adit, but it is said to be 200 feet above the second adit and 243 feet long. It has been caved for many years. With the exception of the winze in the lower tunnel and the high, slick ledge at the second level, these workings seem comparatively safe if you carry the necessary lights and watch your step. Some of the roof areas are low and can give you a good smack on the head. Do not try to access the stopes above the drifts; the rock can be loose, and the rotting shoring or stulls might not hold your weight.

[96] An alternate route, if this road is blocked, is to park just before the gravel pit a short distance off Highway 2 and walk the old mine road on the west side of the pits. This will, after a mile and a half, put you at the top of the hill and near the end of the road.

[97] We measured the depth of this winze in 1991 by using "calibrated, ultra-sensitive depth measurement equipment" (a rope with a weight on it) and found it to be 24 feet deep.

The metals mined here were copper, gold, and silver, and the ore minerals were bornite, chalcopyrite, chalcocite, pyrite, and azurite. The gangue consisted of quartz.

The nearby Honeymoon Prospect, rated at B-2, was no more than a dry prospect, one of hundreds in the area that failed to strike ore and that normally would not be mentioned here. However, because some people have been known to visit it on their honeymoon, and so many are misinformed by well-meaning locals, a description is in order. From the "parking lot," find a foot trail that leads toward Bridle Veil Falls and follow it across the talus slope to the tall timber. Just inside the timber area, turn up the hill[98] until you reach a trail. Follow this trail as it climbs to the base of a small waterfall that tumbles over a sizable cliff. The adit is here. This is a far more comfortable place to camp than the Lake Serene Mine because it is flat and has few large rocks. It is also a more picturesque setting. No ore was discovered in the tunnel, but based on the large cross-section, we can speculate that the tunnel was intended to strike the Lake Serene ledge from that angle but funds ran out before the project was finished. The tunnel is only about 250 feet long, is very large in cross-section, and is bored into solid granite. This is a good tunnel for the amateur mine explorer.

Buckeye Mine

Rated at C-4. This mine dates from 1898. Most, if not all, of the work was done between then and 1907, with the property being surveyed for a patent in 1906. We have found no records that tell how much ore was shipped, but most likely several tons were packed out on horseback in the early days. Little development work was done after 1907.

Follow the instructions to the Lake Serene Mine, but continue left up the small hill instead of right under the power lines. This is the BPA power line road. Follow it for about 4 miles until you reach the wrecked body of an early 1950s Jeep station wagon (cream color with blue trim) on the right side of the road. Descend to the bottom of the hill, where the road again swings out to the left and under the power lines. Park here[99] and find a trail toward the mountain, which is also an old road. Cross the creek where the bridge is out, making sure you return to the road on the other side. Follow this road another 300 feet until it turns hard left, but continue straight ahead. (If you turn, you might end up in the wrong gulch.) Travel cross country, and rejoin the road again within 500 feet. At this point you have a choice: Either turn right and follow the road to its end and turn left up the creek, or climb the bank at any point that will afford you passage through the brush. Either way, you will enter the gulch. It is 300 feet wide, with high, vertical cliffs on both sides. Ascend this gulch to an elevation of 1,950 feet. At this point, the canyon abruptly narrows to about 10 feet in width, still with vertical towering cliffs on both sides. Note the mine workings on the right; this is an old open cut that was also used as a chute to convey ore down to the pack animals who carried the bags of high-grade ore to the railroad below. Climb the bottleneck gulch ahead of you after reading and heeding the warning on the next page.

---

[98] An alternate route is to continue along the trail through the woods while watching closely for the wreckage of the old cabin above the path. Scamper up to it, turn right (back toward the talus), and find a trail to follow until you see a small waterfall tumbling over a sizable cliff.

[99] We made several attempts to locate this mine before finding it. That day we scanned the cliffs with binoculars from a vantage point near the parking area at the base of the hill. We established the location of the correct gulch by spotting a vivid, deep green-purple "peacock" stain along the western side of the gulch, which indicated a richness of copper-bearing ores in that locale.

Index

This ore cart is just inside the lower adit of the Buckeye Mine. The ore cart is in Snohomish County, but a short walk into the tunnel places you in King County. Our first, unsuccessful attempt to locate this mine was in late spring, and we later realized that we didn't find it because the adit was under a large patch of snow in the gully. The walls of portions of this tunnel as well as the sides of the gully are stained with iridescent bornite (peacock) ore. (Vic Pisoni photo)

The gulch soon divides left and right, with the lower adit drilled straight into the hogback between the gulches.[100] It is in solid rock, and chances of a cave-in are minimal. This adit contains about 1,100 feet of underground workings, including two short drifts near the back. You can find excellent bornite samples in stringers in the mine and in the rock below the adit. Two short tunnels were driven into the gulches above this portal, but because of the danger in reaching them we did not visit these sites. However, old maps show them to be short tunnels.

An interesting note: When you enter the mine you are in Snohomish County, and at the back you are in King County.

The metals mined were copper, gold, and silver. The ore minerals were chalcopyrite, pyrite, bornite, cuprite, and chalcocite. The gangue consisted of quartz, calcite, and crushed and altered granodiorite.

Golden Tunnel Mine

Rated at E-4. Located in the eastern part of the Index Mining District 6 miles from Highway 2, this mine was one of the most promising and closely watched properties in the Cascade Mountains. The mine is located in a breathtaking canyon of steep, brushy walls topped by spectacular mountain peaks on all sides. No trails or roads lead into this canyon. The tunnel cannot be seen from the valley floor and can be spotted only from the air or from some of the surrounding high mountain ridges.

---

[100] When you reach this adit, look carefully at the right-hand wall as you enter the tunnel. It is stained from top to bottom with deep purple bornite. The stain is so dark that it appears black unless you look closely.

Looking out of the Golden Tunnel Mine in 1993. The upper aerial tramway wheel is lying on the bottom of the opening. This natural cavern was lined with quartz and pyrite crystal when first discovered. (Phil Woodhouse photo)

The tunnel is a natural cavern, perched 4,200 feet above sea level. It was located in 1895 by a "tall, lank Swede" named John Anderson. It was reported to be 15 feet high, 20 feet wide, and 65 feet long, with streaks of high-grade copper pyrites in large crystals carrying gold and silver. Some early descriptions of the cave called it a crystal-lined cave, containing both quartz and pyrites. Perhaps the most important aspect of the mine was that at least a portion of the ore contained "free milling gold." [101] After Anderson sold the mine to investors, the Golden Tunnel Mining Company began to acquire more claims, and interest escalated. The company's stock rose to 21 cents per share (a good price for undeveloped mining property in those days), and plans were made to build a mill in the valley below with a long aerial tramway to connect it to the mine.

By 1899, the mill was operating, and a puncheon road had been built to it. A sample run of 58 tons of ore was processed to fine-tune the new equipment.[102] The company also hired Vulcan Iron Works of Seattle to build a 250-ton-per-day, all-weather tramway from the mine to the mill, to replace a makeshift tram with an 8-ton-per-day capacity. The tram was scheduled to be completed by the end of 1899, but it was not completed until late 1901 or early 1902. This delay contributed to the ultimate demise of the mine. The completed tramway also had chronic design problems, which thwarted efforts to make it operate efficiently.[103] With no way to ship the ore, and with bond and mortgage payments due, the

---

[101] Free milling gold can be seen with the naked eye and sometimes includes nuggets, making it cheaper to mine and to mill and therefore more valuable to the miner. It is rarely found in western Washington.

[102] The equipment included a device called the "Montgomery Ore Granulator and Pulverizer," manufactured by the A.C.M. Company of Butte, Montana. This machine used three large, 20-inch diameter, 1,200-pound steel balls rolling in a circular trough to crush and grind the ore. (The standard type of ball mill tumbled iron balls with the ore and water; the stamp mill hammered the ore to powder.) We have never heard of another one of these devices ever being used—testimony to its inferior performance.

[103] Most aerial tramways of the time used conventional brakes to control their speed, but this one used a system of pneumatic or hydraulic cylinders (we haven't determined which) attached to the bull wheel via a crank arm. We theorize that this introduced a sinusoidal braking pattern into the cable system that led to oscillations in the cables that the operators could not control.

Index

mine fell into receivership and was closed. It appears that later owners stripped the mine and mill of everything of value and sold them to recoup their costs (a common practice in those days).

High on a mountain ridge lie the remains of the great bull wheel of the Golden Tunnel Mine's aerial tramway. This wheel, situated at the upper tram station, used grippers around its perimeter, which used the cable's own tension to close them tightly and prevent slippage. The crank arm at the top of the shaft was attached to two cylinders that pumped either air or liquid to produce a braking effect. Since this imparted an oscillating rather than a smooth braking action, the cables tended to whip and lash. This might be the reason that this tram never performed as designed. (Phil Woodhouse photo)

The metals mined were gold, copper, and silver derived from ores of chalcopyrite, bornite, and malachite in limestone rock, which comprised the gangue.

Index Bornite Mine

Rated at C-2. This mine was located in 1898 by Alec Watt, Charles. E. Cummings, and York Barington. A year later, the Index Bornite Mining Company was incorporated to operate the mine. Most of the underground work was completed during the first few years of the new century and consisted of two adits, 57 and 522 feet long, including crosscuts, drifts, and a shaft, now flooded, that is reported to be 70 feet deep and might access a sublevel.[104] The adit at the creek is the long one and contains nice ore samples. While we do not recommend that you enter, the rock is fairly stable. The long drift off the main tunnel is hazardous, however, so if you do enter, stay out of this drift and restrict your exploration to the main tunnel.

This mine is located on Lewis Creek, 2^1/$_2$ miles southeast of Index. Drive east on the Index-Galena Road for 1^3/$_4$ miles to Lewis Creek (the first small bridge you come to). Park just past the bridge, or, if the gate is open, drive on the logging road for about a mile until, at an elevation of 1,300 feet, you find the remains of a very old and obscure road turning to the left. Turn and walk this road uphill to its end, about a half mile. (You'll see an old cabin site 200 feet up the road on the left.) At the end of the road, at an elevation of 1,500 feet, a trail climbs the bank in an up-valley direction, gaining a couple of hundred feet of elevation in just a short while, and then levels out and parallels the creek for roughly 650 feet. It meets the creek at the base of a small but long stretch of rapids. As you stand on what seems like the end of the trail, overlooking the foot of the rapids, jump down to the little landing on the bank of the creek and look to the right. There you will see the portal of the lower adit situated at an elevation of 1,620 feet.

---

[104] We located only the long adit and shaft during our visits to the mine in 1991-92. The 57-foot adit might be on the small hill just behind the shaft to the east.

> **Warning** The vertical shaft has a wood collar that is covered with dirt and is completely rotten. Do not step within 10 feet of the shaft or you will be standing on the collar and in EXTREME DANGER! Stay off the collar! The shaft was flooded to within 10 feet of the surface when we visited it and it looked impossible to climb out of without a rope. In the cold water in this shaft, the chances of survival are slim to nil. PLEASE STAY AWAY FROM THE SHAFT.

You can find the vertical shaft by climbing up the hillside, above the mine and around the cliff to the left. As you near the top of the ridge, note the tailing pile at the top. (You must distinguish the tailing pile by its shape because it is largely buried beneath forest litter and is very difficult to see). Finish the climb of the hill and tailing pile to an elevation of 1,780 feet. Heed the above warning: Hang onto kids and pets, and stay away from the shaft. This shaft is so dangerous that the only reason we mention it here is so you will be aware of the danger in case you find it.

The metals mined here were copper and silver derived from the ores chalcopyrite, bornite, and chalcocite. The gangue consisted of quartz, calcite, and crushed granodiorite.

Uncle Sam Prospect

Rated at C-3. Located in 1897 by William Cornwall, this property consisted of four claims and several tunnels totaling about 400 feet of underground workings, plus two cabins.

To find this mine, an altimeter is almost mandatory. The mine is on the north side of the Barclay Creek Valley above the town of Baring. Drive east on Highway 2 to Baring. Turn left and cross the railroad tracks into the old town. Turn left onto Forest Service Road #6024 (toward Barclay Lake Trail), and after about 2 miles you will reach the valley where the road straightens out toward the southeast. Soon an old logging road drops abruptly to the left from the main road. Follow this road either by driving or hiking (your choice) as far as you can. The way will descend to Barclay Creek. Cross the creek and begin climbing the opposite side toward the northwest. At the end of this road, continue straight ahead through the brush in the logged-off area until you reach the uncut timber. Begin a traversing ascent to the west (directly ahead), crossing a couple of gullies until you reach 2,800 feet elevation (about ³/₄ mile into the woods). Contour at this elevation until you reach a small, wooded gully.[105] Ascend this gully to the prospect at 3,050 feet elevation.

> **Warning** Do not climb to the elevation of the mine and attempt to contour the valley wall too quickly, because you will encounter some nasty cliffs hidden in the woods.

The portal you have reached is the lower adit. The tunnel is relatively uninteresting, but some cast iron artifacts and excellent ore samples can be found on the small mine dump at the tunnel's mouth. We did not locate or visit the upper tunnels.

The metals sought here were copper, gold, and silver, which were derived from the minerals chalcopyrite, pyrite, bornite, and hematite. The gangue consisted of quartzite, garnet, and hornblende.

---

[105] As you traverse the hillside, watch for the remnants of old trails that lead to the mine and possibly other features in the area. If you locate one, it might make it easier to hike up to, and locate, the tunnel.

Bitter Creek Mines and Canyon Creek Mines

Rated at C-3 for Bitter Creek, with an undetermined rating for Canyon Creek. Drive east on the Index-Galena Road 3 miles from the Index turnoff, to a small road on the right. Drive or hike this road as far as possible. After about a mile, the road reaches Canyon Creek; this is the closest it comes to the Canyon Creek Mines (also known as the Gunn Peak Mines). If you are interested enough (and you would have to be very interested), make your way up the gulch or the edge after looking carefully for a possible trail.[106] The mines, at about 2,500 feet of elevation, consist of two adits, one 492 feet long and the other 5 feet long. These claims were located in July 1897 by A. M. Watt and Charles. E. Cummings and incorporated on August 10, 1897, as the Gunn Peak Copper Mining Company. The main ledge, called "The Rainbow," varies in width from 1 to 30 feet. The main tunnel is more than 350 feet long, with 100-plus feet of drifts. It was said that this mine had the best constructed and equipped camp and blacksmith's shop in the district at the turn of the century.

The metals were copper, gold, and silver derived from the ores chalcopyrite and bornite. The gangue consisted of crushed granodiorite.

The Index Peacock Mine is reported to be above the Canyon Creek Mines. It consists of a 100-foot-long tunnel driven on the vein. However, no other information is available, except that the metal sought was copper, which was to be derived from the ore minerals chalcopyrite and bornite. The gangue was granodiorite.

To reach the Bitter Creek Mines, continue past the Canyon Creek Mines and up the switchbacks for a couple more miles. When the road enters the valley of Bitter Creek, you can see a 1970s clearcut on the hill along the other side of the valley that extends to the visible top of the ridge. Drive or walk to the Bitter Creek crossing, and follow the road that takes off to the left shortly after you cross the creek. It will soon switchback once and parallel the creek to the gulch at the end of the road. Stop here and plan a route up the left side of this gulch, staying on the hillside above the creek. The mines are within 50 feet of the gulch rim, about halfway up the visible hillside. There are two tunnels on the property: One is about 600 feet long (now caved a couple of hundred feet back) and the other one, almost directly below the upper adit and 100 feet lower in elevation, is 200 feet long.

The metal sought was copper, derived from the ore minerals bornite, chalcopyrite, pyrite, and hematite. The gangue consisted of crushed and altered granodiorite.

Calumet Mine

Rated at C-5. The claims here date from 1897, when John A. Lewis located them and began production. The development work consisted of three tunnels and several open cuts, along with two camps. The upper camp is at an elevation of 3,600 feet, 500 feet below the lower or main tunnel, which is 500 feet long. The upper tunnel is located about 200 feet almost directly above the lower adit and is only 100 feet long. Somewhere up there is a third adit that is reported to be about 45 feet long. In addition to the upper camp, Lewis built a camp at the base of the cliffs and connected the mines and lower camp with a small bucket tram.

This mine is located in the same valley as the Bitter Creek group. Follow the driving instructions for the Bitter Creek Mines, but after crossing Bitter Creek continue right at the intersection instead of turning left up the hill. The road continues up the valley to a dead end.

---

[106] We haven't visited this property, so directions up the gulch are lacking here. However, two of the adits are visible in the gulch from the ridge on the opposite side of the North Fork of the Skykomish River.

Warning Getting to these mines entails climbing steep cliffs and high, unstable tailing piles. (After viewing these cliffs, even we were not crazy enough to attempt to climb them, so we don't have any detailed directions.) This should not be attempted by the faint of heart or the inexperienced. Also remember to look back down behind you from time to time to make sure you want to proceed. Remember: The miners used guide ropes to climb to these mines. The upper tunnel also has a winze or underhanded stope of unknown depth that is now flooded. Watch your step if you decide to enter this mine.

The metals mined here were copper and zinc from the ore minerals chalcopyrite, pyrite, and sphalerite. The gangue was quartz, calcite, and altered granodiorite. One or two mines are rumored to be somewhere across the valley on the flanks of the 3,600-foot peak on the west side of the valley, but we have not yet investigated this.

The Sunset Mine's buildings on Trout Creek during early days of the mine's operation. Notice the railroad tracks of the surface tram that enter at the lower left of the photo. A portion of the water flume that supplied the power to the site can be seen in the woods above the buildings. (Special Collections, University of Washington Libraries, Negative #4267. Lee Pickett photo)

Sunset Mine

The Sunset Mine is rated at A-1, with other mines up this valley rated as high as E-5. The 5-mile-long valley of Trout Creek was once one of the most active mining areas in the western Cascades, and the hills are peppered with mines and laced with trails and old roads. It would be an enormous undertaking to describe all the mines and prospects here, along with their history and minerals, so this section will discuss only the major workings and their histories.

The first discoveries here were the Sunset and Black Bear lodes, made by Ezra and Arthur Egbert in June 1897. Soon after, the Sunset Mining Company was formed. Only assaying and minor development work were done during the early years of the mine. Shipments of crude ore to the smelter in Tacoma began in 1902 and continued through 1905. However, the crude ore shipments proved unprofitable and were discontinued. A surface tram running between the town of Index and the mine,

Index

Sunset Mine
(isometric projection)

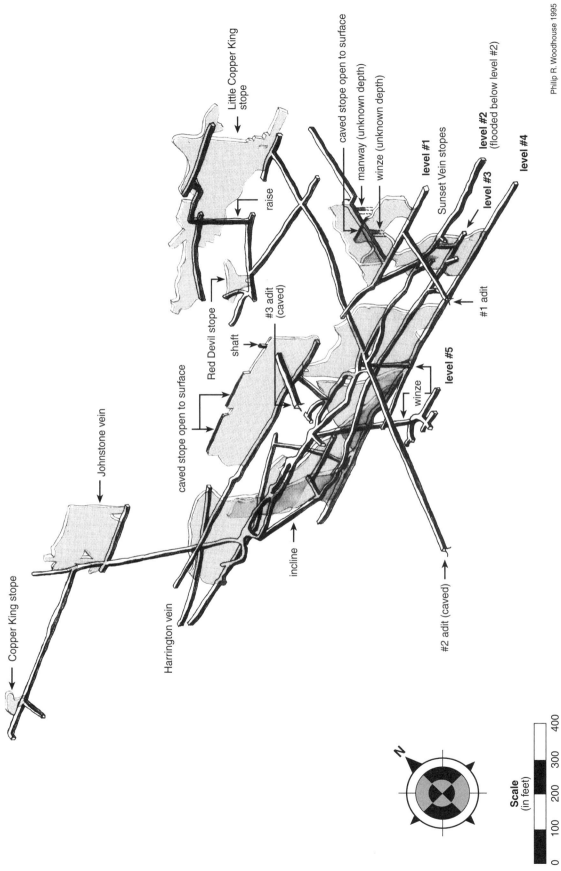

Little Copper King stope

caved stope open to surface

manway (unknown depth)

winze (unknown depth)

level #1

Sunset Vein stopes

level #2
(flooded below level #2)

level #3

level #4

raise

#1 adit

Red Devil stope

#3 adit (caved)

shaft

Johnstone vein

caved stope open to surface

level #5

winze

Copper King stope

Harrington vein

incline

#2 adit (caved)

N

Scale
(in feet)

0   100   200   300   400

Philip R. Woodhouse 1995

built in 1907, was ruined by weather while the mine lay idle. Production resumed in 1916, when a logging railroad was completed from Index to the mine. A 150-ton-per-day flotation mill was completed in 1918, and operations continued intermittently through 1920, when the mine was again closed due to low copper prices after World War I. Production resumed in 1923 and continued until August 1930, when low copper prices and financial problems forced the mine to once again cease operations.

In 1930, while the mine was under option to the Britannia Mining Company, an electrical conductivity survey was made by C. N. Disney of the Radiore Company. The survey covered an area 200 to 600 feet wide and extended 3,600 feet along the western extension of the Sunset vein. [107] The survey indicated an electrical anomaly that extended 2,500 feet west from the Sunset workings. However, Britannia allowed the option to expire before exploring this new find. In 1935, control of the mine passed to the workers, who held labor liens against the property. They worked the mine on a reduced scale until 1940, when the liens were satisfied and the property reverted back to the bondholders.

Miners use gad bars to assist in removing ore from an ore chute in the Sunset Copper Mine. The mine had five levels, including one above the haulage level and three below. The lower tunnels had to be constantly pumped to keep water from flooding the mine. Ore being removed from these chutes was sent down to the haulage level from levels and stopes above. (Lee Pickett photo, Snohomish County Historical Society)

From 1941 to 1943, the mine and mill were operated on a limited scale by Kromona Mines Inc. of Seattle. Some crude ore shipments were also made by lessees from 1941 to 1946. [108] We have found no records of ore shipments after 1946. In July 1950, the U.S. Bureau of Mines began a diamond drilling project on the property, mainly in the area examined by the Radiore Company in 1930. Twelve diamond drill holes were run to explore the anomaly, and two holes were drilled to the eastern extension of the Sunset vein. Three of the holes on the anomaly penetrated copper ore, with the best results coming from the Radiore "B" hole. [109] Drilling totaled 3,746.5 feet. Total production from the Sunset Mine was reported to be 263,500 tons of ore, from which 1,500 ounces of gold, 156,000 ounces of silver, and 12,912,000 pounds of copper were produced, with 90 percent of the production coming from the Sunset vein.

---

[107] The principle of this geophysical investigative method is based on the differences in electrical conductivity of ore and rock formations. (Minerals conduct electricity better than country rock does.)

[108] The mill was built to reduce only low-grade to medium-grade ore, and too much value was lost by milling the thinner high-grade veins. Therefore, these high-grade veins, when encountered, were leased out to independent miners.

[109] In the mid 1970s, the owners ran a 300-foot exploratory tunnel to the Radiore "B" vein but found only a small stringer of ore not worth developing.

The underground workings consist of more than 12,000 feet of drifts, crosscuts, and raises,[110] with 6,200 feet of horizontal workings on the main (#2) level, 1,200 feet on level #3 below that, 2,250 feet on level #4, and 300 feet on level #5. In addition, 1,550 feet of tunnels were driven on the upper workings, or #1 level.

During its heyday, the mill's capacity was increased to 250 tons per day and was powered by two Pelton wheels—one 5 feet in diameter that powered the mill, mine, and camp, and a 3-foot wheel that ran the compressor that powered the drills. These Pelton wheels were turned by water from Trout Creek, 1½ miles above the mine. The water was carried in a 4-by-5-foot flume to a point just above the mill.[111] There it entered a 24-inch-diameter wooden penstock that carried it to the mill and an 18-inch-diameter penstock that split off the 24-inch to deliver water tp the 3-foot Pelton wheel at the portal of level #2. Ore was moved from the main adit in four 1¼-ton mine cars (four of them at a time) that were pulled by a gasoline powered (Ford engine) locomotive capable of transporting 100 tons per day.

Emerging from the main haulage, or #2, level of the Sunset Copper Mine, the little Ford engine tows a consist of four ore cars. (Lee Pickett photo, Sky Valley Historical Society)

To assure an ample water supply to the camp, Sunset Lake farther up the valley was dammed. This raised the level of the lake by 20 feet and increased its size to 65 acres. A siphon was installed at the dam to conduct water from the lake. Concentrates from the mill were carried to Index by standard-gauge railroad when the logging railroad was in operation. When the logging railroad was shut down, a Fordson tractor was rebuilt and equipped with four-wheel drive to haul two 5-ton cars with regular-type railroad braking wheels down the tracks on a steep grade that at one point included a 12-percent slope to the mouth of the valley and on to Index. When the tractor was in operation, two trips per day could be made, with men and supplies being brought up to the camp on the return trips. When the mine was not producing, miners and mail were transported on a gas speeder.

To get to the Sunset Mine, drive east on the Index-Galena Road and watch for the bridge over Trout Creek 4.9 miles from Index. A few hundred feet past the bridge, take a lesser road leading off to the right. (A high-clearance vehicle is recommended for this road, which is usually quite brushy.) Go up to the left through the large open gate and up the switchback. Ignore the road that heads to the left a mile from the gate; proceed straight ahead another ¾ mile to the big concrete slab on the left side of the road. This was the foundation for the Sunset Mine Mill.

The deep hole with the tunnel or channel running from it was the location of the 5-foot Pelton wheel that provided the power for the mill, mine, and camp.

---

[110] In the early 1980s, we found more underground workings than are shown on any map, bringing the total to more than 13,000 feet.

[111] This flume was later shortened to 2,100 feet, and the remainder of the distance to the original intakes of the penstocks was replaced with a 33-inch-diameter wood stave pipe.

Following a disastrous collapse of two of the main stopes in the Sunset Mine, a miner and company official inspect the damage. The chasm that resulted is up to 17 feet wide at this point in the mine. Notice the mine rails at the bottom of the photo. They once ran along a ledge within the stope but now trail off into the abyss. The collapse of these stopes caused massive cavities to open on the surface of the mountainside; these were so large that a 10-story building could fit into them. (Pickett Museum photo, Index Historical Society)

Look around this area for some nice ore samples, and then walk up the road and look for a small stream coming down the road. Follow it to the portal of the main haulage tunnel (level #2). This adit is caved just a few feet back (a good thing too, because it accesses some very dangerous workings!). This tunnel strikes the Sunset vein 600 feet from this portal and was drifted both left and right on the vein. During the 1930s, the main stopes, which are located just to the left and right of the #2 crosscut tunnel, collapsed. The tunnel was redug through this debris and shored. To reconnect the #2 crosscut to the vein, a tunnel was driven on a curved path to the left from the crosscut to connect to the vein beyond the collapse, while a curved tunnel was driven to the right to connect directly into one of the collapsed stopes. In this stope, a deep, blue lake formed as the lower tunnels became flooded, and one could look hundreds of feet up into the cavity that remained after the stope collapsed (when the area was still accessible). To access other veins behind the Sunset, a crosscut tunnel was driven straight ahead more than 500 feet to the Blank, Red Devil, and Little Copper King veins. A crosscut driven from the left drift of the Sunset vein accesses the Harrington, Johnstone, and Copper King veins. On the same drift, a two-compartment winze was sunk to a depth of 365 feet, and it accesses sublevel #3 at 92 feet below #2, sublevel #4 at 185 feet below level #2, and sublevel #5 at 335 feet below level #2. The hoisting room for the winze is carved out of the solid rock on level #2, and the hoisting machinery is still there, along with the big overhead pulley above the shaft. These lower levels account for about 3,750 feet of workings and are now flooded to the main level.

After the reconstruction, the #2 crosscut continued through the collapsed stope area for more than 500 feet into the Red Devil and Little Copper King workings far back in the mountain. In 1964, one member of Northwest Underground Explorations entered the #2 crosscut, walked to the back of the Little Red Devil drift, and then climbed a 120-foot raise to level #1. The upper level was badly collapsed, and little exploration could be done along it. As he ate lunch, sitting on the mine rails of the #1 tunnel amid the spectacular blue and green (azurite and malachite) stains from the copper ore, small rocks tumbled from the ceiling as the mine slowly collapsed.

From the portal of this tunnel, walk up the road a short distance and locate a badly brushed-over road (now no more than a trail) just off the main road to the left, 200 feet from the #2 portal. Walk, climb, and beat brush over to it, and follow it as it climbs up the hillside and then switchbacks left. Just

200 feet after the switchback, look for mine tailings (with ore samples present) dropping toward the road on the right. Climb the tailings to find a small creek flowing from a collapsed mine adit. This is the portal of the #1 tunnel.[112] This tunnel was driven to cut the Sunset fissure at about 120 feet below its outcrop. This was accomplished when the tunnel reached a horizontal length of 225 feet, where it crosscut the ore body. The tunnel was then drifted to the right and left, with the right drift running for 150 feet to a dead end. A raise was driven to the surface near the intersection of the #1 tunnel and the drift, while the left drift ran for another 150 feet where a winze was sunk to the main level of the mine.

Hike around to the right of this adit, climb the mountain for a distance of about 250 feet, and locate a thick cable wrapped around a large stump. Just above this stump is a small landing. Prepare yourself for quite a sight as you walk up to the landing. There, before you, is a large cavern. Step down into it, look to your right into the darkness, and let your eyes slowly adapt. A large building will appear. This was apparently constructed to protect the ore chute and manway used by the miners to move workers and ore after the stopes collapsed in the 1930s. This building is three stories tall and hangs against the back wall of the stope. This cavern is large enough to contain a five-story structure.

Deep in a major stope of the Sunset Mine, these miners pose for a picture. The concentrates extracted from this area ran to 40-percent metal content. This is a good showing for copper. (Lee Pickett photo, Snohomish County Historical Society)

Warning You are looking into the collapsed roof of stope #1. DO NOT VENTURE UNDERGROUND HERE! The roof or floor could collapse further at any moment, either bringing down tons of rock on you or plummeting you 75 feet to the bottom of the lower workings—or both. Look from a distance, pick up ore samples on the ground, and leave to enjoy a long life.

Down to your left as you stand on the high point of the stope facing the mountain is a small opening. This is the top of stope #3.

---

[112] It is possible to enter this portal through a small hole above the adit, but we do not recommend this because the tunnel accesses the bottom of a raise that is collapsed 75 feet above the floor of this mine. It would not take much for this collapse to come tumbling down on you. Use your head as something other than a rock stopper, and stay out of this mine.

Warning Do not enter this stope! It drops sharply for about 80 feet to a very small landing, and from there 15 feet into a funnel that was once an air hole for miners working in stope #4 below. There is nothing to grab onto if you slip and little chance that you would survive the 100-foot fall.

Now exit the cavern and turn right as you face away from the mountain. Walk, staying at the exact same elevation, for about 500 feet, passing the caved portal of adit #3 just below you along the way. Pass a small open cut, and watch where you step!

Warning The old air hole for stope #11 is wide open and usually unmarked. It is a vertical shaft 4 by 6 feet in diameter and descends 80 feet to the rocks below. You will pass it or come near to it as you proceed.

Pass the air shaft and, staying just below the treeline at the top of the old clearcut, proceed with caution to a large trench. Follow the rim until you are able to turn and look back over your right shoulder to the large cavern at the end of the trench. This resembles the one you just left, but it is much larger and deeper. Do not attempt to descend into this chasm. More ore samples can be found here along the edge of this abyss.

Warning The ceiling of this stope is very unstable and always in danger of further collapse. On our last visit, the roof gave way a little, and rockfall crashed into the depths of the cavity. You can peer down into the darkness and see where you would land if you were to fall into the air shaft, but DO NOT ENTER.

Shift change at the Sunset Mine. Taken on November 7, 1929, this photo features the little Ford engine and the level #2 adit in the background, along with the miners. (Lee Pickett photo, Everett Library Collection)

On your way out, you have the option to descend the hillside through the brush to your car, because you are just above the level #2 adit. If you do, you might find the old steel rings from the aging, disintegrated wood-stave penstock that carried water to the mill and Pelton wheel. Four other tunnels are on the property, with only one of any interest. That is the Copper King adit, which you can reach by driving back down the road $^{3}/_{4}$ mile, turning hard right on a poor road, and following it (by driving or hiking) as it climbs to the treeline above the clearcut. At the treeline, find a road leading off to the right and follow it almost to its end. Watch the bank above the road for the mine tailing pile. The mine is at the top of the pile and is about 160 feet long. Some copper ore samples can be found on the pile. Two other tunnels (the Wet Tunnel and the Radiore B adit) are on the road below this one. Both adits are completely collapsed and not worth the effort to visit. The last tunnel on the property is known as the Ravine Tunnel. It is located well above and to the right of the main mine workings at 3,000 to 4,000 feet elevation. We have not visited the Ravine Tunnel and cannot give its exact location. [113]

The metals mined here were copper, gold, and silver derived from the ore minerals bornite, chalcopyrite, covellite, pyrite, native copper, and native silver. ("Native" metal is the actual metal itself, as opposed to ores containing the metal.) The gangue consisted of quartz and calcite.

Non Pareil Mine

Rated at C-1. The claims here were located in 1898 by John A. Lewis. In 1903, they were incorporated as the Non Pareil Consolidated Copper Company, with a capitalization of $1 million at a dollar a share. The underground workings amount to about 1,700 feet, with 1,051 feet of that being the long crosscut tunnel, including drifts and crosscuts. A 300-foot adit is reported to be located above the main workings. [114] There are numerous open cuts and short tunnels on many of the 32 claims, with most of the workings being on the Blue Mud, Imperial, and New Lone Star claims.

From the Sunset Mine, drive or hike up the road (which gets really bad from here on) $1^{1}/_{4}$ mile beyond the Sunset #2 adit. About 200 feet past a major washout, watch carefully for a granite tailing pile well above the road on the left at an elevation of 1,860 feet. Climb the tailing pile to an elevation of 1,920 feet. You are at the lower, main adit, which was driven as a crosscut to intersect the vein. This vein is exposed in a short adit in the creek bed above and to the left of this tunnel. However, only small "trace veins" are present in the main tunnel, and it appears that either the vein didn't go as deep as expected or else they didn't crosscut far enough to reach it.

The metals were copper, gold, silver, cobalt, and a very rare mineral in western Washington, nickel. These were extracted from the ore minerals chalcopyrite, bornite, pyrite, chalcocite, and malachite. The gangue was quartz and calcite.

Merchant Mine

Rated at E-4. The majority of the Merchant claims were located from 1891 to 1896 by Andrew Merchant. Other claims in the Merchant group with sizable workings include the Ore and No Go claims, with 150 feet of underground workings, the Fred P. claim with 500 feet, and the Big Goat claim with 175 feet. These claims are located downstream, closer to the lower camp. The best time to visit this mine is late summer or early fall because of high water crossings.

---

[113] The claim maps show a Ravine claim in the area of a large gully on the mountain, so one could surmise that the mine is in the gulch on that claim. The tunnel is reported to be 200 to 300 feet long.

[114] It's possible that this 300-foot tunnel is the Ravine Tunnel mentioned above, but this is only speculation.

The compressed-air engine that operated the haulback aerial tram at the Merchant Mine. This engine originally shared its base with the winch drum and gears for the tram. Compressed air was piped up the mountainside from the mine's headquarters camp on Trout Creek. The air was also used to run the drills in the mine. (Daryl Jacobson photo)

Caution You must use a high-clearance vehicle with four-wheel drive to reach this mine, or else you will have to hike.

Follow the Trout Creek Road past the Sunset Mine to road's end about 2.8 miles from the Sunset Mine. Find a trail descending to the right toward the north fork of Trout Creek, and make a crossing at some point near where you reach the creek. On the opposite side, a trail leads downstream and then cuts left at a 45-degree angle across a marshy scrub forest[115] to the south fork of Trout Creek and a log that crosses to the old lower camp of the mine. This is an historic and interesting spot to explore before continuing to the mine. The camp contains some old drills and household items of various sorts, lying in and around the rotting logs that at one time were the cabins and buildings of the main headquarters camp.

After exploring the camp, recross the log, turn right, and follow the trail. (This is usually not a place to hike in shorts and T-shirts because the valley has more stickers and brush than you might ever encounter on any other hike; a pair of good gloves will be useful too.) Work your way to the left if the trail is overgrown, and find the road again. Follow it up the valley for about 1,000 feet until you are just across the creek from a major gulch and (in season) a small waterfall.

---

[115] This trail is usually flagged with surveyor's tape. However, if the flags are missing, watch closely for the foot path. If you get lost, remember that the camp is located on the opposite side of the south fork of Trout Creek at a point where the evergreens end and the brush takes over. This is as good a reference as we can provide.

> **Note** The mine tailings are immediately to the right of the waterfall, but because they are gray, not red like most tailings, they tend to blend into the surrounding mountainside.

Descend to the creek, cross, and make your way to the base of the cliff on the right of the waterfall to find the old miner's trail leading into the scrub brush. Follow it until you lose the trail, and begin to climb via your own route up alongside the cliff to a point where you can safely move left on the hillside, above the cliff, to the long tailing pile.

> **Warning** Do not get too brave on this tailing pile. If you slip and tumble, you could go right over the cliff. BE CAREFUL!!

Carefully ascend the tailing pile to the top, where you will come face to face with the cliff. By following the base of the cliff to your right over a small ridge hump, you will see the upper camp. Or, by moving left toward the gulch area, you will come upon the portal of the main tunnel. (Note the air receiver tank mostly buried in the rock at the left of the adit.) These are the main workings of the Merchant Mine, which consists of 2,040 feet of tunnel and a raise of unknown height.[116] The first few hundred feet are flooded by a backup of water created by rockfall at the portal, so if you plan to enter the mine (and we don't recommend that you do), be prepared for deep and cold water for a bit. To get to the upper camp from the mine, backtrack around the base of the cliff the way you came, but at the head of the tailing pile, continue straight ahead and over the small hump to the view of the camp across the small, brushy ravine. Work your way around the side of the ravine, passing the large, flat area that was the likely location of the bunkhouse and cookhouse for the mine, and cross to the landing. Here are the remains of what appears to be an old compressed-air engine and winch. This was installed by M. E. Downs (who held a bond on the mine) in 1897 or 1898 to power the small haulback aerial tramway. The tram was a very small bucket tram of perhaps a 5-ton or 10-ton capacity. It connected the upper and lower camps, a distance of about 2,800 feet. Other small relics also lie scattered about.

The metal mined here was copper, taken from the ore minerals chalcopyrite, bornite, pyrite, magnetite, and hematite. The gangue was quartz and crushed country rock.

Other Trout Creek Prospects

From the Sunset Mine to the end of the Trout Creek Valley are many mines and prospects, located mostly on the west side of the valley. They are accessible by crossing Trout Creek within $1/2$ mile southeast of the Sunset Mine and following a long-forgotten road that drops from the main road to the creek. The bridge is long gone, so you have to ford the creek. (This is best done, and almost certainly only done, during periods of low water.) On the other side, find the old road. From here, it is best to seek out the mines for yourself, because they are scattered and numerous. They consist of tunnels ranging from a few feet to several hundred feet in length and are all at elevations of several hundred feet above the road. Look for clues to their whereabouts such as trails, roads, and cabin sites. It is interesting to examine some of the old equipment and vehicles abandoned over on the west side in bygone days. The mine and prospect names include the Miss Helen, Dorian, Aimee, Judge Extension, Ridenour #3, Venus, and Hidden Treasure.

---

[116] Somewhere on the claim, there is reportedly a vertical shaft of unknown depth.

Kitanning Mine

Rated at B-3.[117] This mine was first located in 1900, but a relocation was made in July 1909 by Judson C. Hubbard. The mine consisted of five claims—the Wonder, Cuprite, Copper Pick, Copper Idle, and Copper Bar. The mine later grew to include nine claims.

From the bridge over Trout Creek on the Index-Galena Road, continue east toward Galena for $1^1/_2$ miles to a small pull-off space on the left side the road. You will see this turnout just as the road turns slightly left and at a high point just as it descends slightly. Park here at an elevation of 1,050 feet. Hike away from the river into the woods, and climb as you move slightly to your right until you are walking along the banks of the little creek. Continue climbing until you reach an elevation of 1,300 to 1,400 feet (or until the cliffs begin to loom above you on your left). Leave the creek at this point, contouring to your left until you are just below the cliffs. Continue with the cliffs on your right side. You will cross a small draw and encounter another cliff slightly lower than the one that you have been following.

Looking down the upper tunnel of the Kitanning Mine. It took us three years to locate this elusive 525-foot adit. When we finally found it, we discovered that on the maps of the area the location was off by $3/_4$ mile, and the published elevation was off by 160 feet. Note that the ore car rails are still in place. (Vic Pisoni photo)

At 1,300 feet elevation, you will spot the remains of a cedar shake cabin at the base of the cliff across the draw. It is an easy scramble to this one-room cabin with a dirt floor. The lower tunnel (elevation 1,350 feet) is located just past the cabin at the east edge of the cliff and is about 250 feet long with some signs of mineral stain on the roof and walls. The main adit is above this one at an elevation of 1,850 feet, and you can reach it by climbing the draw to the left of the lower tunnel until more cliffs force you into a tighter draw just to the right. Ascend this draw to an elevation of 1,750 feet, and look for a faint trail leading from right to left across the gulch. Follow this trail along the cliff to your left, looking uphill, to what appears to be a dead end. Turn and find the trail climbing above you as it switchbacks to the mine, which is blasted into the rock face of the cliff along a very impressive vein.[118]

The tunnel is 525 feet long and contains a small stope or raise near the entrance. The vein is very impressive, especially near the back of the tunnel, where you can scrape away some light mud and dirt

---

[117] This mine can be found more easily with the aid of an altimeter, calibrated at the Trout Creek Bridge for 950 feet elevation.

[118] The trail is much more of a danger here than the mine itself. If you suffer from acrophobia, this might not be the hike for you. At any rate, be careful as you ascend the steep miner's trail.

to expose a nice chalcopyrite vein. But if you plan to take samples, be sure to bring a good, heavy hammer, a chisel, and face protection, because the ore is very hard. When you search for this mine, don't bother looking for the large tailing pile that should be at the base of the cliff, because the entire contents of the tunnel were shipped to the smelter near the turn of the century by the Twentieth Century Alaska Copper Company (a good indication of the size of the ore body).

The metal mined here was copper, extracted from the ore minerals chalcopyrite, bornite, chalcocite, and pyrite. The gangue consisted of quartz and crushed granodiorite.

Lost Creek Mines

Rated at D-4. Several claims were located here in February 1897 and were operated by the Lost Creek Mining Company. The mines are in the Lost Creek Valley 8 miles northeast of Index on the Index-Galena Road.

Park at the west side of Lost Creek, and find the old brushed-over logging road leading upstream. (This road might be too cluttered to use, in which case you should find a route just above it to the right). Follow the contour of the hill as it turns into the Lost Creek Valley. It is a good idea to carry, and to know how to use, the USGS 7.5 Minute maps for this area (the Baring and Monte Cristo quadrangles).

None of the mines contains a great deal of workings, and minerals are scarce. On the west side of the valley near the mouth, and just above the creek, is the Kipling Prospect: a 30-foot adit that failed to strike ore. The other prospects of note are on the east side of the valley at elevations above 3,500 feet. They consist of the Roosevelt Tunnel, with one 56-foot adit and a 10-foot drift; the Upper Roosevelt Prospect, with a 17-foot adit and another 10-foot drift; and the Marion Prospect, located in January 1909, with a 38-foot adit and connecting 30-foot drift.

The metals mined here were copper, gold, and silver, derived from the ore minerals chalcopyrite, bornite, chalcocite, and pyrite. The gangue was quartz and quartzite.

Howard Creek Mines

Rated at C-4 for the lower tunnels and E-4 for the upper tunnels. The claims were first located in 1897 by Charles R. Howard and sold later that year to the Cooperative Mining Syndicate, which did the major development work. (The mines are also known as the Cooperative Group Mines.) Despite much underground and surface work, however, it appears that little if any ore was shipped from the mines. Most underground tunneling consisted of exploratory work. Assays by the USBM indicated poor mineral showings. These mines are arranged in two groups on Howard Creek. The lower group comprises four claims: the Phoenix, Vulcan, Pennsylvania, and Keystone. At the head of the basin and extending up to Howard Lake is the upper group of 12 claims.

Follow the Lost Creek Logging Road as described in the previous section, but follow the road until it makes a hard right switchback. If you can still see the trail ahead, continue on it or make your own way cross-country into the Howard Creek Valley and locate the remains of two old cabins at an elevation of about 2,700 feet. This is the lower camp. The main workings of this group are on the Keystone Claim well above the cabin site on the small stream and gulch on the east side of the creek. A trail is said to lead from the cabins up the hillside about 1,000 feet to the Keystone Claim. On this claim are two adits; one is 267 feet long with a 20-foot upraise, and the other, 200 feet above, is 96 feet long. Also, just above the cabin sites on the west bank, at creek level, is an adit of unknown length. The upper mines are located on the west side of the basin at its end, at an elevation of about 3,500 feet. Development at this camp consisted of two cabins on the Lester Claim and two adits of 684 feet and 59 feet. Also, a shaft whose ore assayed mostly in gold is reportedly located near the lake.

The metals mined here were copper, gold, silver, lead, and zinc from the ore minerals chalcopyrite, pyrite, and bornite. The gangue was quartzite and granodiorite.

Daisy Prospects

Rated at D-4. These are part of the unofficial Troublesome Creek Mining District, which enjoyed only a sporadic and uneventful life. It was overshadowed by its well-known neighbor, Silver Creek. We don't know exactly when the first discoveries were made, but according to L. K. Hodges[119] the first discovery was made by J. C. Lillis (who later died in a mine accident at Monte Cristo). The Daisy Mines, which are not readily accessible, are situated high on the flanks of Hubbart Peak, on the divide between Troublesome Creek and Silver Creek in Section 9, T28N, R11E. There are four adits totalling 1,440 feet of underground workings, one caved adit, and one shaft. These comprise the known workings of the Daisy Mines.

These claims produced gold, silver, and lead, although we know of no ore shipments made from the mines. The ore minerals were galena and arsenopyrite, and the gangue was granite. Zinc and antimony were also reported in assays by the USBM.

Good Luck Prospect

Rated at B-2. Also part of the Troublesome Creek Mining District, this area can be reached by driving the Index-Galena Road for 0.6 mile past the bridge over the North Fork of the Skykomish River and parking along the road just downstream from the Troublesome Creek Campground. Climb the hillside to a trail 50 feet above the road in the timber. Follow the trail to the right and uphill just before the large gulch. Soon you'll find the tailing pile of two of the adits. The lower adits are within 450 feet elevation of the road. Ascend the tailing pile and find two short tunnels. To the left and above these adits is another short one. Several open cuts are also on the property. This is a fairly scenic setting and is worth a visit, but be careful! The area is also home to many cliffs and steep hillsides. Note the old Ingersoll Rand two-lung air compressor lying on the hillside to the left of the lower tailing piles. The three adits are 18, 28, and 46 feet long and reasonably safe.

The metal sought here was copper, with the deposit lying in schist, quartzite, and granite, in which there is a quartz pegmatite dike containing sparse mineralization.

Shamrock Prospect

Rated at C-2 from the highway. This property, part of the Troublesome Creek Mining District, is worth a quick look. On the Index-Galena Road, turn off onto an old road 0.4 mile east of the bridge over the North Fork of the Skykomish River, between Silver Creek and Troublesome Creek. This road switchbacks steeply up to 2,400 feet elevation, where you'll find two adits that are 66 and 72 feet long. These mines were first mentioned in written records in 1915 and were worked as recently as 1978. Not much mineralization can be found here, only small stringers of copper ore with minor amounts of gold.

119 L. K. Hodges, *Mining in the Pacific Northwest*, Seattle Post-Intelligencer, 1897.

Ethel Mine

Rated at B-2 for the lower tunnels and C-3 for the upper tunnels. This mine was located before 1900 and was incorporated as the Ethel Copper Mining Company in December 1905. Later it became the Ethel Consolidated Mining Company. In its heyday, this mine sported a bunkhouse and cookhouse for the crews, two dwellings, a 10,000-foot-per-day sawmill that supplied wood and timbers for the mine and camps, two stables, an 80-ton-per-day capacity concentrator,[120] and an electric power plant. The main (#4) tunnel is completely collapsed about 600 feet back from the portal.

We believe that this is the lower tunnel of the Ethel Mine. This mine was located in the "copper belt" that included other noted mines such as the Copper Belle and Sunset. Notice the horse pulling the train of ore cars standing at the adit in the background. (Pickett Museum)

At one time, the mine owners, who were based in Pennsylvania, planned to extend the #4 tunnel for 4 miles to undercut all their holdings in the area. This ambitious project was abandoned after only 2,000 feet. This large cross-section crosscut was intended for use as a haulage tunnel; it would have been connected by raises to the upper workings where the ore was being mined. This would have eliminated the 4,000-foot gravity and surface trams that ran from the lower tunnel.[121] In 1902, an immense body of copper ore was uncovered at the mine, with assays that showed 77 ounces of silver, $5 in gold, and a whopping 1,180 pounds of copper per ton. This, no doubt, brought a rush of excitement to the camp, and plans for a 400-ton-per-day concentrator and a smelter were made. It was said that even before the large strike, enough ore was in sight to run the 80-ton mill for a year and a half. The new mill and smelter never materialized, however, and the mine was finally closed after it was learned that the ore slimed badly at the mill.[122] The mine had been developed and equipped under the direction of the manager who was also the promoter of the property but not a skilled mining

---

[120] This concentrator was later expanded to 100 tons per day.

[121] The "lower tunnel" is actually above the main tunnel and headquarters camp.

[122] During the concentration process, the ore is crushed as fine as flour and mixed with water to create a slurry. Fine bubbles of air are introduced at the bottom of the tank containing the slurry. The heavy ore particles sink to the bottom of the tank, dragging the attached air bubbles with them. The lighter gangue particles are carried to the surface and skimmed off. The ore "slimes" if the ore particles are so small and light that many of them are floated and skimmed off as well.

engineer. When things started going wrong, the manager reportedly sold out his entire holdings and resigned from the company, leaving the owners, who were mostly eastern businessmen, high and dry. Not being mining men, the stockholders allowed the mine to remain idle.

This patented mine is located on Excelsior Creek on the north side of the North Fork of the Skykomish River, opposite the mouth of Trout Creek. Cross the river at any point that is feasible, and hike toward the hogback between you and Excelsior Gulch. Stay low because the main tunnel is at quite a low elevation. Once you locate the main tunnel on the Skykomish River side of the hogback, you are standing just above the old camp.

The main haulage adit of the Ethel Mine. Notice the drainage channel on the left. The mines were bored on a slight uphill slope with such channels next to the haulage rails to allow for efficient water drainage. (Index Historical Society)

From the main tunnel, walk around to the right toward Excelsior Creek, find the large bull wheel from the old gravity tramway, and then look up the long swath that marks the tram path from the upper workings. Climb these "seven hills of misery," and find the remains of two old log cabins near the top. These were two of the old camp buildings that served the upper tunnels, which were the producing mines of the group. At the end of the swath, just past the cabin sites, you can descend to the stream and climb slightly up the creek to the portal of the lower, or main, working tunnel (not to be confused with the main crosscut tunnel at the lower campsite). This tunnel is caved about 350 feet from the entrance, but at one time it totaled 1,250 feet of horizontal tunneling with a 200-foot raise in the underground workings. The raise was connected to the upper tunnel 200 feet higher and almost directly above the lower portal. The upper tunnel is partly caved and flooded at the portal.

Warning Inside the right-hand drift of this mine's upper tunnel is a small collapse. On the other side of this rockfall is the top of the raise from the lower tunnel. Do not attempt to cross this rockfall. It is 200 feet to the bottom.

This tunnel runs as a crosscut for 225 feet, where it intersects the vein. Drifts were driven in both directions on it for some distance. Tunnel #3, which is 200 feet to the left and 50 feet higher, also runs as a crosscut for about 300 feet and ends with a short drift to the left and a hand-filled, inaccessible drift to the right. In all, about 3,200 feet of underground workings were dug in these mines, and an additional 150 feet were bored in the Edmonds Discovery tunnel 1,200 feet east of the main tunnel.

The metals mined here were copper, gold, and silver, derived from the ore minerals chalcopyrite, bornite, chalcocite, and pyrite. The gangue consisted of quartz, calcite, and granodiorite.

North Star Mine

Rated at D-2 to D-5, depending on where the adit is actually located. This is truly a "lost mine." Since 1991, we have been trying to locate this mine in North Star Gulch just northeast of Index. We are accustomed to searching for months or even years for particular mines, but this one presents little teasers along the way that make the search more suspenseful than most. We'll give you the information that we have gathered a little later in this section so that you, too, can try to solve the puzzle.

The first three claims were located on April 7, 1900, by C. E. Larson; three more were recorded on June 7 of that same year. Eight more were located by S. E. Illig in January 1903. The main ore strike was made in a tunnel about 140 feet long, high up on the mountain, with ore values averaging a little over $100 per ton, mostly in copper, with some silver, gold, and lead present. However, an ore sample taken from the face of this tunnel showed an assay of 12.2 ounces of silver, 10 ounces of gold, and 32.2 percent copper per ton. While this tunnel was being extended at least another 60 feet on the vein, plans were made for a crosscut tunnel to be driven nearly 600 feet to the vein at a lower elevation. This tunnel was driven in 1903 by steam drills. A total of 960 feet of underground workings were dug in the lower crosscut tunnel.

To reach the area of the mine, take Reiter Road just east of Gold Bar to the Deer Creek Flat Road. Follow it as it winds and climbs (and stay alert for motorcycles and off-roaders who often enter and exit without warning). Keep left at all intersections with side roads, and stay on the main road.[123] After Deer Flat, the road again climbs, making two sharp switchbacks. After the second switchback, continue for $1^1/_4$ miles to a lesser road to the right. Turn and follow the road a short distance to a junction, and proceed left.[124] In a short distance you will have to abandon your vehicle. (Even a bicycle should be parked.)

Hike along the old road another mile to North Star Gulch, where the creek pours over the road and drops 100 feet over the face of the cliff to the right of the road. You are now at an elevation of 2,400 feet. Geologist Charles E. Weaver's 1912 report[125] states that the main tunnel is at a elevation of 2,570 feet. But Weaver's stated elevations are 160 feet higher than established elevations used today.[126] Therefore, 2,570 feet minus 160 feet equals 2,410 feet—right about the elevation where the road crosses the gulch. We have been unable to locate a portal or tailing pile anywhere in the area, but we did find an old strongbox and some small pipe in the creek, at road level. Also, on the approach to the gulch, walking from the car over the bank on the talus slope beneath the road, we found a 4-inch-diameter pipeline descending toward the creek far below. Just beyond, on a small ledge below the road, between

---

[123] This road might be gated or water barred at any point, so be prepared to walk, bike, or turn around. At the very least, a high clearance vehicle is recommended.

[124] For a great view of the valley and the Gunn Peak Mines area as well as the Bitter Creek Valley, go right instead, to the log landing.

[125] *Geology and Ore Deposits of the Index Mining District Bulletin #7,* Washington Geological Survey, 1912.

[126] We encountered the same situation with the Kitanning Mine. We searched for this mine for years, until we practically stumbled on the property. The old references placed the location almost a mile from where it actually is.

the 4-inch pipe and the point where the road crosses the creek, is a pile of pipe and wood, suggesting a storage site. If you follow the 4-inch pipe down the talus and hillside to a point where the pipe approaches the creek, you'll see what appear to be the remains of the powerhouse, with pieces of the old generator or dynamo scattered about. If you feel the desire to look for the mine, here are the clues:

- One of the tunnels should be at about the elevation where the road crosses the creek.

- The drilling was done with steam drills, so the mine must be at a location where a boiler could be installed next to or in front of the portal and near water.

- The long tunnel was run as a crosscut, so no ore vein or mineralization need be present that would give away the location. Since the tailings were country rock and not acidic minerals, vegetation, including moss, could have grown over them, camouflaging everything.

- The road might have run right over the portal, destroying it, and the tailings might have been used to surface the road. This situation is common when a road passes near an abandoned mine.

- The mine might be somewhere else on the hillside or in the gulch.

- The mine might be close by but in dense brush or covered by a rockfall.

- The shorter tunnel might be at the location where the modern road crosses North Star Gulch. R. A. Stretch's 1903 map of Index shows a short trail from the Index-Galena Road leading up North Star Creek that could have led to the portal of the lower tunnel. If this is accurate, the lower tunnel would be on the east side of North Star Gulch at a low elevation.

Warning This is tough country, with high sheer cliffs, loose talus, dense brush, and heavy devil's club. Never hike alone, stay in contact with one another, and know where everyone is at all times. Negotiate the talus side by side to reduce the risk of sending a boulder down on a fellow explorer.

The metal sought here was copper, to be extracted from the ore minerals chalcopyrite, bornite, and pyrite. The gangue was quartz and crushed and altered granodiorite.

Miscellaneous Mines

The American Arsenic Company Mine, rated at B-2, is reportedly located in Section 1, T27N, R9E, and Section 6, T27N, R10E, near the headwaters of Hogarty Creek, at an elevation of 2,400 feet. Organized in 1920 and encouraged by the high price of arsenic, this mine reportedly has a 150-foot drift and a shaft of unknown depth on a deposit of realgar, with subordinate amounts of orpiment. Slight encrustations of the white arsenic oxide are said to occur. In July 1920, a 15-ton mill was completed at the property 300 feet below the mine, and water to operate it was collected from a small stream nearby and carried to the mill in a 6-inch-diameter wood pipe.

The Charlotte Mine, rated at B-2, is reported to be in the southwest $^1/_4$ of Section 35, T28N, R10E, about $^1/_2$ mile west of the Ethel Mine. It is on the northwest side of the North Fork of the Skykomish River, at an elevation of 1,000 feet. It reportedly has a 150-foot drift, a 35-foot drift, a 20-foot drift, and a short winze. The metals sought were copper, gold, and silver from the ore minerals chalcopyrite, pyrite, and chalcocite. The deposit consists of small lenses of ore along a shear zone in granodiorite.

Miller River and Money Creek

This region consists of two separate watersheds. We will discuss them together because of their physical, topographic, and geologic similarities. The area is situated near the town of Grotto on Highway 2 east of Everett on the way up to Stevens Pass. Miller River has an east and a west fork. The primary source of the east fork is Lake Dorothy, located within the Alpine Lakes Wilderness Area high in the central Cascades. The river flows north to join the Skykomish River just 2 miles above Grotto. Along the way, it picks up the shorter west fork, which gets its start in the Cleopatra Basin and Gouging Lake region northwest of Lake Dorothy. Just across the river from Grotto, Money Creek joins the Skykomish for their mutual rush toward Puget Sound.

The buildings of the Apex Gold Mine above Money Creek in northern King County. An aerial tramway transported goods to the mine and allowed the ore to be shipped down to the surface railroad, which then carried it to the town of Miller River (formerly Berlin). (Washington Miner cover illustration)

The scenery in both watersheds is similar, with rich carpets of lush, green forest extending from the valley floors high up onto the surrounding mountainsides. Above the timberline, hanging valleys and alpine basins present meadows and rock fields of unparalleled splendor. The rock walls of these basins laid bare the mineral veins that crisscross the area, making this a prime spot for prospecting. You can often trace the veins for hundreds of feet along the cliffs.

As you drive into this area, you begin in Snohomish County and travel south and east into King County. The West Fork of the Miller River was the largest producer of silver in King County, with mines such as the Cleopatra, the Aces Up, the Mono, the Great Republic, the Triple S, and the Coney Basin leading the way. Farther downstream, near the confluence of the West Fork and the East Fork, the

Miller River–Money Creek Mining Area

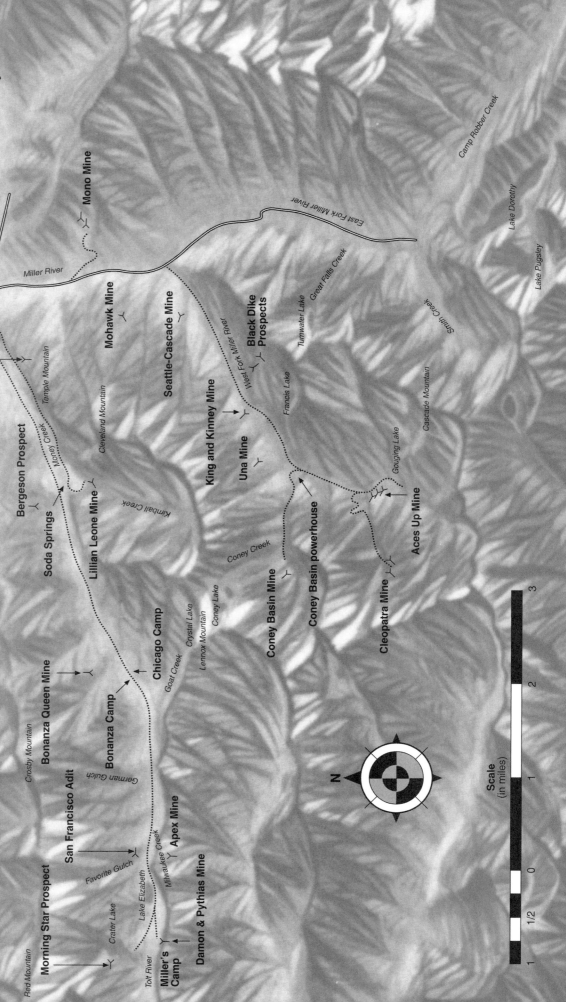

Skykomish

U.S. Highway 2

Mono Mine

East Fork Miller River

Miller River (formerly Berlin)

Miller River

Grotto

South Fork Skykomish River

Mohawk Mine

Seattle-Cascade Mine

Grand Central Mine

Temple Mountain

Bergeson Prospect

Money Creek

Cleveland Mountain

Soda Springs

Lillian Leone Mine

Kimball Creek

King and Kinney Mine

West Fork Miller River

Black Dike Prospects

Francis Lake

Tumwater Lake

Great Falls Creek

Camp Robber Creek

Lake Dorothy

Lake Pugsley

Smith Creek

Cascade Mountain

Una Mine

Lowe Creek

Crosby Mountain

Bonanza Queen Mine

German Gulch

Bonanza Camp

Chicago Camp

Goat Creek

Crystal Lake

Lennox Mountain

Coney Lake

Coney Creek

Coney Basin Mine

Coney Basin powerhouse

Gouging Lake

Cleopatra Mine

Aces Up Mine

Red Mountain

Morning Star Prospect

San Francisco Adit

Favorite Gulch

Milwaukee Creek

Apex Mine

Lake Elizabeth

Crater Lake

Tolt River

Miller's Camp

Damon & Pythias Mine

N

Scale (in miles)

1   1/2   0   1   2   3

mineralization changed, and the metal antimony played a key role in the prospecting, though little was ever mined. Money Creek, entirely in King County, exhibits mineralogy similar to the lower stretches of Miller River, which is not surprising given their close proximity to one another. Along Money Creek, gold, silver, and some antimony were the primary metals of interest, with mines such as the Apex, the Grand Central, the Kimball Creek Mines, and the Damon and Pythias leading the production.

The mountains that top the valley walls bear names such as Mount Phelps, Mount McCartney, Red Mountain (there are two), and, separating Miller River and Money Creek, Mount Cleveland.

History

Because of the remoteness of the Miller River area, no record of prospecting or mining exists from before the routefinding and surveying of the Great Northern Railway began in the late 1880s and early 1890s. This effort began to open the valley of the Skykomish River to more than railroad workers. In 1892, W. L. Saunders and Archie Williamson were among the first men known to have ventured into the Miller River region with the intent of finding minerals there. In 1889, Alexander McCartney located the Apex group of claims on a galena ledge above the south side of Money Creek. This mine, also named the Apex, was the first to ship ore from the district. Prior to the cutting of a major wagon road into the mine in 1901, the Apex shipped about $80,000 worth of ore on horseback.

The greatest mining activity in the Money Creek area was between 1900 and 1905. In 1906, a fire destroyed most of the little town of Berlin (now Miller River). The fire was said to have burned everything in town except the barns of the Apex Mine. It had burned in nearby timber for a day prior to reaching the town. The buildings burned included a mine concentrator, sawmill, shingle mill, stores, hotels, and five saloons. In 1909, a narrow-gauge railway was completed between the town of Berlin, near the Great Northern tracks, and the Apex Mine. By the time the locomotive for this new narrow-gauge railway arrived, the rails had had plenty of time to gain a generous coating of rust and dead leaves. This, combined with the moderately steep grade, caused the locomotive's drive wheels to slip as it neared the top of the grade near the mine bunkers. The slipping turned to sliding as the little locomotive began an uncontrollable journey back down the tracks to a curve where it jumped the tracks and turned over. There it remained until it was removed for scrap years later. For the remainder of the small railway's life, cars were moved up the track by horses. On the return trip to Berlin, the cars were allowed to coast down the line.

What to See

Unless you are willing and able to do a fair amount of hiking and climbing through an area with few trails and fewer roads, you will have to be satisfied with some tantalizing glimpses of the cliffs and basins high above you. This is an area where the faint of heart might not want to tread too heavily. (There is only one fair-sized mine in this area to which you can actually drive.) If, on the other hand, you enjoy the thrill of traveling cross-country and challenging your routefinding skills, this is the area for you!

For the Rockhound

The upper reaches of Money Creek have been known to yield large, spectacular quartz crystals several inches in length and of startling clarity. The area also has produced large cubic and pyritohedric crystals of iron pyrites that range in color from brassy to gun-metal gray. Most of these have been found high in the Red Mountain area.

Getting There

Head east on Highway 2 past the town of Index, and continue through the town of Grotto, where a cement plant once stood. Within about $^3/_4$ mile, you will approach a small tunnel (the first on the highway). Instead of entering this tunnel, turn right and cross the Skykomish River. The signs will point the way to the Money Creek Campground. You will cross the tracks of the Burlington Northern's main line between Wenatchee and Everett. About a mile past the campground, the Miller River Road forks to the right, taking you to the old town of Miller River (formerly Berlin). Continue on this road if Miller River is your goal. If you want to reach Money Creek, take the Miller River Road fork and then immediately make a 90-degree right turn past a small house onto Money Creek Road.

How far you travel up each road will be determined by two things: where you are going and the clearance of your vehicle. Because of desultory maintenance in this area, it is difficult to predict the road conditions. A winter of heavy snowfall followed by massive spring flooding can make the region unreachable until repairs can be made. The West Fork Miller River Road is impassible by all but helicopters, because the river has a nasty habit of flowing down it during flood season. Money Creek Road usually fares better, but check beforehand and proceed with great caution.

Geology

Considering that this area has provided the leading silver mines of King County, the geology of the Miller River and Money Creek basins is relatively uninteresting. It is certainly not as varied as the Mountain Loop Highway or Darrington areas. The rocks that predominate here are Tertiary granitics with joint planes along which the ore-carrying veins formed. The entire upper region of Miller River and Money Creek are so structured. At about the confluence of the East and West Forks of the Miller River is a contact zone with Eocene-Oligocene volcanic rocks running in an east-west direction. It appears that the occurrences of antimony can be located along this contact or very near it.

Money Creek is somewhat more interesting geologically. Its upper reaches are also Tertiary granitic rocks, but there are also bodies of low-grade, pre–Upper Jurassic metamorphic rocks consisting of greenschists and some limestone, which cut the granitics at several places along the valley's length. Along with these, the Eocene-Oligocene volcanics also present themselves at some of the contact zones along the creek. This makes for a more varied mineral inventory than Miller River. Money Creek has antimony near its eastern end, silver and gold farther upstream, and some reports of copper thrown in for good measure.

The Mines

Mono Mine

Rated at B-2. These claims are patented, so you should get permission from the owners of the property before visiting. Drive south along the Miller River Road past the Miller River Campground. About 3 miles from the turnoff from Highway 2, you will notice what appears to be an abandoned logging road turning to your left. This is the road to the Mono Mine, which is on the other side of Miller River from the road. Park here and hike down the road. About 100 yards after leaving the main road, you will come to the river and discover that the old bridge has been washed out. Cross as best you can. The task is much easier later in the year, long after the spring runoff has subsided, but even then, hip or chest waders might be required. The mine is in the southwest $^1/_4$ of Section 3, T25N, R11E, with the lowest adit located at an altitude of about 1,700 feet.

The lowest adit, to which the road originally ran, is designated tunnel #3 and is 760 feet long. This tunnel contains a 250-foot raise/incline angled at about 80 degrees, which connects with a winze driven downward from the lower part of the higher #2 adit.

> **Warning** A flooded winze of unknown depth is located at the end of the left-hand drift. Watch your step!

To reach the #2 portal, you must climb a steep bank about 300 feet down the road from the #3 adit. From there, a trail leads to the #2 tunnel.

> **Warning** In the 1960s, a trespasser and his dog entered the #2 adit.[127] The dog slid down the winze to its death. This mine is dangerous, and entry to the #2 adit is not recommended.

The mining records indicate that tunnel #1 is located on the mountainside above tunnel #2. We did not attempt to locate it during our visits to the site. A 60-foot winze has been driven downward 55 feet inside the adit, which is located at an intersection with a drift that runs left and right. Watch your step!

The mine produced primarily copper, showing about 2 percent of the ruddy metal. About $1^1/_2$ ounces of silver and less than $1/_2$ ounce of gold per ton were also produced. Some zinc and arsenic made a showing here as well. The ore minerals were arsenopyrite, chalcopyrite, bornite, sphalerite, and pyrite. The gangue consisted mostly of apatite and quartz.

Great Republic Mine

Rated at A-2. Much of the development work at this antimony mine was done between 1902 and 1905, when the Great Republic Gold Mining Company ran the operation. The ore that they found contained only a small portion of gold; antimony and silver were the main constituents. The ore minerals found were stibnite and pyrite, with gangue of quartz and calcite.

This mine is located in the north $1/_2$ of the southwest $1/_4$ of Section 33, T26N, R11E, at an elevation of about 1,250 feet. Drive about 2.2 miles up the Miller River Road after leaving Highway 2 until you reach Happy Thought Creek crossing the road. Park and ascend the creek until you reach the mine at the first falls that you encounter. Both the upper and lower adits are located in the creek bed and are hard to miss. The lower and upper tunnels are not far apart and are connected underground by an incline. In the 1980s, the lower adit could be negotiated to the incline, but not too much farther. Apparently, during heavy runoffs of Happy Thought Creek, debris is washed into the upper adit and finds its way down the incline. This is gradually filling and choking off the lower tunnel. The tunnel is in hard rock and is basically sound but is definitely not a place for claustrophobics. The upper portal is only 20 feet elevation above the lower, and about 240 feet farther to the west. Several small stopes were driven above the upper tunnel, where most of the development work was done.

---

[127] Rumor has it that when the dog took the plunge, the man notified the mine owner, the Forest Service, and the sheriff that his son had plummeted down the shaft. After the rescuers located the body of the dog, the man had to confess the deception, saying that he feared there would be no rescue effort mounted for a dog!

Mohawk Mine

Rated at B-2. This mine consists of four tunnels that add up to about 400 feet of underground workings. It is next to a seasonal stream near the base of a scenic waterfall. Many people visit the area to see the falls in the early part of the year. The mine appears on Anderson's Mining Map of the area, published in 1897.

Drive up the Miller River Road until about ⅛ mile before (downstream from) the West Fork Road junction. Park along the road, and seek out a seasonal creek coming down the mountainside from the west. This will be a dry wash later in the summer. Just to the right (north) of this stream bed, locate a trail that leads up the hillside for about ½ mile to the base of the waterfall, at an elevation of 1,520 feet, where the mine adits are located. The tunnel that the trail leads you to is the main adit. This and another of the tunnels are on the north side of the creek, while the other two are across the creek on the south side, slightly lower in elevation.

The ore in this mine is the same as that in the Great Republic—largely stibnite, with gold and antimony being the primary metals sought here.

Seattle-Cascade Mine

Rated at B-3. Also known as the Triple S, the Silver Dollar, the Copper Plate, and the Alexander Mine. The mine was operated primarily by the Seattle-Cascade Mining Company in 1908 and 1909. Many ownership and name changes followed, and subsequent work was not well documented.

Drive about 4 miles from the Money Creek Campground up the Miller River Road to the fork of the East and West Fork Miller River Roads. The West Fork Road tracks to the right and was essentially impassible during our recent visits. About ¼ mile up the West Fork Road, at an elevation of 1,560 feet, locate a gulch with a seasonal creek that has entered the roadway and washed it out badly. Travel up this gulch just a short distance until you notice a narrow but long and badly weathered slide area to your right as you move up the gulch. Turn and ascend this rocky slide to the top. Here you will find a large ore dump. This was near the site of a mill that was constructed to process the ore from the mine. The ore was found to be incompatible with the milling equipment and the project was abandoned, leaving this ore where it lies just above the road. The ore had been carried down the hill from the mine on an aerial tramway 1,100 feet long.

To reach the mine, find a route up the hill parallel to the gulch you first entered from the road. (Do not attempt to climb up the gulch itself; you will encounter impassable cliffs.) The lower (main) adit is located at the base of a cliff at an elevation of 2,100 feet. The main tunnel here is about 1,050 feet long. The plan was to run this adit another 600 to 800 feet into the mountain to crosscut the vein at that depth. At 575 feet from the entrance, a 6-by-8-foot raise was begun to provide easier access to the upper tunnel. This raise is said to connect with the short tunnel in the gulch 80 feet above and to the left of the mine. This lower tunnel and raise were required because of the extreme difficulty the miners had getting supplies and equipment up to the lofty discovery tunnel some 584 feet higher in elevation. As noted, the upper tunnel is well above this lower tunnel and is about 300 feet long. If you venture up there, and we don't recommend you do, be careful! This adit contains a flooded winze of unknown depth, and the route is treacherous. There is a third adit on the property, which we have not visited.

The mine produced mostly silver and lead with zinc, copper, and gold also making a small showing. The ore minerals were sphalerite, galena, pyrite, arsenopyrite, and chalcopyrite. The gangue consisted mostly of quartz.

Lynn Prospect

Rated at C-2. The Lynn Prospect is about 1.3 miles up the West Fork Miller River Road, on the northwest side. The lower adit, at an elevation of 1,965 feet, was driven as a crosscut for 185 feet to the shear zone; it contains 15 to 30 percent quartz, 10 to 25 percent clay, and 3 to 5 percent sulfide minerals. It follows this zone for a distance as a drift for an additional distance of 160 feet. The upper adit, at an elevation of 2,165 feet, runs as a drift along the shear zone for 45 feet and then crosscuts 30 feet to another zone where the tunnel is apparently in a state of collapse. Both of these zones contain fine-grained pyrite, galena, chalcopyrite, sphalerite, and lenses of quartz. Both adits are on the left side of the gulch.

King and Kinney Mine

Rated at C-2. At this mine, located on the West Fork of Miller River, two adits pierce the mountain at 400 and 800 feet above the river.[128]

A member of Northwest Underground Explorations surveys a collapse in the King and Kinney Mine. (Phil Woodhouse photo)

The mine is reportedly on the southeast corner of Section 17, T25N, R11E. Drive the Miller River Road 3.4 miles from the town of Miller River (formerly Berlin), where it forks to the right, and park at the entrance to the West Fork Miller River Road. Hike 1.4 miles up the road until you encounter a very large cedar tree on the right side with a large (1¼-inch) cable and some old pieces of wood attached to it at about 10 feet above the ground. Turn so that the river is behind you, and look straight up the mountainside. You will see brush-covered talus to your right and forest straight ahead and to your left. Climb into this forest at a convenient spot and begin to ascend. Stay as close as you can to the boundary between the forest and brushy talus on the right side of the woods without encountering too much brush. You'll find the mine's powerhouse 300 vertical feet above the roadway, just on the edge of the trees. The mine, which was open as of 1995, is about 10 feet higher and 60 feet farther out on the talus slope.

---

[128] There is quite a bit of confusion about the locations and names of some of the mines and prospects in this area, and this mine might be the same property as the Lynn described above. These tunnels are about 300 feet of elevation above the road.

Steve Reeves, left, and Jeff Schempp, right, examine a gasoline-driven air compressor at the ruins of the small power plant at the King and Kinney Mine in 1995. (Phil Woodhouse photo)

Judging from the machinery that remains, the mine was last worked during the Depression years. The tattered remnant of one of the powerhouse walls still stands precariously on the south side, while the rest of the building has collapsed. A bunkhouse that was immediately to the south is completely gone. The site still contains the air compressor, which consists of a four-cylinder gasoline engine clutched through a multiple V-belt system to a two-piston, single-stage air compressor manufactured by the Gardner-Denver Company of Denver, Colorado, and Quincy, Illinois. These are mounted on the same steel frame along with an air receiver tank that is about 6 feet tall and $2^1/_2$ feet in diameter. The 10-gallon gas tank now hangs at a crazy angle to one side, and the radiator is gone. Just below the powerhouse is the only aerial tramway bucket that we could locate at the site—but what a bucket it is! This is the largest tram bucket that we've seen on the western slopes of the Cascade Mountains. It is still connected to its hanger, but the carriage and wheels are missing. The tram appears to have used a fairly simple haulback system in which a single bucket was raised and lowered along the stationary cable[129] by a lighter-weight hauling cable. We found no trace of the haulback mechanism or its pulleys.

As you make the slight climb up the dump to the mine adit, you will notice a few more artifacts lying about. Most notable is the ore cart frame, now stripped of its wheels, axles, and body. As you approach the portal, look down the mine dump to your right and you will see the body of the cart down in the brush. This tunnel is strikingly similar to the Lynn Prospect's lower adit, which leads us to believe that they might be the same mine.[130] It is a crosscut driven straight into the mountainside for almost 200 feet, which then turns gradually to the left and back sharply to the right. It continues for about 35 feet until it encounters the vein, whereupon it turns sharply left and drifts for about another 200 feet.

Warning If you have elected, on your own, to enter this mine, the rock will appear firm until the tunnel reaches the vein. The vein material is soft, kaolinized (clayey) material that has already caused extensive collapsing of the rotting shoring. Do not enter this portion of the tunnel.

---

[129] This cable is still there. It is the same cable that is fastened to the tree at the roadside below. You could follow this artifact to the mine, but it would lead you through almost impenetrable brush.

[130] Through the years, names and descriptions of mines and prospects often changed as new owners and investors came and went. It is difficult to know for certain who is describing what properties and exactly where they are actually located.

Right where the tunnel reaches the vein, there is a small air receiver tank on the floor of the mine, which was connected with piping to the power plant. This is the first mine we've seen that was not bored on a slight uphill slope to allow for water drainage. As a consequence, the water is about a foot deep throughout the tunnel.

The upper tunnel of this mine is about 400 feet of elevation above the lower adit (described above). This adit is said to be about 525 feet in length but is caved 10 feet beyond the portal.

The metals sought here were copper, lead, zinc, silver, and gold. The minerals consisted of chalcopyrite, pyrite, galena, sphalerite, and malachite, which were disseminated throughout a quartz and kaolin gangue that comprised the vein material.

Una Mine

Rated at C-3. While the King and Kinney Mine was reopened in the Depression era, the Una was not, but some light work was done there in the 1950s. The mine's 130-foot adit produced ore in 1908 while under the ownership of Consolidated Gold Mines Company. The ore was copper, gold, and silver. This is also said to be a good tourmaline hunting area.

The mine is located in the southeast corner of Section 17, T25N, R11E. The building site is 650 feet of elevation above the West Fork Miller River Road on a steep hogback between two treacherously steep gullies. All that remains of the original structures is the shattered wreckage of two cook stoves that once heated the building(s) and the food for the men who occupied them. On one fragment of stove is cast "Detroit St." The complete statement might have once read "Detroit Stove Company." A few samples of ore are also scattered about the site, along with what appears to be a small base for a forge, built of hand-fitted stones. Surprisingly, a wagon road 5 to 6 feet wide was run from the river road to the cabin site.

The ore at this mine is unusual because the gangue material is composed of fine crystals of black tourmaline, or schorl. Green malachite stains this matrix in places, creating an interesting display. Other ore found here is similar to that described for the King and Kinney—a decaying clay/quartz containing disseminated crystals of pyrite.

> **Warning** The ascent to this mine is not for the timid or the out-of-shape. Avoid the gullies to the north and south during your climb to the old campsite, because one slip into them will be your last. To reach the mining area, you must actually climb into and up the south gully. BE CAREFUL.

Members of Northwest Underground Explorations visited the Una Mine in 1995. The following is our first-hand account of that adventure.

To reach the cabin site, hike the West Fork Miller River Road as described for the King and Kinney. When you reach the large cedar tree to which the cable is fastened, continue up the road a few hundred feet until you can see the steep gully up to your right as you face up the valley. Early in the year, there will be a splendid waterfall here. You will notice some brownish-stained rocks partway up the gully. Continue along the road until the forested slope of the mountainside meets the right shoulder of the road. Leave the road and ascend about 100 feet of elevation into the forest. At this point, begin to climb to your right, ascending at about a 45-degree angle to the horizontal. As you approach the gully, which you saw earlier from the road, again begin to climb directly upward. If you are lucky, you will come upon the wagon road, which is difficult to discern. Follow it to the right until you encounter dense brush, which comprises mostly vine maple. Head straight up at this point until you reattain the road, which now ascends to your left. Follow it through vine maple into the trees of the hogback. Now climb directly up for about another 60 feet of elevation to reach the building site. Be extremely cautious as you explore this area, as noted above. To descend, carefully retrace your steps to avoid ending up in one of the gullies or having to thrash through excessive brush.

To reach the workings from the cabin site, climb just to the right of straight up the mountainside, at about a one-o'clock angle from the forge area. A 30-yard hike will bring you to a switchback going left. This will lead you to the gulch about 40 yards to the south. The ascent up the creek's gulch is steep and requires scrambling experience. Samples of ore from the mine are noticeable in the creek bed and consist of a fine crystal matrix of black tourmaline that contains gold, silver, and copper. We found some pieces weighing up to 40 pounds.

About 150 feet of elevation above where the path enters the gulch is an embankment (left side bank, looking up) that crests 30 feet above. From the top of the crest, you can see the main tunnel in a large rock outcropping, not more than 40 feet from the crest. At the tunnel opening, a post with a rusty can nailed to it leans against the outside. This contains the claim notice, dated September 28, 1957. It is signed by the past owners and witnessed by Mike Kinney of the King and Kinney Mines. It renames this adit the Janet adit.

The 15-foot entrance tunnel is 6 feet by 6 feet in cross section. Just inside, you will see an ore-stacking chamber 8 feet in diameter that contains some items of interest. Along the right side going into the adit is a shelf 4 by 3 by 3 feet, which seems to comprise a work area of some sort. Next to the shelf is a drying oven with four racks, 2 by 2 by 1 feet. A few feet past the shelf is the ore holding section. Ore and burlap sack remnants indicate that this was where the miners placed the sacked ore to be trammed down and across the gully to the cabin site area and then, presumably, sent on to market on pack burros or mules. From the ore holding space, the tunnel turns 90 degrees to the left and then makes a gradual bend to the right for 35 feet. Here it forks to the left and right for 15 feet in both directions. From the appearance of the remaining ore on the walls and the artifacts left behind, it seems that the ore was not mined out. Ore samples of iron, malachite, and crumbling quartz along with the coal-black tourmaline can be chipped off the walls.

A second claim notice is located 30 feet from the Janet adit, next to a shallow, 10-foot-long pit. Downhill, below the prospect pit, is a 15-foot snub tunnel with some low-grade, iron-stained ore of no appreciable consequence. The same participants from the Janet adit named this property the Troyce. Fifty feet over and 30 feet higher is a natural cave of what seems to be a whitish calcite mixed in a darker rock. Low at the entrance, it is roomier inside—about 15 feet in diameter. Just outside, and protected from weathering factors by overhanging rock, is a large and well-preserved blacksmith bellows. It appears that this operation was interrupted by an unfortunate event of some sort—perhaps weather, lack of funds, politics, or litigation in one form or another. The blacksmith bellows, with all its hardware still in working condition, has not been used.

For the Rockhound

The ore at these adits is very unusual, especially for this area. Microscopic examination reveals tiny sprays of black tourmaline (schorl), which are seldom found in the Miller River area. Interspersed among these sprays are various metallic sulphides.

Coney Basin Mine

Rated at D-3. The first claims were staked here in 1892, and development work began in 1894. By January 1896, a hydroelectric plant—one of the first ones west of the Cascade Mountains—had been installed. Work continued until 1897, when an explosion outside the mine killed several men. The resulting litigation caused the mine to close. Mining activity was intermittent after that time. Almost 3,000 feet of tunneling was done at the mine, and several shafts were also reportedly bored on the property, but we failed to locate them during our recent visits. The upper adit is stoped upward to daylight immediately inside the portal. The mine is located just north of the center of the east $^1/_2$ of Section 13, T25N, R10E, at an elevation of 3,100 feet.

Travel up the West Fork Miller River Road about 2.2 miles past the separation of the East and West Fork Roads. At an elevation of 2,040 feet, you will encounter an older road that ascends to your right toward Coney Creek. Before it leaves the side of the creek, look for old pieces of iron and other debris between the road and the creek. This is the old powerhouse. A little farther up the road is the lower camp for the mine. Continue up the road through two switchbacks, and at about 2,400 feet elevation, you will begin to enter Coney Basin, a hanging valley on the western wall of the West Fork Miller River Valley. As you enter the basin, you will be able to locate the area of the mine portals on the cirque's back wall. The vein is denoted by a wide, red streak that slashes the wall above the portals, and the mine dump is located where the wall contacts the scree. Continue via the way trail that runs from the end of the road to the scree below the portals, and scramble up to the mine. At one time, a 2,000-foot aerial tramway connected the portals to the end of the road in the center of the basin below.

About 40 feet inside the upper adit, just past the glory hole, the tunnel was enlarged to contain an Ingersoll-Sergeant double-action air compressor. The compressor is still here! The flywheel is about $7^1/_2$ feet in diameter, and a special notch had to be carved in the ceiling to accommodate it. It rests on a wooden timber frame and was powered by a DC electric motor. A portion of the motor is also still here, along with its resistance-box speed controller. The power for this machine was generated by the falling waters of Coney Creek at the powerhouse alongside the road, which you passed on your way up. It is amazing that such a massive piece of machinery was hauled to such a remote location. This machine dates back to the 1890s.

This air compressor powered the drills in the Coney Basin Mine in the 1890s. It was produced by the Ingersoll-Sergeant Drill Company of New York. It was driven by a DC electric motor. A flat belt ran from the motor and around the flywheel. Electrical power was provided by a water-driven Pelton wheel located far down the basin near the West Fork of the Miller River. (Phil Woodhouse photo)

As you probe deeper into this tunnel, you will find other, smaller artifacts along the way. The tunnel continues directly into the cliffside for several hundred feet and then turns left and parallels the cliff face for hundreds more feet. This is mostly a crosscut tunnel, and every stringer or vein that was crossed enticed the miners to drift into the mountain in search of ore. One such drift is along a vein that contains a great amount of calcite, and the tunnel is festooned with speleothems (stalactites and stalagmites) of a pure white color. The lower tunnel accesses stope-work, and it is clear that most of the ore extracted here came from this level. When we visited this mine in 1996, a rock slide had completely obliterated any trace of the lower tunnel.

This mine is now in the Alpine Lakes Wilderness Area and is thus off-limits to future mining ventures. The ore assayed highest in gold, with silver, copper, zinc, and lead also making a strong showing.[131] The ore minerals were chalcopyrite, galena, sphalerite, pyrite, and tetrahedrite, with quartz as the gangue material.

Black Dike Prospect

Rating undetermined. Northwest Underground Explorations has not visited this area. With the aid of a USGS 7.5 Minute map for Grotto, locate Francis Lake in Section 29, R11E, T25N. Note the steep gully just to the northeast of (downstream from) Francis Creek, near the center of Section 20. Our research shows that the four Black Dike adits are in this gulch. Adit #1 is at an elevation of 2,590 feet and has 80 feet of crosscut and drift and one winze of unknown depth. Adit #2 is at an elevation of 2,900 feet, with 170 feet of drifts and crosscuts, and a raise of unknown height. Adit #3 is at an elevation of 2,940 feet, with 30 feet of drift and crosscut. Adit #4 is at an elevation of 2,970 feet, with 60 feet of drift and crosscut. All four adits are on the west side of the gulch.

Aces Up Mine

Rated at E-3. This is the farthest major mine up the West Fork of the Miller River. There are four adits on the property, three of which we visited in the spring of 1995.

The mine is in the southeast 1/4 of the southwest 1/4 of Section 30, T25N, R11E, at 2,400 feet elevation. Hike the West Fork Miller River Road about 4.2 miles past the point where it forks from the East Fork Road, until you reach the property at the road's end. This is about 1/2 mile beyond the old Cleopatra Mine campsite. As you approach the end of the road, you will notice a large mine dump on the mountainside about 100 feet above you. This is the #2 adit at an elevation of 2,430 feet. First visit the lower tunnel, still ahead, and then you can take any number of pathways and old roads to tunnel #2.

The lowest adit on the property, at 2,360 feet elevation, is partially caved and flooded, and is thus inaccessible without chest waders.

> **Warning** The timber shoring is totally gone in this adit, and the massive rocks that make up the roof of the portal create a real and immediate hazard to the explorer. Do not enter this tunnel.

Since the tunnels were numbered from the upper tunnel downward, this is tunnel #3. It was the main adit and appears to have been intended as the haulage tunnel for the complex. A total of 670 feet of tunneling was done in this adit. The bore goes straight into the mountainside for 100 feet and then splits, with the left-hand tunnel continuing straight ahead. The right-hand tunnel Y's about 30 degrees for 80 feet and then terminates. A trace of ore was found in this crosscut.

The left, or main, tunnel continues directly into the mountain for another 320 feet, until it is 420 feet from the portal. If the miners thought they were following a vein, they were mistaken, because no ore was ever detected along this distance. At 420 feet from the portal, the tunnel makes an abrupt

---

[131] It is rumored that a quantity of ore was helicoptered from this mine in the 1980s, but this has not been substantiated.

right-angle turn to the right and crosscuts for 90 feet where it intercepted the vein. The remaining 80 feet of tunnel was drifted along the vein, where a small amount of gold and silver value was found. We have not entered this tunnel; our information comes from other mining records.

Just outside the #3 tunnel are the remains of a large side-dumping ore cart, along with the remnants of compressed-air hoses and other odds and ends. A small brick structure that appears to have been a fireplace or forge is also located here. This tunnel is at the site of the main camp, and the decayed remains of buildings litter the spot. A large, broken log with stair steps notched into it crosses the West Fork of the Miller River at this spot. The original trail crossed the river here and continued upstream along the eastern side, where early maps hint at additional mining activity.

Now head to the #2 adit previously mentioned. On the way up, near the bottom of the mine dump, is an old six-cylinder Chevrolet engine lying along a section of the access road. It lies with what appears to be compressed air pipes, but the engine seems to have been automotive in nature and was not used for power at the mine. On the dump, just a few feet above the engine, is a moose of an industrial four-cylinder gasoline engine, which has about a 7-inch stroke and a 6-inch bore. This probably powered an air compressor, but no sign of the compressor can be found. On the other side of the access road, near the river, is a portion of a stationary engine radiator upon which is cast "Gardner Denver." This company manufactured air compressors, and this radiator might have belonged to the larger engine. As mentioned in the section for the King and Kinney Mine, the air compressor there is a Gardner Denver; this unit might have been salvaged from the Aces Up property to be used down the valley in later years.

You will notice that the #2 adit is open and accessible. It was blasted just over 400 feet along the vein straight into the mountain. Just over 200 feet beyond the portal, a winze was sunk along the vein.

> **Warning** This winze is flooded and quite deep. Be absolutely certain that you have adequate light when entering this tunnel, and stay clear of the winze. To be safer yet, STAY OUT!

High-grade ore was reportedly removed from this winze. In this vicinity, a 15-foot stope was driven above the tunnel at a point where the vein widened to about 2 feet. Rich ore was also reported to have been removed from this stope. Especially high-grade ore was discovered between 300 and 400 feet from the entrance. The remainder of the tunnel is relatively uneventful, but you can see the vein along which the tunnel was drifted the entire way.

From debris discovered on the river side of the property access road, we have determined that an aerial tramway of a basic haulback design once connected the #2 adit and the road. Whether this was used during the mine's operation or a temporary affair used to strip machinery from the area in later years is a matter of speculation.

To reach the highest tunnel that we visited, the #1 adit, you need considerable cross-country skills and some luck. This tunnel is at about 2,580 feet elevation and is located above and down-valley from the #2 adit. Climb into the woods immediately above the #2 portal, and ascend about 40 degrees to the horizontal while traveling to the north. You might find vestiges of the old access trail or mine dump material in the forest. You have to look carefully, because this tunnel does not have a prominent dump, and the rocks are scattered down the mountainside and mixed with the forest litter. When you locate this tunnel, you will find it open and easily accessible. Be sure that you have good lights before entering the tunnel, and look out for the winze 25 feet inside the portal!

> **Warning** There is a winze along the left side of this tunnel, as there is in the #2 adit. This winze, however, is only 25 feet inside the portal and must be carefully circumvented.

This winze is also flooded, and the records do not indicate how deep it is or what value, if any, of ore was removed from it. The tunnel was drifted along the same vein as the two lower drifts and was driven 175 feet into the mountainside. The vein that the miners were following is in evidence the entire way.

The fourth tunnel listed on the property is about 60 feet above the #1 adit and was drifted only about 20 feet along the vein. We did not attempt to locate it.

Lead, copper, zinc, and gold were found in the ores here along with the silver. The ore minerals were pyrite, arsenopyrite, sphalerite, chalcopyrite, argentiferous galena, and jamesonite, with a gangue of quartz and calcite.

Cleopatra Mine

Rated at D-4. Originally located as the King Solomon Mine, this is one of the larger of the many mines on the West Fork of the Miller River. It produced intermittently from 1897 until as recently as 1941, during which time about $250,000 worth of ore was dug from the property. It was forced to close only because it was classified as nonessential at the outset of World War II. In the early days, a primitive tramway transported ore down to a point near the throat of Cleopatra Basin, where it was loaded onto mules for the remainder of the journey to the railroad. In 1940, a newer tram was installed that was aligned along roughly the same right-of-way as the older tram. It is unclear if any ore was ever shipped over it. In 1958, 1959, and 1960, the Cleopatra Mining Company built a $1^1/_2$-mile bulldozer road from the West Fork Miller River Road to join with the old mining road just inside the basin.

The underground workings of the mine consist of about 2,000 feet of drifts, crosscuts, adits, and winzes, and one large raise of about 200 vertical feet.

The mine is in the center of the east $^1/_2$ of the east $^1/_2$ of Section 24, T25N, R10E, at an elevation of 3,400 feet. Travel up the West Fork Miller River Road for 3.6 miles to the Cleopatra camp. You will notice the remains of an old truck off to the right (west). Go back down the road about 100 feet from this point, and locate the old bulldozer track leading directly away from the river into the brush. Carefully follow this through its tight, steep switchbacks until you gain about 400 feet of elevation. You will then encounter the original road to the mine; begin a climbing traverse through variable brush heading in a southerly direction toward the stream that descends from Cleopatra Basin. As you hike you will approach a small gully containing a small seasonal stream. Here the road makes a final switchback, crosses the stream, and begins to turn to the west into Cleopatra Basin. You will hear the stream flowing from the basin as you head west. The early upper camp of the mine was situated here. An old mine rail lies twisted next to the roadway.

Old maps indicate that a trail to a tunnel that was also part of the Cleopatra Mine[132] left the road at or near this spot where it made the last switchback before entering the basin. The trail angled uphill to the north toward the base of the cliffs. We did not visit this tunnel.

Take some R and R at this point, because the going gets rougher up the trail. From the West Fork Miller River Valley into Cleopatra Basin, the forest cover rapidly becomes more sparse. Small trees and brush proliferate along the way, and it takes a sharp eye to maintain your heading along the old

---

[132] This small tunnel is not located in Cleopatra Basin but was bored as an exploratory adit along a promising lead just outside the Cleopatra Basin entrance.

Cleopatra Mine
(isometric projection)

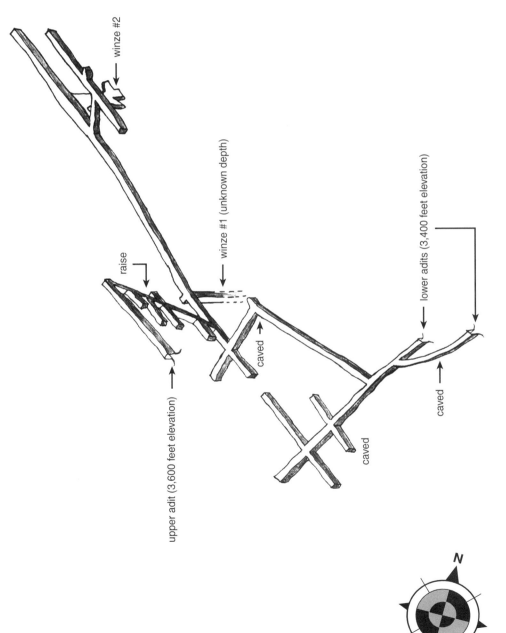

winze #2

raise

winze #1 (unknown depth)

upper adit (3,600 feet elevation)

lower adits (3,400 feet elevation)

caved

caved

caved

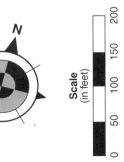

N

Scale
(in feet)

0   50   100   150   200

Philip R. Woodhouse 1995

road. You cannot stray far, however, because beyond the south side of the road, the slope plunges far down into Cleopatra Creek, while the slopes of the mountain define the northern edge of the track. Eventually, you will get good glimpses of the basin and, in the early part of the year, the many grand waterfalls that cascade down the cliffs. As you enter Cleopatra Basin on the old roadway,[133] the track will become more difficult to discern. At times, it is completely obscured by brush or destroyed by rockslides.

From the lower part of the basin, you can see the location of the mine and its attendant buildings (what remains of them) high on the left (south) side of the cirque's wall. The upper adit is defined by the mine tailing pile, which shows clearly as a reddish splotch against the greenery of the steep slope. About 200 feet of elevation below this and slightly to the left, you can see the ruins of the buildings that accompanied the lower, or main, adit.

> **Note** The basin might be more easily traversed in the springtime, when it is covered with snow. But do not try this too early—there might be excessive snow on the slope below the buildings, making it very difficult and dangerous to ascend and descend.

This is where you are headed if you want to visit these workings. Continue to follow the track of the roadway as it leads you around the bottom of the northern slope of the basin, until you arrive at some relatively open rock and low brush. Between your position and the mine lies the main stream, which drains this basin and other hanging basins high above. Climb amongst the brush through a stand of vine maples while heading to the south, until you reach the stream. Cross at a convenient place, and scramble up the bank into the brush. Staying near the stream bank, climb to an old trail that switchbacks up to the base of the building wreckage. Carefully scramble up the mine dump material onto the old timbers, and you are there!

You will find newer material among the building's ruins because of renewed activity in 1948 and again in the late 1950s and early 1960s. It's strange to see a large coil of $^3/_4$-inch PVC plastic tubing lying next to the cast-iron wreckage of an earlier era. Just below the building timbers are the remains of a large aerial tramway wheel that was probably 7 or 8 feet in diameter when it was assembled. All that is left are one and a half segments of the rim, with a small portion of one spoke still attached. The wheel was assembled in three or four sections, making it easier to haul it to the site. Records show that a tramway was constructed from the mine to the West Fork Miller River Valley in 1941, but this wheel dates to the turn of the century, most likely the late 1890s.[134]

Explore the buildings with caution because the wood is badly decayed and could give you severe splinters. Furthermore, much of the timber now lies at crazy angles on the cliffside. It is evident from the cables still in place that these structures were fastened to the slope to prevent their sudden removal due to avalanche or defective foundations.

After getting your fill of the building site, you can visit the mine itself. Much of it is no longer accessible due to collapses within the tunnels, but the tunnels that remain open are worth the trip. Follow the mine rails along the cliffside toward the gully to the northwest. The portal is partially blocked by large boulders that have dropped from the cliffs above, but you can still enter this tunnel.

---

[133] This road was originally built in the late 1890s and was rebuilt in the late 1930s. It was again rebuilt, with bulldozer assistance, between 1957 and 1960.

[134] It was common practice to scavenge equipment from abandoned mines to use in current operations, and this wheel might have been so obtained.

Warning This tunnel, like all mine tunnels, is dangerous to enter. If you decide to go inside, you do so at your own risk.

The first 100 feet of the adit was used as a storehouse, and it is stuffed with bedsprings, ore cart components, massive timbers, and a large steel strongbox. This strongbox contains many sticks of old dynamite. Step lightly past the box without jolting it. Just beyond this material is a large ore cart in splendid condition, still on its wheels and on the mine rails. Just to the left of the cart, a tunnel runs sharply back in the direction of the adit but slightly to the right of it as you face outward. It appears that the location of the original entrance caused problems due to debris from the cliffs, so the miners bored this adit so that it would emerge nearer to the camp buildings along the side of the cliff. This adit is now caved and is not accessible from the outside. The collapsed-adit tunnel was used for additional storage and contains a large pile of 2-inch galvanized iron pipe with fittings in wonderful condition. Beyond the pipe, however, is a case containing more dynamite. The box has deteriorated, and the explosives are scattered about the area.

Warning Old explosives, especially dynamite, can detonate at the slightest jolt. DON'T TOUCH THIS MATERIAL.

Continuing back into the mine, you will notice how close together the ties were placed and the heavy grade of mine rail used. Most mines used light rail and widely spaced ties because it was faster and cheaper, but not this one. This was a producing mine, not just a prospect. The tunnel was bored straight ahead, and several side tunnels were bored along its length. The main tunnel, however, turns to the right and crosscuts toward the main lode. In the producing part of the mine, a raise ascends 200 feet to the upper adit, with several sublevels along its height. Two winzes and stopes in this area contained most of the ore that was shipped from this lofty place. Most unfortunately, this is the part of the mine that you cannot reach! As you approach the shoring that signals that you have reached the stope and raise work, a massive collapse bars the way. The terraces of red material that have built a lacework of pools on the tunnel floor only hint at what might lie beyond this barrier, along with the possibility of neck-deep water. This is as far as you can go, so turn around and enjoy the small calcite speleothems that lace the ceiling of the tunnel in places as you depart.

We have not yet visited the upper tunnel. If you do, beware of the 200-foot winze toward the back of the 200-foot adit.

Warning Unlike many of the winzes in these mines, this one is *not* flooded; a sudden trip down it would be fatal. Also, just outside the upper portal, there is a 20-foot-deep shaft to stay away from.

Compared to the other mines in the Miller River area that we have mentioned, the Cleopatra is very large and has a relatively complex tunnel system. The main portal is at 3,400 feet elevation and leads to a maze of crosscuts and drifts. If the tunnel were not caved, about 450 feet of twisting and winding would take you to the bottom of a raise that connects, through a complicated series of steep inclines and small sublevels, to the upper adit 200 feet above. Another 60 feet along the tunnel, you would reach the top of winze #1 along the left wall. Another 200 feet and you would encounter the steep incline of winze #2, where the entire tunnel drops away ahead of you. The ore in the vicinity of the raise and the winzes is all of commercial grade, making it worth mining and shipping to market. It is clear that most of the mining was done in the area of the winzes and the raise.

> **Warning** In any mine with a substantial amount of vertical workings, such as the Cleopatra, there is danger at every turn, both underground and on the surface. Do not exceed your level of expertise in these situations.

The metals wrested from this mine were silver, lead, and copper, with some zinc, antimony, and gold. The ore minerals closely match those of the Aces Up Mine; the two are only 4,200 feet apart and are situated on the same vein structure. Argentiferous galena, chalcopyrite, tetrahedrite, arsenopyrite, pyrite, jamesonite, sphalerite, and possibly dyscrasite make up the ore minerals, while the gangue material is quartz.

Apex Mine

Rated at B-3. This was one of the first and largest producers in this district. Around the turn of the century, Abner Griffin, the president of Apex Gold Mines, spent about $100,000 to develop the mine, its encampment, and its transportation systems. In 1901, about $80,000 worth of ore was produced. This was a great amount of money for that time. From the mine's discovery until its closure in 1941, about $300,000 was produced from its ore.

A group poses on one of the supply cars for the Apex Mine. This was hauled up to the mine by horse power (notice the horse at the far left) and then coasted back down to the town of Miller River. Posing on the car are, from the left, Millard Smith, Lou McKean, Ester (Slocum) Smith, Maude Slocum, and in the front, a young man who might be John Maloney, Jr. All were residents of Miller River (formerly Berlin). (Pat Streeter photo)

The tunnels are located in the center of the southwest ¹/₄ of Section 34, T26N, R10E, at an elevation of 3,150 to 4,100 feet. Drive the Money Creek Road for 5¹/₂ miles past where it leaves the Miller River Road. As you near the 5-mile point, you will drive through a prominent switchback, turning first sharply to the right then sharply to the left. About ³/₄ mile after the second turn, notice a wide spot off to the left (south) side and find a foot trail that leads down toward Money Creek. Follow it down and you will discover a road leading to the left and right; follow it to the right for a few feet, and notice the remains of the lower terminal of the aerial tramway that served the mine. This building was still standing in the mid-1960s, but all that remains now is a large concrete pedestal upon which sit the remnants of a diesel engine and other mine-related debris. To get to the mine, cross the creek here and ascend the steep trail to the old puncheon road. Continue along this road to its end, looking closely for an old wood-stave pipe that at one time crossed the road. Remnants of it should be visible along either side of the road; but it will be found mostly intact only at one point, and you might have to look hard for it. If you locate it and feel adventurous, you can make a side trip over the side of the hill—it is steep, so be careful—and down to the old powerhouse, which sits on the bank of Milwaukee Creek. At the end of the puncheon road, a trail continues on across a talus slope and into the vine maple and brush. This trail leads to the base of the mine tailing pile and an old tram cable, which will guide you to the top where the upper tramway station once stood and where evidence of later mining can now be found. The old tram cable can also assist you on your steep climb up the pile. At the top, make your way through the debris toward the mountain. You will pass a latter-day snub tunnel about 35 feet long (this was an attempt to intersect the lower #4 adit behind the now-caved portal) as you proceed along the old ore car track to Milwaukee Creek. On the other side of the creek is the site of the #4 adit, now blocked by rocks and logs (at an elevation of 3,600 feet). Retrace your steps to the old camp just beyond the snub tunnel, and turn left to ascend the brush-covered hillside to the ridge above. From here, you can look down on the lake in the cirque below and notice the tailing piles of the upper tunnels in a row on the opposite side of the lake. A pipe lying on the floor of the lake can be seen from here. This pipe once provided water for the camp and power for a large ventilation fan at the #4 portal. Between your location and the upper mines lay the camp used by the miners who worked these adits. Notice the old rusted cookware and broken glass from a bygone era. The portal just above the lake is the #3 tunnel and is now caved at the entrance. The next one up is the #2 (open as of 1989), while the #1 above the #2 is just a small opening, if it even exists anymore.

> **Warning** All the adits are connected underground by a system of stopes and raises covered only by a few rotten boards. Please stay out! A fall here could put your mangled body too deep for recovery.

About 300 feet below tunnel #4, a crosscut tunnel was driven into the mountain in a futile attempt to reach the vein at depth; we did not find it during our visits to the site in the late 1980s and early 1990s. This adit is also reportedly caved. Keep a sharp eye out if you explore in this area!

The Apex Mine buildings cling to the side of the cliff in this 1926 photo. The covered walkway led to the main adit of the mine located behind the trees to the left. An aerial tramway connected this site with the valley bottom. (Mining Truth magazine photo)

This mine assayed highest in gold, with silver, lead, and copper also being produced. The ore minerals were arsenopyrite, pyrite, chalcopyrite, galena, and arsenolite lying in a quartz vein.

Damon and Pythias Mine

Rated at A-1. This mine was located about the same time as the Apex and at times was operated by the same owners. A map made during the time that the National Gold Corporation operated both the Damon and Pythias and the Apex (1928-32) indicates that the company intended to connect the two properties underground. This would have required a haulage tunnel several thousand feet long. Like many plans in the mining industry, this came to naught.

The mine is located in the center of Section 33, T26N, R10E, at an elevation of 3,200 feet at the headwaters of Money Creek. Drive about $1^{1}/_{2}$ miles past the Apex parking area until the road forks.[135] The Damon and Pythias Mine lies at the end of the left fork. Several adits and test pits are reported to be on the property, but the main adit is the only one that we investigated.

The portal area of the Damon and Pythias as it appeared in 1928. This mine was bored in deposits that were thought to connect with those at the Apex about 3,000 feet down the Money Creek Valley. At one time, the mine operators proposed connecting the two workings by a crosscut tunnel. (Mining Truth *magazine photo*)

The main adit, whose location will be obvious when you reach the site, crosscuts about 1,425 feet into the mountainside in a southerly direction and accesses two veins along the way. About 1,500 feet of driftwork was driven along these veins. At 900 feet beyond the portal, the crosscut tunnel intersects the Damon vein, along which 560 feet of tunnel was drifted to the left (east) and 200 feet of tunnel was drifted to the right (west). It also contains a small stope and short raise. This vein varies in width from about 1 inch to over 5 feet, and it carries gold and silver. Following the crosscut 450 feet beyond the Damon vein, you will encounter the Priestly vein. This vein is drifted 300 feet to the left (east) and 160 feet to the right (west). The Priestly vein is wider than the Damon, but it carries fewer sulfides and thus is not as rich a prospect. Closer to the portal of the crosscut tunnel, another exploratory drift was driven during the late 1950s and early 1960s. This tunnel was bored about 10 feet to the right (west). The value of ore removed from this drift and its attendant workings is unknown.

The metals taken from the Damon and Pythias Mine were gold, silver, and lead. The minerals were arsenopyrite, pyrite, chalcopyrite, and galena, along with a gangue of quartz.

Morning Star Prospect

Rated at C-3. To reach this scenic mine, drive the Money Creek Road as if you are going to the Damon and Pythias Mine. But when the road forks to the Damon, take the right track to the end, where you will find a small parking area. Stop here and take the fishermen's trail to Crater Lake. There are no

---

[135] The small lake that you'll see to your left is the reservoir for the Apex Mine power plant, located just downstream on Milwaukee Creek. The bridge is a remnant of an old surface tram.

signs, and the trail is not maintained; expect mud and steep pitches along the path. In a few places it is easy to lose your way, so keep a sharp lookout for unexpected dips and turns. You will reach the lake after about 1 mile and about 500 feet of elevation gain. Crater Lake is a small tarn nestled in the arms of Red Mountain on your left as you approach.

Walk to the shore of the lake, turn left, and cross the outlet stream. Continue hiking along the shore at the base of Red Mountain. Shortly after you are required to do some fancy footwork to get around a pile of large rocks without falling in the lake, you will come to the base of a large rock slide that descends to the water from the mountain cliffs above. Looking up to the scarp above you, you will notice a groove or small ridge cutting the face from the lower right, at the top of the rock slide, up to the left where it meets some small trees and brush. This is the location of the mine.

Carefully climb the loose rocks and look for samples of pyrite ore along the way. Ascend to the right to meet the groove at the cliff's base. The groove is a crude trail that will take you to the adit.

> **Warning** You will cross a very steep part of the cliff. If you don't feel comfortable here, go back. It looks worse coming down, and a fall could easily be fatal.

If you choose to proceed, the mine is at the end of this trail where it meets the brush. The tunnel is short, not more than 100 feet long. About two-thirds of the way back in the drift, you will encounter a vein of pyrite ore. Spectacular cubic crystals of sulfide have been taken from this narrow lode. Bring a rock hammer and rock chisel if you plan to collect, because it will require some work.

Enjoy the view from the mouth of the adit. The lake is far below, and you are looking to the east. Perhaps this is the reason for the mine's name. To return, carefully descend along the trail you climbed earlier, return to the lake shore, and go down the trail.

The metal sought here was gold, with an ore mineral of pyrites. The gangue is country rock.

Bonanza Queen Mine

Rated at B-2. This mine is located in the lower reaches of an awesome chasm on the north side of Money Creek Road.[136] Drive the road for about $3^1/_2$ miles beyond the point where it leaves the Miller River Road in the town of Miller River (formerly Berlin). Park off the road just beyond the creek that descends to Money Creek. Hike the creek bed up to the tunnel, which is reported to be driven into the eastern wall of the creek bed. When we visited the site in the spring of 1995, we did not locate the tunnel. There is said to be considerable debris that sloughs across the adit, and identifying the site is difficult.

If you ascend the mountainside to the west (left) of the gully for about 700 vertical feet, you can glimpse the spectacular upper chasm, with massive chock-rocks and tree trunks littering its path. There is a small prospect in the gully about 640 feet of elevation above the road.

> **Warning** We recommend that you do not enter the gulch at any point above the mine tunnel; the area is decidedly life-threatening. Any climb into the gulch at this elevation above the road would be rated at C-5.

---

[136] L. K. Hodges, in his *Mining in the Pacific Northwest,* got the locations of the Bonanza Queen, Paymaster, and San Francisco mines terribly confused. It is doubtful that he ever visited the sites. From his description, they were all located in the same side gulch off Money Creek. Exploration and careful examination of the records have allowed Northwest Underground Explorations to unravel the mystery.

There were eight claims in the Bonanza Queen group, with the principal metals sought being gold and silver.

Paymaster Prospect

Rated at C-4. This prospect reportedly consists of two tunnels located about 35 feet apart toward the head of German Gulch (a name that does not appear on modern maps). We have not visited this property, but we will describe how to get to it based on the literature and map record.

Drive the Money Creek Road about 4.2 miles from the point where it leaves the Miller River Road in the town of Miller River (formerly Berlin). You will find the gulch just before the only switchback in the road. If you reach the switchback, you have gone too far. The maps show this prospect at about 1,100 feet of elevation above the Money Creek Road near where German Gulch begins, high up on the mountainside. This would be a good exploration trek for those who are well versed in cross-country routefinding and survival skills; it is definitely not for the novice hiker or climber. Expect heavy forest with thick underbrush in many places.

San Francisco Mine

Rated at B-3. This small tunnel, only about 110 feet long, can be difficult to locate if you are not very observant. It is situated on Favorite Gulch (another name not found on current maps).

Drive the Money Creek Road for about 5½ miles beyond the point where it leaves the Miller River Road in the town of Miller River (formerly Berlin). This will take you past the switchback on the road. Drive a short distance beyond the first gulch after the switchback, and park where you can just make out an old road on the north side. Hike along the road as it parallels the Money Creek Road back toward the gulch that you just crossed. Upon reaching the gulch, hike upstream for about ¼ mile while carefully inspecting the gulch wall on your right. The tunnel is almost hidden by a rock that has dropped from above, and it might be hard to see. You can enter the tunnel, if you choose, by dropping down behind the rock. The tunnel floor is usually fairly dry.

You can see the vein along which the San Francisco tunnel was drifted in the upper left-hand corner of the tunnel as you walk in. You can use a rock hammer to obtain some interesting specimens, although the mineral is dull gray in color and probably consists mostly of arsenopyrite. Gold and silver were the primary metals sought here.

Bergeson Prospect

Rated at B-2. This property, also known as the Normandie Prospect, presents the appearance of a Hollywood set when you approach it across its mine dump. The adit is located on the opposite side of a small stream from the dump and is first glimpsed beneath a huge fallen tree that straddles the gully. A trestle must have been placed across this stream to allow the conveying of gangue rock from the mine to the dump.

Drive 2.1 miles beyond the point where you turn onto Money Creek Road in the town of Miller River (formerly Berlin). Here you will notice an old road grade that parallels the present road, heading up the valley on your right at a slightly steeper angle. There is, conveniently, a good place to park on the right at this point. Hike up the old road grade, which climbs steeply as it rises above its modern counterpart and then turns to the right to follow a small stream. You will continue to climb as you walk away from Money Creek until the road once again turns sharply to the left and continues its ascent. When the road again begins to turn to the right, the mine dump will be immediately ahead of you.

Follow the road about 75 feet until it is adjacent to the dump. Climb the dump and walk toward the stream where the large log has fallen across the gully. Looking under the log, at an elevation of 1,760 feet, you will see the adit, just to the left of the waterfall.

There is not much in the way of artifacts here, just some old compressed air piping and a few pits where the miners probably placed a water wheel and air compressor. It's a fairly easy walk to this spot. Should you decide to enter the tunnel, bring hip or chest waders, or expect to get wet. The water is about thigh-deep just inside the portal, but the tunnel gradually climbs above the water level. The mine is 835 feet long, with a few short exploratory drifts and one 100-foot drift. It is reasonably stable but is also very wet, with many rivulets sprinkling on your head as you pass through. These waters have carried down a considerable amount of dissolved minerals and deposited them on the tunnel ceiling and walls as small stalactites and stalagmites whose colors vary from jet black to blood red and white.

Apparently, no ore of any import was ever shipped from this prospect, and no ore body large enough to stope was discovered. The metals sought were gold and silver, and the only major mineral was arsenopyrite. The gangue material consisted of quartz.

Grand Central Mine

Rated at A-2. This mine, located very close to Miller River (formerly Berlin), is on the south side of Money Creek, not too far above the road. Records show that this mine produced a little ore around the year 1908 and was operated off and on until about 1920. The mine is in the northwest 1/4 of the southeast 1/4 of Section 29, T26N, R11E, at an elevation of about 1,300 feet. Leave the Miller River Road for the Money Creek Road, and proceed about a mile to the concrete bridge. Just before the bridge, turn left onto a road that travels up the south side of Money Creek.

Caution This road is quite rough, with small waterbars dug across it. A high-clearance vehicle is advisable.

At 1/2 mile after you turn off the main road, park and begin to hike upward from the road. The forest is fairly open, and you will have to search for the mine dump as you climb. About 400 to 500 feet elevation above the road, you should encounter the upper portal of the Grand Central. This will be near the base of the first cliff that you see in the forest.

Warning A winze is located toward the back of the upper tunnel; it is about 80 feet deep and does not always contain water. Carry plenty of light into this mine, and watch your step closely. Entering any of these mines is your choice, and you must take the responsibility for the consequences.

Far to the left of the main adit in a steep gully is a small, caved tunnel, which might have been the discovery point of this mine. Records for the mine show a 1,200 foot crosscut tunnel of unknown elevation. We believe that we found the caved remnants of that portal below the roadway.

Antimony and gold were the major metals found here. (Note the similarity to the lower Miller River region just a short distance over the divide.) The ore minerals were stibnite and pyrite, with a gangue of quartz and calcite.

Kimball Creek Mines

Rated A-1 to C-3. This property consists of 29 patented claims along Kimball Creek. Some of these adjoin the western edge of the Grand Central properties. The claims are mostly situated in Sections 31 and 32 of T26N, R11E, at elevations ranging from 1,400 to 3,800 feet.

Proceed as you would to reach the Grand Central. Continue until the road is completely washed out at a large gully. This is about 1 mile from the turnoff at the concrete bridge. Park here. The logging road that you have been following switchbacks at this point. Do not follow this switchback, but cross the creek that caused the washout, and find the old mining road on the other side that continues following Money Creek. About 150 feet beyond the washout, a trail cuts sharply up the mountainside to the left toward the Clara Mine, one of the many small tunnels in the Kimball Creek Group. After about five minutes of hiking from the road, you will encounter a large tailing pile in the forest. The adit is at the top of this pile. This tunnel is about 300 feet long, with about 35 feet of drifting.

> **Warning** This tunnel was driven through loose, unconsolidated soil and rock to reach the firmer rock of the mountainside. The wooden shoring has completely disintegrated, creating a portal that, while open, is terribly dangerous. Stay out of this mine.

Another mine in the area, about which little is known, can be reached by crossing the washout and continuing along the old road for several hundred feet until you cross Kimball Creek on a decaying log bridge. (Watch your step!) A short distance beyond the bridge is a large, caved tunnel of unknown depth from which a great amount of muddy, mineralized water issues. This was apparently the haulage tunnel of the mine on the Lillian Leone Lode claim. Leave the road just before the mud tunnel, and ascend through the woods to your left. Good routefinding skills are required here. After about 50 feet, turn up the mountainside to reach a ledge at about 80 feet elevation above the road. Several buildings that serviced this mine were located on this flat. Follow the flat to the left for about 200 feet, and then once again turn abruptly uphill through denser forest. If you have hit it right, at about 150 feet elevation you will come upon a very large mine dump in which cast iron and mine rail debris are visible. Climb this dump to reach the upper adit of the mine. The tunnel is about 570 feet long, and a collapsed raise ascends from it. We do not know if this raise connects with a 65-foot-deep shaft 100 feet higher up the mountainside above a switchback of the road that you followed to this mine. The portal is caved, but the shaft is not! If you attempt to locate the shaft (it's difficult to find), use extreme caution; one slip into it will be your last. Judging from the size of this dump, there must have been extensive stoping above the tunnel, because there is far too much material here to have come from a 570-foot tunnel. This mine could very well have produced a considerable amount of ore in its heyday.

Foss River

The Foss River area features not only mines but splendid scenery as well. The many lakes of this area are set in basins with walls of steep granitic rock. This region lies immediately to the east of the Miller River Valley and shares some of its geologic structure. Like the East Fork of the Miller River, the Foss River never created the interest or the mining fervor that the West Fork of the Miller River did, and few mines were located there. High mountains and long, steep ridges provide the backdrop for the river's west fork. Some of the better-known peaks are Iron Cap Mountain, at 6,347 feet, which lies at the head of the valley; La Bohn Peak, at 6,585 feet, which lies at the head of the valley between the East and West Forks of the Foss River; and Malachite Peak, at 6,261 feet, which is situated between the East Fork of the Miller River and the West Fork of the Foss River.

As you hike into the area, you will visit several lakes along the way. Trout Lake, a short trek in, is surrounded by the wonderful scenery described above. This jewel lies at only 2,030 feet elevation. Past Trout Lake, the trail switchbacks up 1,931 vertical feet to reach Copper Lake, which glistens in subalpine meadows at 3,961 feet. Beyond, the trail ascends to Little Heart Lake at 4,204 feet, and then on to Big Heart Lake at 4,545 feet. Since the trailhead is at 1,600 feet above sea level, the total elevation gain amounts to over 2,900 feet, clearly not a venture for the uninitiated.

The properties described in this chapter are all in the vicinity of Trout Lake, but this should not prevent the scenery-hungry from continuing up the valley.

What to See

This scenic part of the Alpine Lakes Wilderness has an added feature—the mining properties. Mines are scattered throughout the ridges and cliffy terrain of this lightly mineralized area, from the lower Trout Lake Trail up to Copper Lake. The 5-mile trail takes you to or along Trout Lake, Lake Malachite, Copper Lake, Little Heart Lake, and Big Heart Lake. The historic mining properties are concentrated near Trout Lake.

You can get a feel for this journey into the past by consulting the USGS 7.5 Minute maps for Big Snow Mountain and Skykomish.

Getting There

Drive east on Highway 2 toward Stevens Pass. At 1.8 miles past the town of Skykomish, turn right onto Foss River Road No. 68. After 4.2 miles, you will pass the East Fork Foss River Trailhead, and at 4.8 miles you will arrive at the West Fork Foss River Road, No. 6840. Veer left onto this road and travel 2 miles to its end and the trailhead. The hike to Trout Lake is a cool, pleasant 1½-mile stroll and accesses the majority of the mines described here. If you choose to continue on to the higher lakes, you will find yourself leaving the cool of the forest for the heat (if it is sunny) of the exposed mountain slopes. Prepare yourself accordingly.

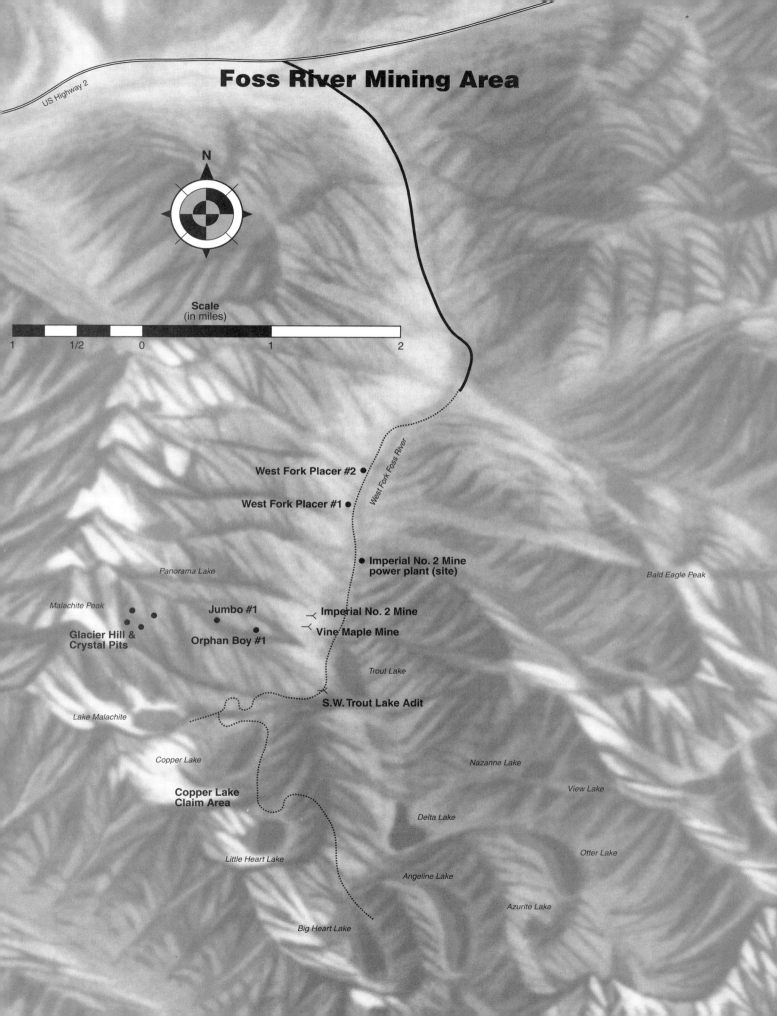

Foss River Mining Area

US Highway 2

N

Scale
(in miles)

1 1/2 0 1 2

West Fork Foss River

West Fork Placer #2 •

West Fork Placer #1 •

• Imperial No. 2 Mine
power plant (site)

Panorama Lake

Bald Eagle Peak

Malachite Peak

Jumbo #1 •

Imperial No. 2 Mine

**Glacier Hill &
Crystal Pits**

Orphan Boy #1

Vine Maple Mine

Trout Lake

Lake Malachite

S.W. Trout Lake Adit

Copper Lake

Nazanne Lake

**Copper Lake
Claim Area**

View Lake

Delta Lake

Little Heart Lake

Otter Lake

Angeline Lake

Azurite Lake

Big Heart Lake

Geology

The lower portion of the Foss River Valley, through which you will be driving, consists of Paleocene and Cretaceous nonmarine rocks comprised mostly of arkose, which is massive, cross-bedded, and brown-gray to light brown in color. Also included are conglomerates and siltstones. These rocks are not known to produce an abundance of minerals in the Cascade Mountains. In the Trout Lake area, however, the Eocene and Oligocene volcanic rocks consist mostly of a light green andesite breccia along with interbedded andesite and basalt flows. These are an extension of the rocks found along the lower Miller River, where they carry small amounts of antimony and copper. It is in these rocks that most of the properties described in this section are found. As you leave Trout Lake and climb to the vicinity of Copper Lake and beyond, you will encounter Tertiary granitic rocks consisting mostly of granite, quartz, monzonite, and quartz diorite. These rocks make up the terrain all the way to the head of the valley and are the extension of the rocks found in the upper Miller River district, which have produced the largest silver mines in King County. Little mineral content has been reported in the Foss River area, however.

The Mines

West Fork Placers #1 and #2

Rated at B-1. These two former placer claims extend for about 3,000 feet along the river bed and are (as of this writing) open to recreational gold panning. Materials that make up the river bed at this point range from fine gravel to 10-foot boulders. Recent panning has shown a trace of gold per square yard—not too encouraging even for sport panners.

These claims are ²/₃ mile from the trailhead, where the river turns westward for about 100 yards. On the Skykomish USGS map, they are near the number 31 that designates that section.

Imperial #2 Mine

Rated at C-3. This interesting tunnel is situated in the eastern side of Malachite Peak just below the point where the cliffs meet the talus. It is the longest known tunnel in the area. Its 772-foot adit cross-cuts many mineralized shear zones, with the richest veins at 142 feet and 570 feet from the portal. Finding the tunnel is both difficult and unpleasant due to the quantity and size of vine maple and devil's club flora through which you must thrash to reach the property. Before you go, it is a good idea to check with the ranger to learn what rules to follow when traveling off-trail in this wilderness area.

When you hike to Trout Lake, after you cross the West Fork of the Foss River and pass the "big tree" (You'll know it!), the trail begins to climb through the ancient, virgin forest, and as you head up-valley toward Trout Lake you will see a very rusted 2¹/₂-inch pipe crossing the trail. This was a shield for the ³/₄-inch compressed air pipe that runs through it. This air pipe conveyed the compressed air from a power plant on the West Fork of the Foss River to the mine tunnel. There it ran a small compressed-air engine that was connected to the ventilation blower for the mine. It also supplied air to an air receiver tank just inside the adit, from which air was conducted through a 2-inch pipe to the drill at the end of the mine tunnel. The drill is still at the mine, along with the dismantled remains of the air engine and the blower. An ore cart and other assorted tools litter the site. It appears that few people have visited the area since it was abandoned.

This vertical tank standing along the wall of the Imperial #2 adit served as an air receiver for compressed air delivered from the power plant on the Foss River. A blacksmith bellows also lies abandoned in the tunnel. (Vic Pisoni photo)

A view deeper inside the Imperial #2. The light rail used for the mine cars is still intact; the large pipe visible in the upper left conducted air into the mine for ventilation. (Vic Pisoni photo)

This mine is just south of the first seasonal runoff stream (shown as intermittent blue lines on the Big Snow Mountain USGS map) about 400 feet south of the placers mentioned above and west of the river. The tunnel is at about 2,400 feet elevation and 200 yards south of the stream (or stream bed, depending on how dry the weather has been).

Upon reaching the air pipe crossing the trail, start upward through the forest by contouring to your right as you face uphill.

Warning Do not attempt to follow the pipe, because it will lead you into a great thicket of vine maple and devil's club.

After about 100 feet, head uphill, where you will encounter the dreaded plants. Ahead and above are large fir and cedar trees that form a line up the steep valley wall. Cross through stretches of dense brush, always climbing toward the next tree or group of trees. If you follow the correct strip of trees, you will arrive at the mine portal just as the brushy scree over which you have been climbing meets the cliffs of the awesome eastern flanks of Malachite Peak. Someone in the distant past dismantled the little air engine here, and there are copious amounts of drill bit steel lying about the area. Carefully turning over the heavy forest litter at the site might yield more artifacts. View them, photograph them, and then leave them exactly where you found them.

Visiting the tunnel is an experience, because about two-thirds of the way in, the crosscut encounters several active underground streams, which are guaranteed to soak the unwary. We saw no substantial mineralization of the rock in the spring of 1995. The way back is just the reverse of the nasty experience that you encountered going up!

Gold, silver, and copper were found in the ore here.

Vine Maple Discovery Prospect

Rated at C-3. The Vine Maple was driven 112 feet on a shear zone 4 to 5 feet wide. This mine is about 300 feet to the south of the Imperial #2, at an elevation of 2,600 feet.

Ascend to the Imperial #2 as described above, and climb around the south side of the adit and head straight up until you arrive at the base of the cliffs. Head south while hugging the cliffs for about 300 feet until you reach the tunnel. The rock is minimally mineralized, and we found no notable specimens when we visited the site in the spring of 1995. Return the way you came; it's miserable but far easier than any alternative.

Silver and copper were the principal values sought. No production information has been found for this property or any of the properties in the immediate area.

Orphan Boy #1 Claim

Rated at C-4. This property consists of a mineralized shear zone, 1 to 5 feet wide, in metavolcanic rock, bearing traces of gold and some silver. These metals created the interest at this claim. This dig is a true prospect, because no tunnel development or open cuts produced anything of shippable size.

This claim is 1,000 feet east of the Vine Maple tunnel, at an elevation of about 3,600 feet, where the section line defining the boundary between Sections 31 and 36 intersects the creek, which flows from the center of Section 36 to the West Fork of the Foss River. Follow the section line north for 500 feet. The prospect is in those cliffs.

During our visit to this area in the spring of 1995, we were told by a forest ranger that in 1991 a large snow and rock slide had come thundering down the creek bed from high on the slopes of Malachite Peak. It dammed the Foss River for several years until the river finally cut through the mass. During this time, Trout Lake rose 10 feet, and the forest at the upper part of the lake was killed due to inundation. Along with the rocks and snow, the slide also carried a large mine rail down to the very edge of the Trout Lake exit where the West Fork of the Foss River begins its journey down the valley. This would suggest additional prospects up this formidable draw.

Jumbo #1 Claim

Rated at C-4. This property is situated in silver-bearing metavolcanic rock, with a mineralized shear zone 1 to 3 feet wide. It is similar in all respects to the Orphan Boy #1, described above. It is 1,000 feet west of the Orphan Boy #1, is at an elevation of 3,600 feet, and is 300 feet north of the creek.

Copper Lake Claim

Rated at D-5. This working is in granodiorite rock. There is one caved pit and a caved adit of unknown length that was driven into a tourmalinized shear zone 10 to 15 feet wide. Its ore assayed a trace of gold, up to 3.3 ounces of silver per ton, and some lead.

Available information on the location is vague, but the claim appears to be 1 mile south of Malachite Lake on a ridge west of Copper Lake.

Glacier Hill and Crystal Prospects

Rated at D-5. South of Malachite Peak, just southwest of the center of Section 36, are four digs. They consist of a pit and some minor work done to some of the outcrops on the property. One outcrop is 50 feet wide. Mineralized shear zones in metavolcanic and sedimentary rock are the host material surrounding these veins. Two of the prospects are at 5,200 feet elevation, and the others are at around 4,600 feet and 5,400 feet, according to USGS and USBM surveys.

Trout Lake Mining Company Properties

Rated at C-2. The main properties are on or right near Trout Lake. The camp was on the west shore and consisted of two cabins, a kitchen and dining hall, bunkhouse, blacksmith shop, power plant, and all the modern machinery for up-to-date (1908) mining. Three areas were worked, beginning in the spring of 1907: a tunnel on the west shore, a tunnel on the east shore, and a developing prospect at the north end of the lake. We have not visited the east shore tunnel, although we did notice an overgrown road leading to a flat, brushy area where the tunnel might be located.

The Trout Creek Mining Company buildings as seen from across the lake. This was the largest mining effort in the Foss River district. (Washington Miner photo)

The west adit, or main tunnel, is south of the camp. It was driven 465 feet to intersect outcroppings of several veins running in a westerly direction through the mountains, where it crossed a gulch. In this gulch the several veins meet. The plan was to blast the tunnel along a ledge to the point below the outcropping and, from that spot, crosscut the workings to the veins' meeting point, with the expectation of driving into richer ore toward the multivein terminus in the gulch.

Looking toward the portal from inside the west tunnel of the Trout Lake Mining Company's workings above Trout Lake. Notice the clearly defined hanging and foot walls along which the tunnel ran. No commercial quantities of ore were ever taken from this tunnel. (Vic Pisoni photo)

To reach the west tunnel, hike the wilderness trail to and along the edge of Trout Lake. Where the trail is nearest the lake, you will see a very large rock (above a well-worn campsite area). The flat area around this rock is believed to be the site of the buildings that housed the many functions of the Trout Lake Mining Company. Continue hiking until the trail begins to climb above Trout Lake toward Copper Lake and Malachite Lake far above. After the first little uphill spurt, the trail crosses a gully that presents a vertical drop of about 20 feet to a seasonal stream below. Backtrack about 30 feet down the trail, and find a steep path that leads down to the adit immediately below the trail in this gully. You can explore all 465 feet of this wet tunnel in relative safety; the rock is stable and firm. In fact, it is composed mostly of granite and is very hard. The last, uncompleted pattern of blasting holes at the end of this crosscut suggests that the miners had a difficult time driving this hole as deeply as they did.

While no vein was detected along this tunnel, the sediments on the floor produce a curious glitter. The glittery particles appear to be tiny cubes of pyrite or perhaps flakes of the mica component of the native rock through which the miners were tunneling.

The east adit was also run for 465 feet and, with continued drilling, was expected to strike a ledge of ore another 400 feet beyond. This ledge was discovered 2,000 feet above on the mountainside.

The last development work found a large ledge of ore on the north end of the property. It surfaces a couple of hundred feet above the river valley and is 200 to 300 feet thick. A 15-foot tunnel was run into high-grade ore that assayed at $10 in gold and $14 in silver and copper per ton (based on the 1908 standard of pay). To accommodate this new discovery, the powerhouse was moved there and a tramway or railroad was considered. A prominent engineer who came to the lake was impressed with the immense water power reserve there, and he stated that if it were fully developed, it could equal that of the hydroelectric power being generated at Snoqualmie Falls, where an underground power plant built in 1907 still supplies power to this day. Although exploratory work could have been carried out very economically, it never was, even in light of the highly touted mineral expectations. And, alas, there is no further development or production data to provide an ending to this saga.[137]

Dutch Miller–Seattle-Boston Copper Company Claims

Rated at E-3 to E-4. In 1905, the Seattle-Boston Copper Company tried to sell stock in the Dutch Miller Mine. A. J. Walters, a writer for *The Westerner* magazine, featured these properties in the December issue. It is not known whether this attracted investors to the venture. Because it would have been easier to ship ore to the north, the company planned to build a railroad from the Skykomish area, 8 miles

[137] *Washington Miner,* December 15, 1908.

up the Foss River via the East Fork, to a mill site. At the mill site, which was about $^3/_4$ mile north of Jade (Success) Lake, a cabin and horse barn were built in anticipation of the railroad's arrival. An aerial tram was to be erected to carry ore from the mines over Crystal Pass to the mill site. This was to run from Crystal Pass, several thousand feet down Necklace Valley, past Opal Lake, Emerald Lake, and Jade Lake, to reach its destination.

Southwest of Crystal Pass is Crystal Mountain, whose summit rises to an elevation of 6,585 feet. Fifteen hundred feet west of this peak are a caved adit and two trenches. One thousand feet south of these, at Chain Lakes, are the Dutch Miller and Seattle-Boston Copper Company Claims. Near Crystal Pass are two prospect digs in an enormous basin composed of white syenite, with numerous red-capped ore outcroppings. The great amount of glacial action in this basin has exposed the rock and makes finding the ore easy.

The Seattle-Boston Copper Company had 14 men opening up veins in several high-grade ore deposits. Foreman James Cosgrove was in charge of determining the lode's value. If the lode turned out to be promising, the company planned to let a contract to mine 75,000 tons of the minerals, which would be taken by tram to the mill site. A tunnel was proposed that would run under Crystal Mountain from northwest to southeast to reach the ore body at depth, but work was never begun due to the remoteness of the site and lack of investment capital. The claims are still owned, however, and attempts to renew mining activity have been made in the last 20 years. These efforts have not been brought to fruition.

To get to these properties, refer to the USGS 7.5 Minute maps for Skykomish, Mount Daniel, and Big Snow Mountain. The trail is a long 11 miles, with some difficult sections, and scenic all the way. You should allow two or three days to make this trip. Drive east on Highway 2 to Skykomish, and (using the Skykomish map) drive up the Foss River Road to Section 17. There a pack trail goes southeast up along the East Fork of the Foss River for 3$^1/_2$ miles. Using the Mount Daniel Map as a reference, continue for another mile. Continue to follow the trail for an additional 2 miles up a feeder creek to the center of Section 6 as shown on the Big Snow Mountain map. Hike another mile to Jade Lake and the start of the Necklace Valley. Then continue to hike past Emerald Lake and Opal Lake back into territory shown on the Mount Daniel map. A half mile later, you will begin to climb switchbacks toward Crystal Pass (not named on the USGS maps). The peak on your right is Crystal Mountain (toward the southwest on the map). The trail ends at the pass. You will now have a spectacular view of an enormous basin spread out below you. From here, you will have to route-find your way to any areas that you want to visit. Cross-country skis might be handy from this point on, because much of the year the basin is covered in snow.

For the Rockhound

There is ample ore to sample in the area. Bornite, chalcopyrite, and other minerals abound.

The cabin at the proposed mill site of the Dutch Miller Mine. The Seattle-Boston Copper Company planned to run a long aerial tramway from the mine to this location on the Foss River. The mine was never developed to a point where it was practical to ship ore, so the tramway and mill were never built. (The Westerner magazine, 1908)

North Bend

George W. Carmack poses with a windlass bucket full of ore at the head of an unnamed shaft. Carmack was active in the mines of the North Bend Mining District. (Washington Miner *photo*)

This district is only a 45-minute drive from Seattle and thus is one of the most heavily visited areas of the Cascade Mountains. Its accessibility prompted many early prospectors to seek their fortunes here. The mountains rise to peaks higher than 5,000 feet above sea level, forming the ridges along the many valleys that cut through the landscape. The valleys have laid open the ancient rocks, revealing their mineral wealth (or lack of it) to all who would investigate. Many of the mountains in this area have names familiar to the hikers and climbers of the Seattle area: Mount Si, Chair Peak, Kaleetan Peak, Mount Garfield, and many others.

Interstate 90 cuts through this area, but most of the roads that penetrate deeply into the region are old logging access grades, and many are very rudimentary. Some are impassible due to lack of maintenance.

History

Mount Si (originally named Mount Uncle Si) is the first bare rock mountain you come to when you travel eastbound from Seattle on I-90. If you are of an earlier generation, names such as the Yellowstone Trail or Sunset Highway might evoke pre I-90 memories. Today's town of North Bend, the backdrop for the *Twin Peaks* television series and the gateway to a multitude of outdoor sports, was the site of a

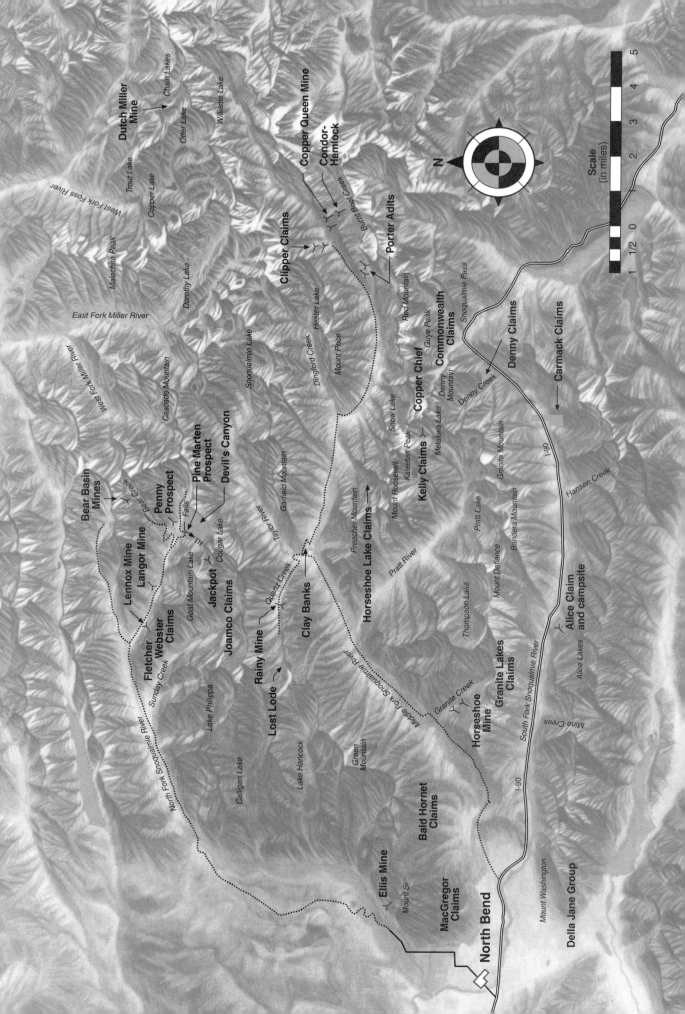

North Bend Mining Area

N

Scale
(in miles)
1 1/2 0 1 2 3 4 5

Dutch Miller Mine
Chain Lakes
Otter Lake
Trout Lake
Copper Lake
Williams Lake
West Fork Foss River
Malachite Peak
Dorothy Lake
East Fork Miller River
Copper Queen Mine
Condor-Hemlock
Burnt Boot Creek
Clipper Claims
Porter Adits
Hester Lake
Dingford Creek
Mount Price
Red Mountain
Snoqualmie Lake
Snow Lake
Mount Roosevelt
Kaleetan Peak
Guye Peak
Snoqualmie Pass
Commonwealth Claims
Denny Mountain
Copper Chief
Denny Claims
Denny Creek
I-90
Carmack Claims
Hansen Creek
Kelly Claims
Melakwa Lake
Pratt Lake
Granite Mountain
Bandera Mountain
Mount Defiance
Thompson Lake
Pratt River
Horseshoe Lake Claims
Preacher Mountain
Garfield Mountain
Taylor River
West Fork Miller River
Cascade Mountain
Pine Marten Prospect
Devil's Canyon
Falls
Goat Creek
Bear Basin Mines
Penny Prospect
Langor Mine
Lennox Mine
Fletcher Webster Claims
Sunday Creek
Jackpot
Cougar Lake
Goat Mountain Lake
Joamco Claims
Lake Philippa
North Fork Snoqualmie River
Rainy Mine
Quartz Creek
Clay Banks
Lost Lode
Lake Hancock
Caligan Lake
Green Mountain
Middle Fork Snoqualmie River
Granite Creek
Horseshoe Mine
Granite Lakes Claims
South Fork Snoqualmie River
Alice Claim and campsite
Alice Lakes
Mine Creek
Bald Hornet Claims
Ellis Mine
Mount Si
MacGregor Claims
North Bend
Mount Washington
Della Jane Group
I-90

war in 1855 in which the Snoqualmie Tribe and the U.S. Army sought out Yakima and Nisqually trouble-makers. The Snoqualmie warriors received $20 for each enemy brave's head and $80 for the head of a chief. The U.S. troops and the Snoqualmies came out ahead.

Jeremiah Borst, a farmer and prospector, settled the area, called Rangers Prairie, in 1858. He started with 160 acres, which included the abandoned Fort Smalley. Later he became owner of the largest hop farm in the world, with a trading post and stopover facilities for the cattle drives that came over Snoqualmie Pass. Borst learned of mineral deposits from his Indian wife, and he prospected the South, North, and Middle Forks of the Snoqualmie River. In 1869, Borst and Arthur Denny, one of Seattle's founders, discovered iron near the Snoqualmie Pass area, prompting speculation that an ore smelting center would be established near North Bend. As a result, a railroad and several towns were built in the Snoqualmie Valley. No industry developed, but the mining prospects did, which led to the first decent road over the pass. Today there are many accessible mines in this area, which can be enjoyed by hikers, rockhounders, and history buffs.

What to See

While there are many small prospects scattered throughout this area, no major mining operations were ever undertaken. The contact zones mentioned later in the Geology section provide a spectacular array of minerals for collectors, especially those interested in crystals. Many of the prospects and small mines are located in these areas of contact between sedimentary and igneous rocks. The scenery also provides a grand panorama for those energetic enough to climb into the higher reaches of the mountains and elevated cirques. Fishing and whitewater boating also find their practitioners in this wonderful place.

Getting There

The approach you take depends on which locale within the North Bend district you intend to visit. To reach the Taylor River area, drive east on I-90 past North Bend for 1 mile and take the Edgewick exit to a stop sign. Turn left under the freeway, and continue past Ken's Truck Stop. At $1/4$ mile beyond are signs pointing toward 18 miles of good dirt road to the Middle Fork of the Snoqualmie River and Taylor River. You will pass over two concrete bridges along the way—one of them midway along the drive and the second, crossing Taylor River, near the trip's end. After crossing the second span, stay left where the road splits, following it $1/2$ mile to a gated foot bridge.

If you intend to visit the Middle Fork of the Snoqualmie River, follow the same instructions as those for Taylor River, but after crossing the second bridge span, turn right when the road splits.

> **Caution** The Middle Fork Road is often in very poor condition, so you should use a high-clearance vehicle to explore the area. The road might even be washed out, so we have included some long walks and mountain bike rides to access the area.

To reach the Mount Si area, take I-90 east past North Bend to exit #32. At the stop sign, turn left and cross over the freeway. Continue until the road T's at the old US-10 pavement. Turn left and drive west about $1/4$ mile to the Mount Si Road, and then turn right and continue north across railroad tracks and the Snoqualmie River. The mountain directly ahead of you is Mount Si.

Most of the mines and claims mentioned for the South Fork of the Snoqualmie River can be accessed from I-90, because the freeway follows the upper reaches of this river almost to Snoqualmie Pass. For mines located at or above the Alpental ski area, you have to leave I-90 at the first Snoqualmie Summit exit and turn left under the freeway at the stop sign. Turn right onto the Alpental Road, and drive to the gate. Park in the public parking area.

For the Chair Peak mines, you can also park at Alpental, although some of these areas might be more easily reached by hiking up Denny Creek, over Evergreen Pass, beyond Melakwa Lakes, and over Melakwa Pass to Chair Peak Lake. Chair Peak will be on your right. If this sounds difficult, it is!

To reach the mining areas of Bear Basin, Illinois Creek, and Lennox Creek, on the North Fork of the Snoqualmie River, go east on I-90 and take exit #31. Turn left at the stop sign and continue north into North Bend. At the stoplight, turn right and drive two blocks. Turn left and follow Ballarat Street as it turns half-left. Drive north along Ballarat Street and then east on 12th Street for 1 mile and north again on 428th Avenue SE, staying on the main track the whole way. You will eventually find yourself driving along the base of a hill to your left, and you will arrive at a road that is marked "DEAD END 24 Mi." Continue directly ahead up a steep hill. (DO NOT take the Ernie Grove Road.) After about 5 miles, you will pass spur gate #10. Continue for another 5 miles to the Wagner Bridge. Stay on the main road. The mining area is another 6 miles past the bridge.

Geology

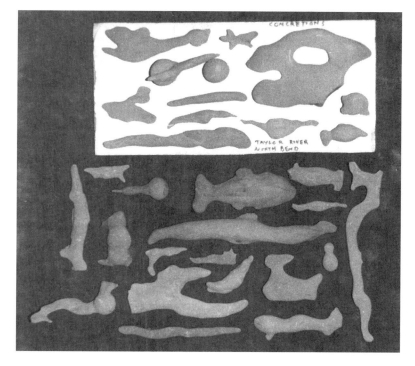

Examples of the concretions found in the Clay Banks area of the North Bend Mining District. (Vic Pisoni photo)

The most interesting features of this area are the contact zones between the large bodies of sedimentary limestones and the intrusive granitics. These provide some pegmatite structures and pipes in which well-formed crystals of quartz, pyrites, and other minerals have formed, some of a great size. Most of the rocks in this region are Tertiary granitics that are in contact with Upper Jurassic and Lower Cretaceous rocks. Also interspersed throughout the area are Eocene and Oligocene rocks. The valley floors are covered with alluvium derived mostly from the surrounding ridges and mountains. Mount Si is composed of Middle Jurassic sedimentary and volcanic rocks, with the emphasis on the sedimentary types. One other area to the north and east of Mount Si also consists of these rocks. The many bodies of sedimentary rock surrounded by the igneous provide a great number of contact zones; this augurs well for the formation of the crystalline mineral forms that are most sought after by collectors.

The Mines

Taylor River Area

Rainy (Quartz Creek) Mine

Rated at C-3. Copper was discovered on Quartz Creek in 1901 when some short adits and a shallow winze were begun. Little development work was done between 1901 and 1951. When the price of copper went up in 1951, a small mill, flotation plant, assayer shed, and bunkhouse were built. A load of concentrates was shipped to the Tacoma Smelter that fall. In 1957, 2,000 feet of diamond-drilled core sampling was done—the last official work at the mine.

This view of the Rainy Mine on Quartz Creek was taken in the 1950s. The small building at the lower left is the headhouse, which led to a short tunnel that accessed a winze driven 106 feet down into the rock. Copper was a main constituent of the ore found here, but some minerals that exhibited radioactivity were also discovered. Sprays of black tourmaline (schorl) form much of the gangue.

You can refer to the USGS 7.5 Minute map for Lake Philippa to locate this property. The mine area is in the northwest ¼ of Section 16, T24N, R10E. Mine shaft and adit symbols are shown. Note that this is a privately owned claim, so you must obtain permission from the owner before entering the property.

Cross the Taylor River at the footbridge and walk ½ mile, taking a left at the road leading away from the river. From here it is 1½ miles to the Rainy claim—a beginner-level hike of 45 minutes to an hour. You start at 1,200 feet elevation and reach the Rainy Mine at 1,800 feet. At this point, watch for a road leading left down toward Quartz Creek. Take this road for about 100 yards to the remains of a log bridge. Go down the gully it once crossed. You will soon rejoin the road. Go left where it ends at a landing built atop the mine tailings.

> **Warning** The portal is caved and covered with dirt and rock. The opening leads to a dome-shaped area 20 feet in diameter and 15 feet high. A double shaft just below this dome, 106 feet deep, is flooded. A winze alongside the shaft is stoped out to 65 feet in depth and is also flooded.

There are two tunnels, one 60 feet long, located behind the shaft, and a 50-footer to its left. A winch over the shaft at the surface, along with the building the winch occupied, have collapsed. The winch dropped onto the timbers over the flooded area of the mine. The surface above the shaft has caved into the tunnel below. Stay away from this hole, located above the caved adit. If you slip in, there will be no way out.

> **Warning** Consider this zone between the portal and upper road off limits. It has collapsed, and is very dangerous.

Besides some concrete foundations above the tailing pile, an ore cart crushed against a tree, and the floor frame of the bunkhouse in the woods east of the property road, not much remains.

The Father's Day/West adit on the Quartz Creek property is 300 feet west of the shaft. A dry stream/path leads you there from the landing road. The adit was driven 100 feet into hard rock. The main mineral is arsenopyrite, with veinlets of chalcopyrite.

For the Rockhound

Remember to obtain the owner's permission before collecting. You can fill your pockets with chalcopyrite, the principle ore mineral on the site. Arsenopyrite, molybdenite, quartz crystals, and smoky tourmaline needle crystals (schorl) can be found in the rock surrounding the portal area. Minerals that have been chipped by other people are sometimes scattered about on the ground for easy picking. If you prefer to do your own gathering, be sure to bring gloves, eye protection, and a rock hammer or chisel and hammer. There is plenty of good drinking water only a stone's throw away at Quartz Creek.

Lost Lode

Rated at C-4. Located upstream from the Rainy Mine, these six claims are dominated by a large-bodied quartz ledge; the cropping is on the bank of the creek. We have not yet visited the site. Several small streams flow across the ledge into the creek. The ledge has a granite hanging and diorite foot wall defining a vein 265 feet wide and a number of feeders ranging from 2 inches to 2 feet wide. There is mineralization throughout, with iron pyrites, copper pyrites, and bornite carrying gold and silver. Very high copper content ranges from 8 percent in the pyrites to 70 percent in bornite. The ledge forms a cliff beside the creek; access was so easy that ore could be quarried out on the surface. The owner made a series of open cuts, creating a flight of stairs 10 feet high. A group of 14 New Yorkers, possibly investors interested in the prospect, visited the property in the spring of 1897, but no sale was made and the claims were not developed.

North Bend

Clay Banks Concretions Area

Rated at B-1. This recreational area on the banks of the Taylor River is suitable for the entire family and for folks who want light exercise. The clay bank is popular for its natural cement art. Solid silhouettes of familiar forms can be easily picked from soft gray clay. Figures of ducks, worms, fish, snowmen, and more contemporary natural creations can be found on the clay slides. They can also be found in the Taylor River, where the concretions have been washed of their clay and are in clear view.

This property is in the northwest $1/4$ of Section 22, T24N, R10E; it is $1/4$ mile downstream from the Taylor River Bridge, on the east side of the river. Park at the bridge, walk to the water's edge, and follow an easy fishermen's trail to the gathering area.

Middle Fork of the Snoqualmie River

Clipper Claim

Rated at B-5. This claim is located in the Hardscrabble Creek area several miles from the Taylor River Bridge. The road is often washed out, especially after the spring floods. The Clipper consists of seven zones: the Clipper, Pedro, Katie Belle, Hawk, Three Brothers, Red Face, and Crawford Creek. Some claims were patented in 1908 following their discovery in 1902. Copper was the dominant mineral sought, and exploratory adits were driven on the property between 1908 and 1912. Diamond core drilling was also done intermittently during the 1960s.

To get to the Clipper, Katie Belle, and Pedro locations, refer to the USGS 7.5 Minute maps for Big Snow Mountain and Snoqualmie Pass. These claims are 1 mile east of the Goldmeyer Hot Springs Road. Hardscrabble Creek is the target area. The claims lie through and on either side of the creek from the road almost to Hardscrabble Lake. Trails lead from the Middle Fork Road north into the claims area. It will take about an hour of steep hiking to get to the claims. This region is not for those who are out of shape. On a difficulty scale of 1 to 5, it's a 5. (Be sure to take a lunch.) Some of these claims are privately held, so permission is required to collect on them. If they're posted as such, RESPECT THE MESSAGE!

Pedro Zone

Located in the southeast $1/4$ of Section 36, T23N, R11E, this is an elliptical breccia pipe created by volcanic pressure. It forced minerals, which had been created by the enormous temperatures and pressures deep under the earth's crust, upward to a point near the surface. Here they vented and were distributed while replacing or adding to the native ore deposits. Mineral sulfides, mainly those of copper, were the primary constituents, consisting mostly of pyrite and chalcopyrite. The brecciated area is 300 feet wide and 600 feet long. A 10-foot adit was driven on a 50-foot wide mineral zone. This zone is steep country, and no known trail leads to it.

East Katie Belle Zone

Located in the southwest $1/4$ of Section 34, T32N, R12E, in a steep area, this minor underground working at 4,300 feet elevation includes a 15-foot adit and a 100-foot adit. One faces east and the other faces west on a gulch near a major shear zone. Between 1963 and 1965, two core-drill holes were completed. There is no trail to this area.

Katie Belle Zone

Located in the southwest $^1/_4$ of Section 34, T32N, R12E. No known trail accesses this area. The Katie Belle lies in a steep gulch 200 to 300 feet below the East Katie Belle in sheared rock. Pyrite and arsenopyrite are the most abundant sulfide minerals. Lensatic ore bodies constitute 10 to 25 percent of the altered zone.

Hawk Zone

Located in the northwest $^1/_4$ of Section 34, T23N, R11E, near an unnamed lake, this area is at an elevation of 4,000 to 5,200 feet. It consists of outcropping ridges with sheared and altered brecciated granitic rock carrying sulfide blebs, with the minerals pyrite and pyrrhotite being most obvious.

Three Brothers Zone

Located in the southwest $^1/_4$ of Section 27, T23N, R12E, $^1/_2$ mile north of the Hawk Zone, this zone is partially covered by talus on its west side. It has a 30-foot adit with a 6-foot winze at the end and three shallow pits on the surface. You can find stringers of vuggy quartz with chalcopyrite, magnetite, hematite, and quartz crystals lining or filling some of the vugs. There is no known trail to this area.

Red Face Zone

Located in the southwest $^1/_4$ of Section 27, T23N, R12E, $^3/_4$ mile north of the Three Brothers Zone, this location is pyrite-rich, with a portal containing many blebs of pyrite, arsenopyrite, and marcasite. There are traces of gold along the flat-lying fractures. You can identify the area by a large zone of leached rock. There is no trail leading to this location.

Crawford Creek and Alp Zone

Located in the center of Section 27, T23N, R12E. Although gold was found here along with other previously mentioned minerals, lack of volume and intensity discouraged any further exploration. No trail.

Last Chance Claim

Rating undetermined. Located in the center of the northwest $^1/_4$ of Section 1, T23N, R11E, this area borders the Clipper Claim's northwest line. A 390-foot adit intersects mineralization from 265 to 310 feet and is stoped along this length. No other information about the workings is available.

These properties are on the USGS 7.5 Minute map for Big Snow Mountain. Some are private claims, so you must get permission to enter from the current owners. There is no known trail to the claims.

Condor-Hemlock Claims

Rated at C-5. The mineralization on these claims is 1,000 feet long, with a thickness of 400 feet and a depth of more than 400 feet. This was determined by 23 drill holes (total footage unknown). The Condor is at the center of this area, and the Hemlock is at the southeast end. The Condor has potential reserves of 25 to 30 million tons of ore, with copper, silver, and gold values being dominant. The Hemlock has three adits totaling 3,200 feet. An adjacent area, the Porter and the Hemlock, have combined potential reserves of 91 million tons of ore. The Condor-Hemlock Claims have the best ore possibilities discovered to date in this area.

The United Cascade Mining Company currently owns these patented and unpatented claims, all located in King County.

> **Caution** The tunnels in these claims have lethal gases in them!

To locate these properties, refer to the USGS 7.5 Minute maps, primarily the map for Big Snow Mountain, along with the maps for Snoqualmie Pass and Chikamin Peak. The claims are in the northern $^{1}/_{2}$ of Section 11, T23N, R11E; the northwest $^{1}/_{4}$ of the northwest $^{1}/_{4}$ of Section 3, T23N, R12E; the southern $^{1}/_{2}$ of Section 36, T24N, R12E; and the southwest $^{1}/_{4}$ of Section 34, T24N, R12E. Take the Goldmeyer Hot Springs Road, park at the river, and cross on the footbridge (if it's not washed out). Go $^{1}/_{4}$ mile, take a left on an upriver trending trail, and after 1 mile make a 90-degree turn uphill and continue for 200 yards. Turn another 90 degrees at this point, until you cross a footbridge spanning a gully. At this point, check the maps; the adit is in the gully.

Dutch Miller Mine

Rated at E-5. For generations, the local Native Americans kept the knowledge of the area's ores a tribal secret. Judging by the massiveness of the surface deposits, this must have taken some brilliant deception. But given the ways that miners had destroyed game and disturbed their hunting, the native people had ample reason for their secrecy. But soon members of the tribe who came into contact with white settlers started offering them specimens to gain favor or in exchange for goods. As a result, the indigenous people were ultimately prevailed upon to travel to the outcroppings and veins in the company of a trapper or miner. Later, transportation solutions were found to access the remote area.

*An adit at the Dutch Miller Mine. This photograph appeared in an advertisement for the mine. The ad stated that this photo showed $100,000 worth of ore, ready to be shipped. (*The Westerner, *November 1905)*

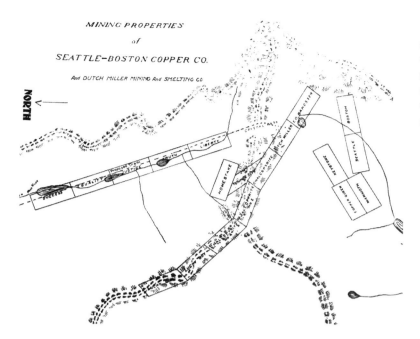

This drawing shows an overhead view of the Seattle-Boston Copper Company's mining properties, including the Dutch Miller claim and adjoining claims. (The Westerner, December 1905)

The mine was located in 1896 at the head of the Middle Fork of the Snoqualmie River near a main divide in the Cascade Range at 5,700 feet elevation. The Seattle-Boston Copper Company was formed to promote and operate it. The topography afforded a choice of three outlets. The shortest route would have required traveling 8 miles to the north and would connect to the Great Northern Railway along the East Fork of the Foss River; it would have required a 2½-mile cable tram system from the mine site through Crystal Pass, down Necklace Valley (which traverses Opal Lake, Emerald Lake, and Jade Lake), to the mill site at the valley's base, and to the railhead. The northwestern route would have allowed a shorter cable line but would have had to connect at a considerably greater distance to the Seattle International Railway at Sallal, near North Bend. The approach from the east side would have gone through a pass near the mine and made an abrupt descent, but not as steep as the northern route. A grade suitable for establishing a railroad would have been attained within 2½ miles, and then track would have been laid along Waptus Lake and the Cle Elum River Valley for 27 miles to the Northern Pacific Railroad at Ronald, Washington. The mine's owner, H. P. Fogh, bought the Fortune Creek Mill[138] with the intention of placing it on Waptus Lake, but alas, the mill was never used and the property was destined for nothing more than speculation and several shipments to a smelter. Prior to 1901, the average return after smelting charges were deducted was $37.65 per ton.

Development on this property is difficult to assess because snow covers the area most of the year. The rugged cirques and sharp ridges have outcroppings with shoots of ore. The richest deposits have been worked. Two 100-foot inclined shafts were dug into the main vein. There are also two adits, one 25 feet long and another 70 feet long, which were driven from an open pit. An adit that was intended to be driven for 2,800 feet was begun near Williams Lake, with the idea that the ore body could be intersected from this angle, but only 88 feet of tunneling was completed.

There are two practical ways to reach this remote area, either via Salmon La Sac or along the Middle Fork of the Snoqualmie River. On the Mt. Baker–Snoqualmie National Forest map, which you can purchase at any ranger station or Forest Service distribution office, locate the trail that continues up the river from the end of the Snoqualmie Middle Fork Road. This is an advanced 8-mile hike; to

---

[138] Fortune Creek is a tributary of the Cle Elum River, located several miles as the crow flies or 20 miles by trail and road upstream from its mouth. Fortune Creek was well known for its placer gold.

make a thorough exploration of the Dutch Miller workings, plan to spend two nights at or near Williams Lake. The USGS 7.5 Minute map for Mount Daniel will show you the trail from Ivanhoe Lake to the Williams Lake tunnel and the Chain Lakes prospects.

The Forest Service trail #1310 that runs from Salmon La Sac to Waptus Lake to Ivanhoe Lake is a 12-mile hike, but it is much more scenic than the Snoqualmie Middle Fork Road Trail. This presents a very gradual ascent to a point $1^1/_2$ miles past Waptus Lake, where switchbacks take you up an 800-foot elevation gain in only $^1/_2$ mile as the crow flies. There is a stone-walled, wooden-roofed shelter at Lake Ivanhoe, with a top-of-the-world view of Bear's Breast Mountain and many ridges.

For the Rockhound

On the Dutch Miller claim, arsenopyrite, pyrite, quartz, tourmaline, siderite, and pink chlorite can be wrested out of the rock with chisel and hammer, or they can perhaps be located on the surface. You might also discover a newly exposed mineralized area due to weather and erosion (a possibility at any mined site).

Horseshoe Lake Claims

Rated at E-5. Swan Hanson, who prospected the Granite Creek Basin in 1896, became manager and president of the Horseshoe Mining Company. He presided over a meeting at the Rainier Club in Seattle on October 15, 1907, where it was disclosed that $749,700 in stock had been issued. Mining engineer Capt. B. F. Hand praised the manner in which the management accomplished a large amount of work for the money expended.

In 1907, 10 men worked in the camps, although the three cabins could house 20 men. On site and in use were two hard-rock Wonder power drills and a Westinghouse steam-driven air compressor run by a 10-horsepower steam boiler.

The properties around and near Horseshoe Lake consist of three groups; the Horseshoe Group, the B & H Group, and the Surprise Group. The Horseshoe Group includes five claims: the Horseshoe, Spur #1 and #2, and Bee #1 and #2. The Horseshoe Group covers three veins of high-grade ore running parallel and only a few feet apart. The veins are 2, 3, and 8 feet wide. The copper ore in each vein is the same type of high-grade chalcopyrite and bornite. Assessment work was done, but the tunnel footage is unknown.

The Spur and Bee claims are all on one ledge, which was traceable for more than a mile and was 200 to 1,000 feet wide in places. No data on the amount of work done beyond the required assessment quota is available.

The B & H Group consists of four claims: the B & H #1 and #2, the extension to the B & H #1, and the Bear Claim. The B & H #1 extension vein consists of gray quartz and galena ore, is 4 feet wide, and carries good copper and silver. The vein is traceable for 2,000 feet up the mountain. The B & H #2 vein is 6 feet wide, runs parallel with the B & H #1, and has good copper values. The development, if any, on this property is unknown. The trail between the B & H camp and the Surprise camp runs on an even grade for about $^3/_4$ mile.

The Surprise Group consists of two claims, the Surprise and the Nelson. An immense ore body was found on the Surprise dig. It is 500 feet wide on the surface in the Nelson location, which is a continuation of the Surprise ledge. There are three tunnels on the Surprise claim. Tunnel #1 was driven 66 feet on an outcrop in broken ground that is heavily mineralized and crosscuts the ore at a right angle. Tunnel #2 is 85 feet of elevation directly below #1 and is 216 feet long, with the first 90 feet timbered because of the unstable country rock. The remaining 126 feet is all in mineralized ground, with several rich pay streaks carrying copper and silver. This tunnel crosscuts an ore body, only one wall of which was disclosed; the breast of the works were still in the ore when digging ceased. We have found no records of work beyond that mentioned above. Below tunnel #2 (down 325 feet, perpendicular to and 15 feet to the left) is tunnel #3. A 340-foot adit was dug in an attempt to reach a projected ore body at a distance of 450 feet and a depth of 400 feet. The first 75 feet from the portal is timbered due to loose ground. The remainder of the tunnel is in solid rock. At 150 feet is a crosscut in a blind vein 2½ feet wide, with good showings of copper. Another 208 feet beyond, the miners broke through a hanging wall of another ledge containing decomposed rock. Tunnel #3 was driven in as a working tunnel. The total amount of work on all the properties is 1,000 feet, along with open cuts.

The mine is on the USGS 7.5 Minute map for Lake Philippa, in Section 2, T23N, R10E, in the lower right corner of the map. The USGS 7.5 Minute map for Bandera will help you locate Horseshoe Lake from the Middle Fork Snoqualmie River Road. Hike about 5 miles on the Pratt River Trail, and then leave the trail and head east between Hatchet Lake and Lake Caroline and then to Horseshoe Lake. This will require experienced map reading, and the trip is for the physically fit only. The hiking and bushwhacking will become very difficult as you work your way cross-country to Horseshoe Lake.

Horseshoe Claim (Granite Creek)

Rated at C-3. This is possibly the same area as the Leona and Rosalie Group on Granite Creek, discovered by Swan Hansen before he claimed the Horseshoe Lake properties. They are in the same vicinity and share the same mountainside. The tunnels were driven into the rock using different techniques, which makes them physically different from each other and indicates two separate sites. The Horseshoe Mine has two tunnels, each about 130 feet long, and an open cut. A small building floor foundation is on the site. One tunnel has dark-colored, football-size nodules in the solid rock, while the other adit is in fractured, unstable-looking rock that litters the floor. A small hole was dug into the side of the adit wall, likely by rockhounds.

The claim was worked for its copper, gold, and silver. Statistics are not available. The mine is located on the USGS 7.5 Minute map for Chester Morse Lake, in Section 14.

For the Rockhound

You can find vugs containing sharp chalcopyrite crystals and octahedral and cubic pyrite crystals over ½ inch in diameter in brecciated zones containing quartz. In the brecciated zones with sulfides, you can find clear quartz crystals up to 1 inch long.

Granite Lakes/Granite Creek Claims

Rated at C-3. The first discovery was made by John Ficher, a farmer and part-time prospector, in 1892. He recorded some locations in January 1897, bonding two groups of six claims each to the Olympic-Andes Mining Company. The company made a trail from the mouth of the creek to the property 1¼ miles away, where a camp was set up. This site could be where the Lower Horseshoe tunnels are presently situated.

Leona and Rosalie Groups

Rating undetermined. We have not located this site. Of the six claims, four belong to the Leona and are on a single ledge running up the mountain from the right bank of Granite Creek. The other two claims are parallel to this ledge. The hanging wall has broken off and slid to the bottom of the mountain.

Outcropped above the slide is the remainder of the ledge. The ledge is 14 feet wide and situated between granite walls. Several streaks carry arsenical iron, sulfides of iron, copper, and zinc mixed in a quartz gangue. A 90-foot crosscut tunnel was driven into the slide below the cropping in hopes of striking the vein. When this failed, the miners went to a point inside the tunnel, 30 feet from the mouth of the adit, and dug 42 feet to the left to reach the foot wall. Then they tunneled back 54 feet toward the surface, parallel with the crosscut. This time they located the ledge and found it to be 10 feet wide, with 3 feet of good ore. Drifting 150 feet further, the ore got richer at depth.

On the Rosalie claims, there are three ledges and a placer on the creek. One ledge is on the creek and runs straight into the mountain. At this point, there is a 25-foot tunnel. The ore on the face of the cut carried iron sulfides and copper pyrites in quartz. As the tunnel penetrated deeper, antimonial silver, brittle silver, and zinc values increased, assaying at a paying value. The other two ledges, 4 and 16 feet wide, run up the mountain to the summit. One ledge was opened and showed a good pay streak.

Granite Lakes Group

Rated at D-3. The property consists of 20 claims in the Granite Lakes area. It is 1^1/$_2$ miles up the creek from the Leona and Rosalie groups. Three men from Seattle, H. B. Pedersen, Swan Hansen, and Louis Anderson, built a camp and developed these claims, later adding three more men to the work force. They had a series of good-sized ledges running east and west from the creek. One ledge, 18 feet wide and running the length of the claim, had 5 feet of ore on the hanging wall, carrying copper sulfides and peacock copper. Another vein was rich in galena, copper, and silver and assayed high in gold. A tunnel of undetermined length was driven in another ledge 50 feet wide, containing fine-grained white iron in a crumbling gangue of silica. The property is located on the USGS 7.5 Minute maps for Chester Morse Lake and Bandera, in the southwest ^{1}/$_4$ of Section 14, T23N, R9E.

For the Rockhound

This area is known to have: chalcopyrite in crude crystals up to 2 inches long changing to malachite, which shows in breccia vugs with quartz crystals; granular purple/pink dumortierite with chlorite and quartz crystals in granodiorite; pyrite in cubic crystals larger than ^{1}/$_2$ inch in breccia zones; quartz crystals up to 2 inches long, colorless but bright, in inclusions of a golden, mica-like mineral; orthoclase crystals, malachite, and chalcopyrite crystals in a breccia zone.

Laura Lindsay Mine

Rating undetermined. The Laura Lindsay is the oldest mine in this district. It is located near the foot of Chair Peak, although it is not known which foot. It has four ledges of ore and a 250-foot tunnel showing $30 to $40 of gold and silver per ton. No site or production statistics are available.

A reference to this mine made on July 11, 1897, in the *Seattle Post Intelligencer* included the following information: "A short distance beyond the end of the road going up to Granite Creek, the trail passes the mouth of the Laura Lindsay tunnel, which runs into the mountain from the river side." By 1897, the property had passed through more hands than even the oldest inhabitants could recall. It was relocated on January 1, 1897, by two men named Bowker and Lee. The ledge was 5 feet wide, carrying iron sulfides in decomposed quartz and talc, and it was very rich in gold and silver. A tunnel had been run by the former owners to a length of 170 feet, but they ran off the ledge. A winze was sunk near the portal to follow the ore down. The final working in the tunnel reached 250 feet.

To reach the mine, use the USGS 15 Minute map for Snoqualmie Pass. Follow the trails to the general area of these claims, which are located in Section 24, T23N, R10E, and then do some cross-country trekking and exploring to locate the sites.

For the Rockhound

A variety of pyrites are probably in evidence.

Mount Si Region

Ellis Mine

Rating undetermined. Fred Ellis located this mine on the northwestern slope of Mount Si, 3¹/₂ miles from North Bend, at an elevation of about 2,000 feet, possibly above present-day Ellisville. The property consists of two drift tunnels, each driven into the mountain for 50 feet. The tunnels are 300 feet apart, tunnel #2 being higher up the canyon. The work was done periodically over 20 years. All work was done by hand, and supplies were carried in on a rough trail and over great boulders, which frequently blocked the creek's canyon. Ore outcroppings were found just above the treeline and were readily traced up the steep mountainside. At no place on the surface was the vein over a foot wide. Heavy rain and yearly slides over the decades have erased any trace of the trail or tailing heap. Mount Si is an erosional remnant of an extensive lava flow. The Ellis workings are probably subject to being sloughed over with dirt and rocks one year, only to be exposed by the elements the next year.

This early textbook illustration depicts miners in a well-shored mine using hand tools. Although the shoring in the Ellis Mine probably wasn't this elegant, these were certainly the tools and techniques used to build the tunnels.

The values in this prospect are gold and silver, occurring in a quartz vein. One assay reported 4 ounces of silver and 0.1 ounce of gold per ton but offered no estimate for the amount of calculated ore in sight. Chalcopyrite is the mineral of copper most commonly found on the property.

MacGregor Claims

Rating undetermined. These prospects are on the southern slope of Mount Si, just behind Little Mount Si. Their workings consist of four shafts, each about 30 feet deep. Rock slides have completely covered all the digs. These claims are also said to contain values in gold and silver occurring in quartz veins, chalcopyrite being the main sulfide.

North Bend

Black Jack Mine

Rating undetermined. Farther around to the southeast on Mount Si, and a little higher up than the MacGregor Claims, is the Black Jack. Several tunnels were driven a short distance on the vein. These have been covered by slides. This mine also has gold and silver values.

Galena Star Claims

Rating undetermined. This claim is located north of and above the Black Jack. The tunnel was drifted 200 feet into the mountain to tap another vein at depth.

The Cascade Gold Mining and Milling Company found gold and silver on Mount Si in 1890, near the Snoqualmie River. (We do not know which fork.) One of the mines showed great promise. The ore was free milling with sulfurets, and there were thousands of tons of ore exposed. Values ran all the way from $18 to $1000 a ton in gold, with more than 50 ounces of silver per ton in some assays (at 1890 prices, mind you). Now, get this: Although this immense vein measured up to 50 feet wide, it showed only a little copper and a small amount of gold and silver in a quartz gangue.

Bald Hornet Claims

Rated at D-3. Three patented digs form this property: the Bald Hornet #1, Bald Hornet #2, and Bald Hornet #3. English immigrant F. M. Guye, the iron prospector and discoverer of the ore-rich Guye Peak claims, found and filed for these three sections in 1890 and 1891 and patented them in 1892. He actively sought out many iron properties in anticipation of the projected Kenmore steel mill in Kirkland, Washington. None of the assays verify that any work was done. Forty-five years after the steel mill idea went bust, the claims were sold for back taxes to M. R. Wood, who never visited the property. Wood sold to Henry Wrightman in 1950.

The development consists of several prospect pits and an open cut, which are now covered over with dirt and rocks and are the only evidence of the limited work done on the claims.

This property is on the USGS 7.5 Minute map for Mount Si, in Sections 31 and 32, T24N, R9E. The 7.5 Minute map for Chester Morse Lake will help you locate the turnoff for the road to the Bald Hornet Claims.

Follow the road past the Mount Si trailhead to Sallal, and watch for the gated dirt road on your left. You can tell by your map that there is a 2,000-foot elevation gain.

For the Rockhound

The rock in the claims area is highly fractured and filled with quartz and pyrite.

Green Mountain Claims

Rating undetermined. The seven properties that make up the Green Mountain group are 1 mile northeast of the Bald Hornet Claims on Green Mountain. They are the Hardscrabble, Everlasting, Good Luck, Franklin, Bessemer, and Crested Butte. The surface deposits were discovered by F. M. and John Guye. Red hematite and magnetic iron forms an ore body 30 feet long and 20 feet wide. Magnetic iron (magnetite) carried 69 to 72 percent ore and hematite 50 to 65 percent ore, almost free of iron impurities. The property was later sold to Henry Wrightman. These properties are located directly on, around the ridges, and down the slopes of the mountain. They are in the southeast $1/4$ of Section 33, which can be found on the USGS 7.5 Minute map for Mount Si. Although the Green Mountain Claims are only 1 mile from the Bald Hornet Claims, getting there involves taking a long maze of interconnecting back roads leading in from the opposite direction.

Obtain the above-mentioned map, and backtrack the shortest, easiest way to Ernie's Grove. You are approximately 12 miles from the Green Mountain Claims. This will be a backroad driving exercise.

South Fork of the Snoqualmie River

Della Jane Group

Rated at D-5. These claims, located on Mount Washington (Profile Mountain), were a gold prospect. They were named for a big cliff that, when viewed from a certain angle, resembles George Washington's profile. The Della Jane Group has seven claims on a true fissure ledge, 2 feet wide. This has been cut by a 22-foot crosscut tunnel and carries free gold in decomposed quartz. A 74-foot tunnel on a ledge the same size has similar ore. These properties are in Section 5, T22N, R9E, as seen on the USGS 7.5 Minute map for Chester Morse Lake. No known trail reaches these digs, and we have not visited these claims.

Last Chance and Alice Claims

Rated at C-3. These two claims could be on different properties, based on the location of the camp site and adit that we discovered. Mining records place the three Last Chance Claims on McClellan Butte, with a true fissure ledge of quartz and pyrites in evidence. The vein is 1 mile long, in an unknown direction. There are three tunnels, with a 60-footer being the longest. The mining artifacts, cabin site, milling equipment, and flooded tunnel that we found are not on McClellan Butte itself, although the trail leading to the butte passes through this lower mining location. Other mining documents indicate that these are the Last Chance and Alice Claims.

*A miner operates a single jack stoping drill as others look on. Machinery like this helped increase production in areas such as the Last Chance and Alice Claims. (*Western Mining and Industrial News, *February 1956)*

The *Seattle Times* of July 13, 1900, reported the start of a surface tramway to connect the Alice Claim's 1,000-foot–level adit to a mill on Revington Creek (now named Alice Creek). The rails of the tram stopped at the mill, where the $1\frac{1}{2}$-mile mine-to-market wagon road hooked up with the county road. At that time, there were three tunnels totaling 300 feet on the 800, 900, and 1000-foot levels, and 30 tons of high-grade, free-milling gold ore on the dump ready for the crusher. (By July 1901 there were 500 feet of tunnels.) The machinery for working the mine was already in operation, and the milling and output equipment was on order. The daily capacity of the mill was 10 to 15 tons of ore, which assayed at $50 per ton.

Use the USGS 7.5 Minute map for Bandera to locate this property. The Last Chance Claims have the vague placement of Section 11, T22N, R9E, while the Alice Claim is in the northwest 1/4 of Section 12, T22N, R9E. Use the Bandera map to find the parking lot for the McClellan Butte Trail. It is a moderate 1 1/2-mile hike to the mining site. About halfway there, you will cross a dirt road, formerly a railroad grade. The next sign that you are getting close is a 10-inch diameter, wire-wrapped, wooden stave pipe running down the middle of the trail. The Alice area is just before the switchbacks. The old mining camp area is on your left. (See the 1-112 circled cross on the Bandera map.) The camp lies between the circle and the first switchback. The flooded adit is within sight of the trail on your left as you turn left on the switchback heading upward.

Hansen Creek

Rated at C-2. Although this is not a mining claim in the true sense, it is a well-dug area. Popular for an abundance and variety of crystals, both of quartz and pyrites, this area consists of several productive locations. Rockhounders are welcome but must obey posted claims and any restrictions listed with them. The Hansen Creek digs are located in Sections 22 and 23, T22N, R10E on the USGS Bandera map. For more precise directions, see *The Rockhound's Guide to Washington* by Bob Jackson.

Last Chance Claim

Rating undetermined. The ore on this claim produced gold and copper. It is located in the southeast 1/4 of Section 15, T22N, R10E. This "other" Last Chance seems to be located in the lower part of the Hansen Creek crystal digs. We haven't found any further information.

Denny Claims

Rated at B-3 to B-5. This group includes the first mineral claim in the Snoqualmie Pass area. Oddly enough, Arthur Denny reached his find via North Bend, through Sallal Prairie, up the Middle Fork of the Snoqualmie River, and finally to what is present-day Denny Mountain. Had he known where the discovery would be made, he could have gone 1/2 mile off the Snoqualmie Pass toll road to claim his find and saved 20-plus miles of bushwacking (although he did save the toll road fee). For his effort, he obtained patents on nine iron claims at 3,500 feet elevation. Denny made this trek to the pass looking for plumbago, a stain the Native Americans used to paint their faces, knowing that iron was the source. Denny spotted an enormous iron stain in a gorge on what is now Denny Mountain. The gorge was a rift in the mountain 150 feet deep. Cliffs rose on each side, exposing vertical ledges of magnetic iron 60 feet wide. That was in 1869, and no improvements were made at that time.

However, in 1882, Denny and three other men located three more ledges of ore in the area. The first ledge they found, which crossed Denny Creek, was named the Denny Lode. Another claim 500 feet to the south and 700 feet high on a cliff became known as the Cliff Lode, while the third was called the Climax Lode. The Denny Iron Mines Company was formed at this time.

In 1883, the company spent $7,000 on improvements, including a 100-foot tunnel on the Climax Lode. The ore contained white arsenical iron, which made it valueless. Some of the rock the company blasted off the cliffs was high-grade Bessemer ore. Unfortunately, surface work done on several claims also produced ore that was valueless because it contained too much sulfur.

The year 1885 was an exciting time, with the discovery of peacock copper believed to be from the Denny Lode. There was a deep drift of snow in the gorge, so the miners had to dig down to the ledge. They drilled into the ore 14 to 20 feet. A ton of ore was sent to San Francisco, where it was pronounced the highest grade of copper ore. Later in 1885, after the snow melted, the miners arrived at their digs only to find the hole 50 feet off the ground, because the snowpack, upon which they had stood to create the tunnel, had melted away.

In 1890, renewed efforts were made to mine the iron ore for smelting at the mill in Kirkland. But a nationwide economic panic in 1893 caused the mill construction to cease. The same turmoil also caused the closure of the Denny Mining Company, and Denny never resumed work on the claims.

For the Rockhound

The Denny Claims are among the more productive collection sites for a variety of gems and minerals. You can find grossular crystals on Denny Mountain. (You will have to split rock to get to the better specimens.) You can also find collectable goethite pseudomorphs, which are common in pyrite and siderite-containing rocks and are often dark brown or black in color. It is possible to find malachite and azurite at the Denny Mountain Claim, where they will be associated with quartz, pyrite, magnetite, and limonite. Specular hematite can be found, with glittering samples perched on large, striated crystals of quartz. Some pyrite crystals have been found with the quartz. Some of the quartz crystals from the area form spectacular sprays, with some individual crystals being several inches long. Small garnets can be found at Rockhound Gulch, and dark green epidote crystals can be found in the lower part of Denny Creek Canyon.[139]

The deposit is located at lower Denny Creek Canyon. (Use a USGS 7.5 Minute map for Snoqualmie Pass.) Park at the Melakwa Lake Trailhead, near the Denny Creek Campground. Hike up the trail about 15 minutes, and then turn left through the woods to Denny Creek. There is a falls and narrow canyon. The garnets are in veins and vugs, up the falls and below.

> **Warning** The canyon walls are almost vertical. People have been injured or have lost their lives here because of lack of good judgment and proper equipment. Use the footbridge to get into the canyon.

It takes about 15 additional minutes from the bridge to reach the area. The best time of the year to collect is July through September, when the water is down.

Chair Peak

Chair Peak Claims

Rated at D-3. At this property, consisting of five claims, magnetic iron was the main ore sought. At the turn of the century, access was by way of the Middle Fork of the Snoqualmie River, to Sallal Prairie by wagon road, and then to Rushing's Ranch at the mouth of Tuscohatchie Creek (now called Pratt River). From there, a trail led to Chair Peak, which resembles an armchair. An impressive cliff of iron

---

[139] See *Gems and Minerals of Washington* by Lanny Ream, published by Jackson Mountain Press, 1985.

rises from Snow Lake on the east side of the mountain. The vein is 82 feet wide. On the west side of the mountain are outcroppings of the mineral from this same vein, with some copper showing. This area is located in the northwest $^1/_4$ of Section 30, T23N, R10E.

Copper Chief Tunnel

Rated at D-4. On the next ridge east of Chair Peak is a 300-foot tunnel bored in the shape of a horseshoe. The surface showings are consistent with those on Chair Peak, although the tunnel also shows sulfides and galena. This property is located in Section 29, T23N, R11E.

Emma Group

Rating undetermined. Adjoining the Copper Chief claim is the Emma Group, which has a 50-foot tunnel that reveals a deposit of copper. The location of the Emma is the same as for the Copper Chief.

Commonwealth and Red Mountain Claims

Rated at C-3. The Commonwealth Claim has a 250-foot tunnel driven into a large body of copper pyrites. Confusion abounds as to the location of this claim. L. K. Hodges has reported it on Red Mountain (which is 3 miles east of Chair Peak). *The Inventory of Washington Minerals* puts it in Section 34 on the trail to Snow Lake. The trail itself is in Sections 29 and 33. The Commonwealth Trail on Commonwealth Creek leads to Red Mountain in Section 34, which seems more convincing as the right area.

This area can be located on the USGS 7.5 Minute map for Snoqualmie Pass. Information on these claims is limited, and the exact elevation and adit sites are not available. The Commonwealth and Red Mountain Claims are located in Sections 29 and 33, T23N, R11E.

Guye Iron Mine

Rated at B-4. Twelve claims make up the Guye Iron Mine on Guye Peak, overlooking Snoqualmie Pass. It is also known as the Mount Logan Mine and the Summit Mine. Magnetic iron outcrops 60 to 70 feet wide were dug to a depth of 100 feet. Another outcropping 150 feet wide was also stripped to a 100-foot depth. These deposits were located at the foot of a cliff on the mountain, while a surface cropping of ore 300 feet long and 100 feet wide was found at the summit, on a round knoll. There is one adit, along with several open cuts and pits, on the claims.

These claims are on the USGS 7.5 Minute map for Snoqualmie Pass in Sections 28, 32, and 33, T23N, R11E, at an elevation of 4,600 feet. Finding these digs is purely a bushwacking proposition. No visible trails are indicated on the map.

For the Rockhound

A vein at the center of one of the claims is reported to have a well-mineralized area 6 feet wide, with garnet, galena, and sphalerite. On a saddle near the top of the peak are grossular garnet crystals, red and semitranslucent, in clusters up to 3.5 inches long.

Honorable Mention

Skookum Gem Quartz Mineral Mine

Rating undetermined. The five claims that make up this group are the Klondike, Cascadian, Florence, Tinker Bell, and Rose Marie. They are located in the southwest ¹/₄ of Section 8, T22N, R11E, as seen on the USGS 7.5 Minute map for Snoqualmie Pass. The land is privately owned.

Crown Quartz Group Mineral Claims

Rating undetermined. These 11 claims are in the same section noted for the Skookum claim and are also on privately owned land.

Past Placer Locations

Rating undetermined. These are located in Section 8 on the South Fork of the Snoqualmie River and consist of the NW Honest Abe Placer Mining Claim, SE Egyptia Placer, SW Black-Eyed Susan Placer, and NW Ilnicho Placer, all of which were controlled by the Christine Treasury Inc. Some workings are located at the site of the present-day Denny Creek Campground, along Lodge Creek, and at the mouth of many drainage creeks flowing into the South Fork of the Snoqualmie River in Section 8.

Carmack Gold and Copper Mining Company

Rated at A-2. In 1900, George W. Carmack discovered gold at his Klondike digs. His first discovery, which proved that the latest purchase of land by the United States was not barren of wealth, started the Alaska Gold Rush. Carmack returned to Seattle after cashing in his gold, but retirement was not for him. He bought some Washington claims from the capable, longtime prospector W. J. McConnell, who located this property in 1899. The claims were the Carmack Lode, Gold Queen, Gold King, and others whose names are not available. The only problem the mine had was the county road, which ran over Snoqualmie Pass to within 200 feet of Carmack's land on its way to North Bend and was always in a state of disrepair. Carmack did more work on the road between his claims and North Bend than the county did. By 1901, ore was being shipped from Carmack's mine by wagon 20 miles to North Bend, where it went via the railroad to the smelting mill. Fourteen teams of mules hauled ore to North Bend. Each trip took three days—two days going down and one returning to camp. A load was 1¹/₂ tons.

Work on the claim consists of a 175-foot-deep shaft with several drifts at different levels, totaling 375 feet. There are three main veins, 12, 2¹/₂, and 1 foot wide. Three shifts worked the mine night and day, allowing ore to be taken out on a steady basis. One drift, at a depth of 150 feet, follows a rich vein under the Snoqualmie River, the stream cutting the pay streak in two. The miners believed that this rich ore would widen at depth, but as they later found, Cascade mineral deposits pinched out at depth! They were unlike deposits in the Rocky Mountains, where veins of ore get richer farther down. The older the mountain range, the more time minerals have to concentrate at depth, a phenomenon known as "secondary enrichment."

By April 1902, things slowed to a halt, and the wagon road was impassable. Twenty tons of ore had been shipped during the earlier years. Documents show the claims being worked until 1918, but no production is shown for those later years.

North Bend

This property is located on the USGS 7.5 Minute map for Snoqualmie Pass, in the southern $^1/_2$ of Section 7 and the northern $^1/_2$ of Section 18, T22N, R11E, straight down the center line. The south end of the claims are about even with the Rockdale site, and the north end runs across the Denny Creek Campground Road. We don't know the condition of these claims; they are most likely flooded, considering that the tunnel cuts under the river.

Gold Creek Area

The Gold Creek Valley extends 6 miles into the Alpine Lakes Wilderness Area. Water coursing down from Alaska Lake, Joe Lake, and numerous feeder streams forms this creek. Lake Keechelus, $2^1/_2$ miles south of Snoqualmie Pass, is fed by Gold Creek at its upper (northwest) end.

In 1889, there were 10 gold placer claims at and around the mouth of Gold Creek and upstream in the valley. These claims were the Mountain Lion, St. Paul, Dominion, Tacoma, Luzon, Golden Fleece, Early Bird, Chicago, De Willoughby, and Boomer. They stretched from Gold Creek to Rocky Run Creek, running parallel with the Lake Keechelus shoreline. The early miners evidently used seasonal runoff from the snow to work the gullies that intersected each dig. The properties are now private or owned by Washington State.

During this time, David Denny (brother of Arthur Denny, one of Seattle's founders) started building a wagon road up the east side of Lake Keechelus. Denny and his crew made two bridges at Gold Creek, one over the main channel and the other spanning an older creek course; they also built a considerable amount of puncheon road over Gold Creek's swampy lowlands. Mining was also pursued by the Flanagan Mining Company, which built a tramway trestle running out of the Gold Creek Valley to the wagon road.

Massive machinery was moved through the woods on very rudimentary roads, or sometimes on no roads at all, using ingenious devices such as the tracked sled shown here. The exact location of this photo is not known, but it illustrates the challenges of moving supplies or equipment into the Gold Creek Area.

Today the lower half of the Gold Creek Valley is a winter sports recreation area, with large parking lots to accommodate the droves of snow sportsters and those engaged in general frolicking. Easy access makes it one of the many popular winter areas on and around Snoqualmie Pass.

Silver King and Silver Queen Claims

Rated at D-3 to D-4. These patented claims are on the west side of Alta Mountain, along the east side of Gold Creek. There is an inaccessible adit with a vein of quartz outcropping south of an extremely steep gully. North of the gully is a caved incline shaft. The incline shaft reached a localized deposit of sulfide minerals that showed gold, silver, and copper. These are on the USGS 7.5 Minute map for Chikamin Peak, in the center of Section 36, T23N, R11E, at an elevation of 3,400 feet.

Tinhorn #3 and #4 Areas

Rated at E-5. The Tinhorn workings are on Alaska Mountain. The tunnel can be followed at least 320 feet; at that point there is a crosscut trending eastward. Mining documents make no mention of more tunnel at this site. There are quartz lenses about 6 inches wide and two surface pits directly over the adit. But for all the labor involved, only small amounts of silver, a little copper, and some lead in low amounts were found.

East Tinhorn Area

Rated at E-5. The East Tinhorn workings are 900 feet east of the Tinhorn #3 and #4 claims. There are two adits on the property. The lower one was driven 330 feet; silver, lead, and gold made a showing in the assays. The upper tunnel is only 22 feet long, with quartz, chalcopyrite, pyrite, gold, silver, and copper found at the portal. This property is on the USGS 7.5 Minute map for Chikamin Peak, in the southeast $1/4$ of Section 22 and the northwest $1/4$ of Section 27, T23N, R11E, at an elevation of 4,400 feet.

Cascade Mining Claims

Rated at E-5. In 1906, Cascade Mining worked two claims at the head of Gold Creek. There are no records of production or development, but mining documents show that in 1951 the property was owned by E. A. Magill.

The main ore was copper, followed by lead, silver, and gold. This wide zone of mineralization was exposed in a crosscut adit and shaft (footage and depth unknown). This area is on the USGS 7.5 Minute map for Chikamin Peak, near the north line of Section 27, T23N, R12E, below a prominent bench in the cirque at the head of Gold Creek. The elevation is about 3,800 feet.

For the Rockhound

The vein is mineralized with lead, silver, copper, and gold.

Giant Lode and Jack Lode

Rated at E-5. The lower Giant adit is caved, and the workings are barricaded with dirt. Assays showed 5 percent mineralized rock containing pyrite, chalcopyrite, and galena.

The upper Giant adit was started on an iron oxide stain 6 feet wide. It heads in an easterly direction with short drifts driven north 8 feet and south an undetermined distance. There is a 32-foot flooded winze close to the portal. This property is on the USGS 7.5 Minute map for Chikamin Peak, in the northeast $1/4$ of Section 27 and the southeast $1/4$ of Section 22, T23N, R12E, at an elevation of 4,000 feet.

The Jack Lode workings are 1,000 feet northeast of the upper Giant adit, where gray rock is exposed on the north and south sides of a small creek. A 3-foot hole undercuts the north bank, and there is an adit on the south side about 30 feet away, which is now caved. The Jack Lode workings showed only a little silver. They are located on the USGS 7.5 Minute map for Chikamin Peak, in the southeast $1/4$ of Section 22, T23N, R12E, at an elevation of 4,200 feet.

Transit Workings

Rated at E-5. The Transit claim is patented and is located on the upper east side of the Gold Creek Valley. It has a crosscut tunnel on the north side of a steep-sided gulch. A drift leads from the adit, and where the adit and drift intersect, there is a winze of unknown depth. Traces of gold, silver, and copper were found here, but not enough to mine.

These workings can be found on the USGS 7.5 Minute map for Chikamin Peak, in the northeast ¼ of Section 26, T23N, R12E, at 5,200 feet elevation.

For the Rockhound

The more northern of the two mineralized zones has a 6-inch-wide vein of pyrite-rich quartz.

Esther and Louisa Mine

Rated at E-5. In 1896, the Esther Gold and Mining Company produced shipments of ore worth $1,000 from this property. The best ore, which reportedly carried 240 ounces of silver and $10 of gold per ton, came from two adits on the east side of a cirque at the head of Gold Creek. The vein they worked was near a wide dike in hard rock; a small amount of ore was in the vein itself. The main ore contained silver, gold, lead, and zinc.

This area is on the USGS 7.5 Minute map for Chikamin Peak, in the northeast ¼ of Section 26, T23N, R12E, at 5,000 feet elevation.

For the Rockhound

Pyrite, ruby silver, galena, and sphalerite are among the minerals you can find at the site.

North Fork of the Snoqualmie River (Buena Vista Mining District)

In 1897, there were over 100 claims on, along, or near the North Fork of the Snoqualmie River, Lennox Creek, and Illinois Creek. This mining claim area starts about 20 miles from North Bend. To reach it, refer to the last paragraph of the Getting There section of this chapter.

Sunday Creek

Rated at A-1. Recent assays of samples from the creek have shown silver, molybdenum, lead, and zinc. The area has the potential for discovery of mineral deposits.

Phil Woodhouse sits on the frame of a large donkey engine high on the side of Bear Basin above Lennox Creek in 1987. This machinery was meant to provide power for an aerial tramway to carry ore from the Bear Basin Mines. The effort was abandoned, and the machinery never quite reached its intended location. The device in the foreground next to Phil is a steam-driven, double-action air pump. (Phil Woodhouse photo)

Joamco Claims

Rated at E-2 to E-5.[140] Copper and gold were the main ores found on these claims, which consist of three sections. There is little information about the development of this area. The trail ends where the creek branches off toward Boomerang Lake to the southwest. (The branch descends from Honey Lake and Mowitch Lake to the southeast.) Here there is a cabin in good condition, which you can use as a base for searching out minerals and traces of past mining efforts.

These claims are located on the USGS 7.5 Minute map for Lake Philippa, in Section 6, 31, and 32, T24N, R10E and in Section 31 and 22 of T25N, R10E. To reach the area, obtain a USGS 7.5 Minute map for Mount Phelps. The road to Sunday Creek has been trenched at the North Fork Road, in Section 11. There is ample shoulder parking space off the road. Journey by foot to your destination.

Fletcher Webster Claims

Rated at E-4. Where the Sunday Creek Road and the North Fork Road converge, a large, cliffy mountain appears on the south side of the road. This is Fletcher Webster Mountain. Although it is not identified on the map, it is between Sunday Creek to the west and Lennox Creek to the east and is bordered by the North Fork Road to the north.

Seven claims are situated on the back (southeast) side of the mountain: the Gold Standard, St. Louise, Colgate, Fletcher Webster, Armada, Highland Mary, and an unnamed claim.

The minerals mined here produced mostly gold and silver. A 40-foot tunnel is located on the property, plus artifacts and building foundations. In addition, there are more surface workings on the site.

This property is on the USGS 7.5 Minute map for Mount Phelps, Section 13, T25N, R9E and Section 18, T25N, R10E. This hike covers 4 to $4^1/_2$ miles of steep switchback roads, so start early and take a lunch and liquids with you. Head for the northwest $^1/_4$ of Section 18 in the steep and cliffy areas. There you will find the old claim properties.

For the Rockhound

The main ledge of ore was from 8 feet to 40 feet wide. The 40-foot tunnel and open crosscut showed enough value in the minerals to pay for processing. Gold brought about $20 an ounce in the late 1800s and early 1900s. The pay ore averaged $32 in gold and silver per ton. If you can locate this area, you might find some ore samples.

Lennox Claims

Rated at B-3 to B-5. In 1898, the 45 claims of the Lennox Mining and Development Company covered more than 10 miles, with Cougar Creek, Bear Creek, and many other streams flowing within its boundaries. These were leased to the Priestly Mining and Milling Company in 1938. By 1946, a substantial camp had been built on a 40-acre flat near the junction of the North Fork of the Snoqualmie River and Lennox Creek. Four bunkhouses, a mess hall, a sawmill, two machine shops, a Pelton water wheel, and an 80-kilowatt generator were on the site. Long-range plans included a 500-ton mill on the flat (after a pilot mill—a scaled down, proof-of-concept mill capable of treating 50 to 100 tons each 24 hours—was tried first). These plans suggest that the value of the ore was high enough to mill on a grand scale.

---

[140] These ratings are based on maps, not on an actual visit.

By 1950, the Priestly Mining and Milling Company was concentrating its efforts on a block of 27 claims. Five adits, two open cuts, and a lower crosscut were the primary workings on the property; but these were only prospects, with no major production ever done. This was due primarily to the lack of access to the ore because of tunnels that were too short, poor roads, and the advent of World War II.[141] The veins varied from inches to many feet in width, with the gold and silver ore exposed on the cliffs and gulches. Most of this is now deeply covered with slide rock or hidden in the dense brush and fallen timber. Many ore croppings remain, visible in the unclimbable cliffs.

> **Warning** These claim areas are located in rock formations that can cause injury or worse if you are inexperienced or lack the proper equipment. The claims are privately held, and unauthorized mineral collection is not allowed.

The Lennox Claims are on the USGS 7.5 Minute map for Mount Phelps, in Sections 7, 13, and 18, T25N, R9E, at elevations between 1,830 feet and 2,870 feet.

Langor Mine

Rated at A-1. The Langor is a zinc prospect, and its 300-foot tunnel has recently been prospected by rockhounders seeking the 4-inch seam of sphalerite, chalcopryite, and pyrrhotite.

The mine is on the USGS 7.5 Minute map for Mount Phelps, in Section 17, T25N, R10E, on the north side of Lennox Creek about $1^1/_2$ miles above its mouth. The adit symbol, a small arrow, is printed on the map. This mine is now the property of the Boeing Prospector's Club, and sample collection is not permitted without permission.

Rainbow Claims

Rated at B-4. The Rainbow properties consist of nine unpatented copper claims. A 6-inch-wide, 75-foot-long vein is located at the base of the cliffs, at an elevation of 2,460 feet. Below the vein, on the mountainside, is an outcropping of rock in which a 10-foot prospect hole was dug. As if to identify the old cabin site, a vintage coffee pot also claims this spot as its own.

The metal sought here was copper, with the main ores being chalcopyrite and pyrrhotite in the iron-stained quartz vein.

The area is on the USGS 7.5 Minute map for Mount Phelps, in the northwest $^1/_4$ of the southwest $^1/_4$ of Section 17, T25N, R10E, across from the Langor Mine on the south side of Lennox Creek.

Washington and Arizona Claims

Rated at C-5. These two claims are on a ledge of ore that is an extension of the well-known Coney Basin Mines. The Arizona has a vein 40 feet wide that stands between perpendicular walls of granite and carries a body of copper sulfides, with gold being found on the surface. The Washington is similar and has a 50-foot-wide mineralized vein carrying 20 feet of pay ore, traceable far up the face of the cliff. The company had a mill site beside two small lakes 400 feet south of the Washington. The outlet streams of the lakes supplied water power for the proposed mill. Their gold and copper ores were never mined and are still there waiting to be rediscovered.

---

[141] Only strategic metals such as copper, molybdenum, nickel, and iron were allowed to be mined during the war. The Lennox ore did not contain enough of the metals.

This site is on the USGS 7.5 Minute map for Mount Phelps, in the northwest $1/4$ of the northeast $1/4$ of Section 15, T25N, R10E, just west of Paradise Lakes at 3,500 to 4,000 feet elevation. You will also need the USGS map for Grotto. Take the Bear Creek Trail off the Lennox Creek Road. Two miles up, a sign will show the way to Bare Mountain. The 2-mile Bare Mountain Trail will bring you to a point near the top where you can bushwack a course to the claims. The trail up is grueling even for seasoned hikers.

Bear Basin Claims

Rated at D-3. The original 25 claims were registered in February 1905 and are located in a horseshoe-shaped cirque at the head of Bear Creek. The 2,165 feet of workings in eight tunnels were driven into the cliffs on various veins by the Snoqualmie Mining Company. Around 1917, the company built a small flotation mill on the creek below camp. In 1922, 360 ounces of silver were smelted from the concentrates of that mill. The mill site produced some high silver assays and some showings of gold. A 1,500-foot gravity tram was built from the portal of adit #3 to the mill, but before it could be used, the property was sold and the new owner moved the tram to the portal of adit #6. Before the tram could be operated there, the mill burned down. That occurred in 1934, and little work has been done there since.

All that remains of the Pelton wheel at the Bear Basin Mill. Water power is abundant in the Cascade Mountains, and the miners made good use of it wherever they could. (Vic Pisoni photo)

North Bend

Bear Basin Adits

Adit #1 is a 10-foot prospect dig situated in the creek, about 100 feet upstream from the mill site. There is no mineralization showing in the tunnel. The mill site can be seen off to the right, from the trail heading into the camp and mining area.

Adit #2 is caved and is hidden under rock and debris. It is about 500 feet south of the mill site and 100 feet higher on the hillside. Adit #3 is on the southeast side of the basin at 4,100 feet elevation. The tunnel is about 450 feet long, with a flooded 20-foot-deep winze 40 feet from the portal.

Adits #4, #5, and #8 are on the east wall of the basin. Adit #4 has a 400-foot tunnel with no mineral values recorded. Adit #5 has spotty zones of sulfides no wider than 6 inches along its 325-foot tunnel. Adit #8 is almost closed from debris being washed into the portal, which is alongside a waterfall. This adit is only 20 feet long and is not worth the struggle to squeeze in and out of to explore.

Adit #6 is on the north side of the basin near Bear Lake Creek and has an ore cart just inside the portal. There is a 70-foot crosscut 180 feet from the entrance. Several minerals can be found in this tunnel.

Bear Basin #6 and #7 Adits

(isometric projection)

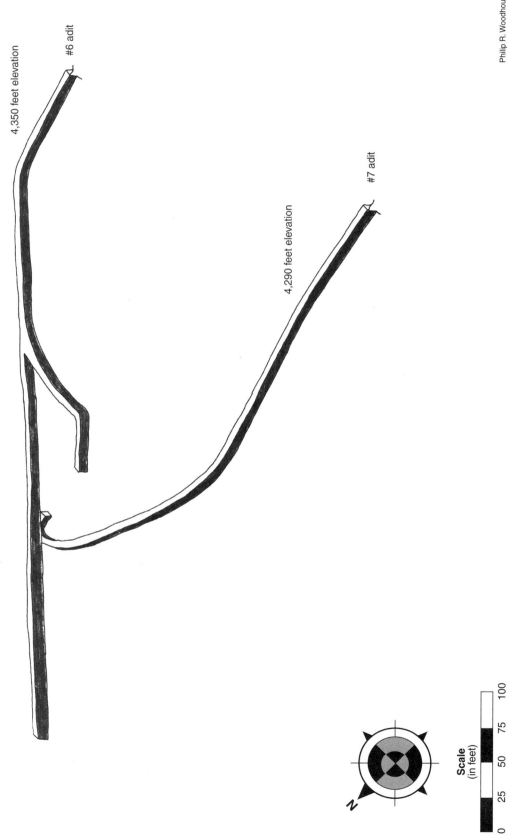

4,350 feet elevation

#6 adit

4,290 feet elevation

#7 adit

Philip R. Woodhouse 1995

N

Scale
(in feet)

0   25   50   75   100

Adit #7 is 200 to 250 feet southwest of #6. It is a crosscut that intersects a 2-inch to 3-inch mineral seam 230 feet from the portal. Forty feet beyond this point, the tunnel cuts some narrow sulfide stringers. The tunnel is about 450 feet long. The campsite once had a bunkhouse, a blacksmith building, a small powerhouse, a compressor, and a Pelton wheel. The basin area is flat, providing a great base camp from which you can check out the claims. The water tastes wonderful, and the scenery is hard to beat.

This scenic basin is on the USGS 7.5 Minute maps for Mount Phelps and Grotto, in the southeast $^1/_4$ of Section 14 and the northeast $^1/_4$ of Section 23, T23N, R10E. The elevation ranges from 4,100 to 5,000 feet. Take the Bear Basin Trail from the Lennox Creek Road. A moderate $2^1/_2$-mile hike will bring you to the Bear Basin Mines.

For the Rockhound

The primary metal sought in this area was antimony. Half-inch white crystals of albite, quartz, tourmaline, and other minerals can be found in small cavities of rock and talus on the east or south sides of the basin. You can dig stibnite from veins or the tailing piles in front of the adits. The adit with the rock wedged over the portal has the best tailings. You might have to do some weeding of the tailings to get to pay dirt, or if you have climbing equipment, you can seek out the veins above the adit in the cliffs. At adits #6 and #7, the tailings also have possibilities. Use a rock chisel, hammer, and eye protection when collecting. Other minerals in this basin include pyrite, arsenopyrite, freibergite, jamesonite, andorite, stannite, and galena.

Penny Prospect

Rated at B-2. The tunnel is about 160 feet long and contains a number of sulfide minerals. Assays show minimal traces of silver. The adit is only 1,000 feet from the road and is flooded. Tailings from the digs are partly hidden by brush and small trees. This mine is on the USGS 7.5 Minute map for Mount Phelps, in the northeast $^1/_4$ of Section 27, T35N, R10E. The prospect and adit are shown on the map but are not named.

Devil's Canyon Claims

Rated at B-3. The four claims on this property were the Devil's Canyon, Vera, Cougar, and Royal Flush, all unpatented. There is a 160-foot adit and cabin site at the north end (mouth) of the canyon, where the trail ends. The last half of the tunnel is mineralized and also cuts quartz stringers up to $2^1/_2$ inches wide. At 725 feet above the adit, and 400 feet higher in elevation, is another mineralized zone. It is 3 feet thick, with several quartz stringers $^1/_2$ inch to 8 inches wide. The largest vein in the canyon has some chalcopyrite, scheelite, and molybdenite occurring along the edge of the ledge in crystals ranging in size from $^1/_4$ to $^1/_2$ inch in diameter. Vuggy quartz can also be found. There are several mineralized quartz veins throughout the walls of the canyon, but rock climbing gear is needed to reach them.

This area is on the USGS 7.5 Minute map for Lake Philippa, in Section 26 and the south $^1/_2$ of Section 27, T25N, R10E, at an elevation of 3,280 feet. Follow the Lennox Creek Road to Cougar Creek. The bridge at Lennox Creek to Cougar Creek has been removed, so the 1-mile hike begins here. Devil's Canyon is about $^1/_2$ mile beyond the end of the road and 900 feet above the east bank of Cougar Creek.

For the Rockhound

Japan law twins (a rare form of quartz crystals) and normal quartz crystals are found in this area. The crystals are mainly in the canyon, and the vugs are on the ridges in the canyon area. In 1985, the people in control of these claims did not welcome collectors. The present ownership status of the properties is unknown.

Pine Marten Prospect

Rated at B-3. This prospect has a short adit, but it is long on potential resources. Possibly as much as 400,000 tons of ore are delineated by the area's outcrops. In 1956, assays showed traces of gold, silver, and copper. The ore bodies, stained by iron oxide, are visible for a distance of 320 feet along the outcrop, reaching a width of 15 to 60 feet and running in an east-west direction.

To reach this area, use the same approach as for the Devil's Canyon area. Take the trail to Dog Mountain. At 3,400 feet, off to the left from the steep switchback trail, is the Pine Marten Prospect. It is 100 feet north of the spring that is shown on the map. Note that this trail is difficult to follow.

For the Rockhound

Pyrite, chalcopyrite, and molybdenite are spread throughout the prospect in irregular masses.

Jack Pot Prospect

Rated at D-4. The Jack Pot had a mill site along with eight claims and several open cuts between 2,840 feet and 4,740 feet elevation. The ore zone was sufide-rich; the two largest, which were lens-shaped, were 140 feet apart. They ran 240 feet along the creek that flows from Goat Mountain. A lenticular vein 2 feet wide at the top of the cliff and 10 feet wide 50 feet lower is the best mineralized area showing. The ore on the claims contains zinc, lead, gold, copper, and tungsten.

The area is on the USGS 7.5 Minute map for Lake Philippa, in the southwest $1/4$ of Section 27 and the southern $1/2$ of Section 28, T25N, R10E. Take the trail that heads up Cougar Creek. The trail on the map stops where Cougar Lake and Goat Mountain Lake meet. An adit is located just inside the Y of this junction; the length of tunnel is unknown. Now the bushwacking to the open cuts begins. Watch for the open cuts on the right side of Goat Lake Creek, starting at 2,840 feet elevation. There are four of them within 100 yards. The other two open cuts are to the left of Goat Creek at 4,700 feet elevation. The first of these is 300 to 400 feet from the creek. The second is about 500 to 600 feet from the first.

For the Rockhound

The most abundant sulfide mineral is arsenopyrite, followed by pyrite, with a matrix high in quartz and mica.

Caution This is rugged country, so only experienced hikers should attempt to tread here.

Cougar Creek Area

Rated at D-4 to D-5. About 16 prospects are scattered between Dog Mountain and Goat Mountain in the Cougar Creek area. The Jack Pot Prospect is also in this region. Along with the previously stated information on the Jack Pot, there are two additional prospects about 1,000 feet downstream from Cougar Lake, at 3,600 feet elevation and about 500 feet west of the creek. Travel 3,000 feet directly east from Cougar Lake, where the 4,800-foot elevation lines converge to form a ridge, and you will find a prospect hole. There are several more workings in this area. One is on top of Dog Mountain. Another is at 4,800 feet elevation and 1,000 feet northwest of Dog Mountain. Northwest of this point, at 4,400 feet elevation and 500 feet away, is the next working. In the center of Section 34, on the east side of a wide cirque, look for a dig at around 3,800 feet. At a point 1,000 feet south of Dog Mountain, you'll find an unnamed lake. About 1,000 feet west of this little lake, at an elevation of 4,900 feet, you'll find yet another prospect. Two more workings are situated 1,500 feet northwest of Anderson Lake, about 300 feet off the trail, at an elevation of 4,400 to 4,600 feet.

Go back down the trail toward Devil's Canyon, and when you reach the 4,200-foot level, head off the trail to the left. Contour, staying at this elevation for 500 to 600 feet as you bushwack to a gulch. The prospects are on both sides along this gully. This ravine leads down to the ridge overlooking Devil's Canyon.

Use the USGS 7.5 Minute maps for Lake Philippa and Snoqualmie Lake, and look in Sections 33, 34, and 35, T25N, R10E. Follow the directions for reaching the Devil's Canyon, Jack Pot, and Pine Marten prospects. An old trail leads to Anderson Lake, but it is not maintained so it's not shown on the map. At about ¹/₂ mile past the place where the Devil's Canyon Creek flows into Cougar Creek, there is an old cabin site alongside the trail. Another 0.6 mile and you come to a falls. From here, the trail goes to the right of the falls and gets vague and intermittent as you head into the areas beyond.

For the Rockhound

Quartz, mica, talc, tourmaline, pyrite, arsenopyrite, chalcopyrite, galena, sphalerite, and molybdenite are the main minerals to be found here; they can be worked out of ore zones and joints.

> **Caution** This is a wilderness area, and there are no trails to most of the places for mineral collecting. Only experienced cross-country hikers and climbers should attempt to find these prospects.

Mount Phelps Prospect

Rated at B-3. The Mount Phelps workings consist of 50 claims and cover what was thought to be a possible bonanza. The 60-foot tunnel angles in and around to the left at a 90-degree angle and is slightly elevated. This keeps it dry year round, as evidenced by 6 inches of mountain goat droppings on the last 10 feet of the floor. A rusty wheelbarrow and several drill bits lean against the wall on the right side as you face the portal. Zinc was the main metal sought, with copper, gold, silver, and lead also reported in several open cuts. However, when a uniform assay was done, it showed only $5 per ton in those minerals.

This area is on the USGS 7.5 Minute map for Mount Phelps in Sections 5, 6, 7, and 8, T25N, R10E. The adit and prospect are in the northwest ¹/₄ of Section 7, and the building remains, 500 feet below the adit, are also in Section 7.

Go to the center of Section 7, leave the North Fork Snoqualmie Road, and head west through the brush until you find an overgrown road. Keep in mind that the roads and trails are generally overgrown with brush and trees, so the going will be slow and sometimes steep. Follow the road to the cabin area; some searching will be required. North of the cabin is a collapsed compressor shed. Above the shed ruins is the prospect hole. To reach the adit from this prospect, go to the northwest up and along a rock outcropping wall. Then follow around and stay near the rock wall. On the northwestern side is the adit, at 1,800 feet elevation.

For the Rockhound

Some magnetite, pyrite, chalcopyrite, and arsenopyrite can be found in dark-colored dike rock in granite, but it is sparsely mineralized along the joints.

Mastodon Group and Brooklyn Claims

Rated at D-5. Although the locations are unknown and little production data is available, these claims created considerable interest in their day. Work was done on a small scale on a series of ledges near the head of the North Fork of the Snoqualmie River, on lofty ridges that traced toward Coney Basin in the Miller River District. A 15-foot shaft that cut a 12-foot ledge produced 3 feet of copper sulfurets and galena. This material assayed high, revealing 80 ounces of silver, $20 of gold, and 29 percent copper per ton. The other ledges also produced strong showings.

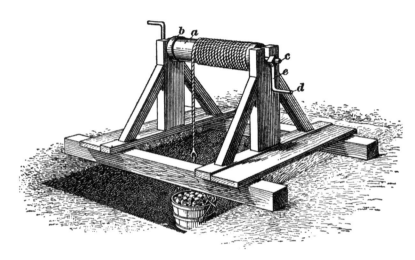

When a shaft was dug, the miners used a simple windlass like this one to bring the ore out of the ground. If the shaft became too deep, the simple windlass would be replaced with a larger hand winch or a winch with powered winding machinery.

These properties are on the USGS 7.5 Minute map for Grotto. They are probably in Sections 11, 12, 13, and 14, around Lake Kanim. This would situate them mainly in a line running from the northwest 1/4 of Section 11, T25N, R10E, southeasterly toward the Coney Mine. The cliffy areas around Lake Kanim are the most likely location.

Lucky Strike Claims

Rated at C-5. For this claim too, there is enough data to entice, but we cannot precisely pinpoint the digs. Three unpatented claims lie within Sections 9 and 10, at an elevation of 3,000 to 4,000 feet. Gold, silver, and copper were the metals sought. An 8-foot ledge, 500 feet long with traceable faults 6 feet apart in granite-type rock, contains quartz veins 12 inches thick. Somewhere there is a 30-foot shaft. The claims were active from 1947 to 1951.

To find the approximate location of this area, obtain the USGS 7.5 Minute map for Mount Phelps. Look for Sections 9 and 10, T25N, R10E. Go 3 1/2 miles up the North Fork Snoqualmie Road. That will put you just inside Section 3, near a south-trending stream bed, which enters the North Fork. Cross the river and bushwack up to the cirque with the twin creeks.[142] The original trail to the property was longer because a switchback pack trail was required to enable the pack animals to reach the cirque area.

---

[142] In 1897, five claims were located on and around the cirque lake: the Lake View, Lert, Kate Sharpe, Gem, and Huckleberry. No other data is available.

For the Rockhound

Quartz veins with pyrite, arsenopyrite, and chalcopyrite can also be found in these two sections.

> **Caution** This is brushy, steep territory, so you'd best be in good physical shape for this one.

Prospector's Ridge Area/Illinois Basin

Rated at C-4. The north end of Prospector's Ridge has many mineralized zones as well as prospect holes. The south end is also well-endowed in mineral deposits. Illinois Basin lies to the north of the ridge and has several mineral outcrops at its upper end.

Quartz, pyrite, mica, and arsenopyrite are the main minerals, and traces of other sulfides also occur, making up as much as 5 percent of the iron oxide–stained rock.

This area is on the USGS 7.5 Minute map for Mount Phelps, in Sections 8, 9, 10, 15, 16, and 17, T25N, R10E. Refer to Section 7 on the map. Take the second road to your right after crossing the Lennox Creek Bridge. It will dead-end at 1½ miles. The map does not show a trail at this point, so bushwacking is the only choice. The overgrown, rock-covered or log-covered pack trail that used to lead to the Beaverdale and other digs went to the left of the falls. After the falls, stay to the right. Beavers have built a dam at the rim of the basin, which causes the lower end of the basin to be swampy. An old cabin site is about an hour's hike from the road. The cabin has collapsed and is hidden by brush overgrowth. Southwest of the cabin, and about 15 minutes away, are the talus slopes and gulches to be dug in search of specimens.

For the Rockhound

Prospector's Ridge has clear quartz crystals up to 1¾ inches long, along with chlorite and epidote. These occur in a brecciated zone. Illinois Creek has miarolitic cavities containing quartz with epidote. The talus slopes and outcrops in the west and south basin areas are also good for collecting.

Beaverdale Claims

Rated at C-4. The directions to this area are covered in the section on Prospector's Ridge/Illinois Basin. The previously mentioned cabin site is at 2,000 feet elevation. There were other buildings on the claims whose whereabouts are unknown. Six patented claims make up this property. The Olympia and Ainsworth are on Illinois Creek and are placer workings. A wide canyon/gulch southwest of the cabin site is host to, from top to bottom, the Cameo, Belle of Washington, and Lanark. The Lanark connects with the placer digs. At this point, the Blakely abuts the others and lies in an eastward trend on the basin floor.

At 1,000 feet above the cabin site on the west side of the basin, the vein outcrops begin; they are exposed intermittently for 1,000 feet. The adits were driven into the vein on the gulch claims. The lowest adit is at 3,280 feet, on the lip of the gulch, to the north below an outcrop. It is caved, and the 400-foot tunnel is inaccessible. The middle tunnel, which is 55 feet long, was driven at 3,580 feet elevation; it too is caved.

The upper tunnel is open, with all 140 feet of it in good condition and relatively safe. The adit is at 3,720 feet, boring into the rock on the north side of the gully, just off of and paralleling the gulch. This vein is continuous and varies from 1 foot to 150 feet in width. It is rich in sulfides; 70 percent of the vein has close to equal parts pyrite and arsenopyrite, these being the sulfide minerals carrying the gold. The portal shows 20 inches of vuggy quartz with pyrite and arsenopyrite. The shear zone with its rich ore might extend 6,500 feet west to the North Fork of the Snoqualmie River area, where there are two caved adits.

For the Rockhound

There are some fine specimens of ore to pick up around the upper Beaverdale adit. The gullies and talus slopes holding the crystals mentioned in the Prospector's Ridge/Illinois Basin section are also good places to find samples.

> **Caution** This is another trailless and steeply rugged area that calls for expert ability and good physical condition.

Monte Carlo Claims

Rated at A-3. The 13 unpatented Monte Carlo Claims lie south to north, on the north trending wall of the North Fork of the Snoqualmie River Valley. Note that mineral collecting is not permitted. South of the North Fork is the Courtney #5. From this point, and in a line heading northward, are the Courtney #2, Courtney #3, Courtney #1, and Courtney #4. The Mac and Cora are blocked against the east edge of the Courtney properties, midway up. The Van #1, Van #2, Procter, Lilly, Constance, and Doggett are a staggered block of six claims bordering on the west line toward the upper (north) end.

A mill site was located on the west side of the Courtney #2, on the river. The cabin that was near the road has been moved to a higher place, in thick timber, by the present owner.

The tunnels were driven in the 1890s. A 335-foot adit with a 15-foot crosscut is located on the Courtney #1. Three shorter workings of unknown length are on the Courtney #3, Procter, and Constance. The composition of the veins was pyrite, quartz, arsenopyrite, and malachite, with some pay streaks measuring up to 16 inches in width. Assays ran high in gold and silver, in association with the pyrites.

While we don't know where this photograph was taken, it illustrates the kind of transportation problems faced by E. P. Courtney while developing the area. The wheels pictured here are probably 8 feet in diameter, made of cast iron, and probably weigh one ton or more each.

When the development was getting underway, transportation was a major problem. Roads and trails needed regular maintenance or repair. Owner E. P. Courtney found a way around this situation. He partially filled wooden kegs with high-grade ore, sealed them watertight, and floated them down-river 3 miles to the junction of the North Fork and Lennox Creek. Problems began when the turbulent waters and protruding boulders objected, in their own way, to these arks of wealth. Almost 100 years later, recreational gold dredgers and sluicers discovered the miners' folly, not knowing the source, as they gleaned the shining high-grade ore.

Another time, thousands of dollars worth of high-grade ore was piled all winter in one of the Monte Carlo's gullies, waiting for shipment. In the spring, a snow and dirt slide in the gully buried the ore forever. Or until the present owner retrieves it.

This property is on the USGS 7.5 Minute map for Mount Phelps, in the northwest $1/4$ of Section 4, T25N, R10E, 3 miles up the North Fork Road from Lennox Creek.

Blackhawk Mine

Rated at B-2. This mine is at the end of a spur road that begins on the Monte Carlo property; it has the same owner. It is shown on the USGS Mount Phelps map in Section 5. The adit is caved. Road washouts prevent driving, and visiting is discouraged.

> **Note**   Please respect signs posted on any property.

North Bend

References

Bagley, Clarence B., *In the Beginning*. Historical Society of Seattle and King County, 1905.

Battien, Pauline, *The Gold Seekers*. Colville Statesman-Examiner, Inc., 1989.

Beach, Willis K., *A Geological Investigation of the Bonanza Queen Mine, Snohomish County, Washington*. Unpublished thesis, University of Washington, 1967.

Black, Jack, *Gold Prospectors Handbook*. Tarzana: California Del Oeste Press, 1980.

Boyd, Robert Jesse, *The Little Copper King and Red Devil Veins of the Sunset Copper Mine, Index, Washington*. Unpublished thesis, University of Washington, 1927.

Boyle, James Ewing, Jr., *The Silverton Mine*. Unpublished thesis, University of Washington, 1948.

Burmeister, Harry Louis, *The Geology, Petrography, and Mineralogy of the Sunset Mine*. Unpublished thesis, University of Washington, 1921.

Campbell, C. M., *Report on the Sunset Mine Near Index, Washington*, 1938.

Campbell, Everett, *A Geological Study of the Ore Bodies of the Copper Bell Mine*. Unpublished thesis, University of Washington, 1921.

Cannon, Bart, *Minerals of Washington*. Cordilleran, 1975

Carithers, Ward and Guard, A. K., *Geology and Ore Deposits of the Sultan Basin*. State of Washington Division of Mines and Geology, 1945.

Clark and Burchfield, *Physical Geology: The Structure and Processes of the Earth*. Charles E. Merrill Publishing Company, 1982.

Clark, Norman H., *Mill Town*. Seattle: University of Washington Press, 1970.

Coats, Robert Roy, *Ore Deposits of the Apex Gold Mine*. Unpublished thesis, University of Washington, May 27, 1932.

"Copper Deposits in the Silver Creek Mining District, Snohomish, Washington." U. S. Bureau of Mines Open File Report 29, 1962.

Crary, Horace Holmes, *The Seattle Cascade Mine and Methods of Treatment of the Ore*. Unpublished thesis, University of Washington, 1912.

Davis, Dwight E., *Ore Deposits and Geology of the Region Around Mount Si*. Unpublished Thesis, University of Washington, 1923.

Deeson, A. F. L., ed., *The Collector's Encyclopedia of Rocks & Minerals*. Clarkson N. Potter, Inc., 1973.

Durkey, Robert E.; Joseph, Nancy L.; Lasmamis, Raymond, "Metal Mines of Washington," Washington Department of Natural Resources, Division of Geology and Earth Resources, Open File Report 90-18, November 1990.

Engineering and Mining Journal, various dates.

Everett Daily Herald, 1900-13.

Everett Herald, 1891-97.

Fleming, Ian, *Goldfinger.* New York: The Macmillian Company, 1959.

Frazer, Robert W., *Forts of the West.* University of Oklahoma Press, 1965.

"From Ocean Shores to Mountain Peaks and Back in a Day." *The Coast,* June 1902.

Gray, Henry L., *The Gold of Monte Cristo.* Seattle, 1969.

Gregory, Carl C. M., *Report of Mining Properties Leased to Cascade Mining Company Known as Cleopatra Mine and Aces Up Mine.* May 26, 1949.

Hodges, L. K., *Mining in the Pacific Northwest.* Seattle Post Intelligencer, 1897 (reprint by Shorey's Bookstore).

Huntting, Marshall T., *Inventory of Washington Minerals Part II, Metallic Minerals Vol. I.* Division of Mines and Geology, State of Washington, Text Bulletin 37.

An Illustrated History of Skagit and Snohomish Counties. Chicago: Interstate Publishing Co., 1906.

Investigation of the Sunset Copper Mine, Snohomish County, Washington. U.S. Bureau of Mines Report of Investigations 4989.

Jackson, Bob, *The Rockhound's Guide to Washington,* Volume 4. Jackson Mountain Press, 1987.

Jacobson, Daryl, *A History of the Early Search for Gold in Eastern King County, Washington.* A report to the U. S. Forest Service, Northwest Underground Explorations, 1994.

Kaiser, A. E., *The Geology of the Yankee Boy Mine, Snohomish County, Washington.* Unpublished thesis, University of Washington, 1934.

Kromona Mine corporate files collection. Sky Valley Historical Society, Sultan, Washington.

Livingston, Vaughn E., Jr., *Geology and Mineral Resources of King County, Washington.* Washington Department of Natural Resources, Division of Geology and Earth Resources, Bulletin 63, 1971.

Lowry, Jack Charles, *Flotation of Ore from the Sunset Mine, Index Washington.* Unpublished thesis, University of Washington, 1937.

Majors, Harry M. and McCollum, Richard C., *Monte Cristo Area, A Complete Outdoor Guide.* Northwest Press, 1977.

McPhee, John Alexander, *The Geology and Mining of the Western Part of the Index Mining District.* Unpublished thesis, University of Washington, 1911.

Meinig, D. W., *The Great Columbia Plain—A Historical Geography 1805-1910.* Seattle: University of Washington Press, 1968.

Mills, Robert Bernard, *Study of Coney Basin Mine.* Unpublished thesis, University of Washington, 1949.

Milton, Charles, and Milton, Daniel J., "Nickel-Gold Ore of the Mackinaw Mine, Snohomish County, Washington." *Economic Geology,* 53 (1958): 426-47, reprinted by permission of the United States Geological Survey.

Mineral Investigation of the Eagle Rock RARE II Area, Snohomish and King Counties, Washington. U. S. Bureau of Mines Report 6054.

Mineral Resources of Alpine Lakes Study Area; Economic Appraisal of Alpine Lakes Study Area, U.S. Bureau of Mines, bulletin #1542.

Mineral Resources of the Glacier Peak RARE II Area, Snohomish County, Washington. U. S. Bureau of Mines Summary Report l6031.

Mining Magazine, 1897-1902.

Moen, Wayne S., and Huntting, Marshall T., *Handbook for Gold Prospectors in Washington.* Washington Department of Natural Resources, Division of Geology and Earth Resources Information, Circular 57, 1975.

Moen, Wayne S., *Silver Occurrences of Washington.* Washington State Department of Natural Resources, Bulletin 69, 1976.

Nordlund, Enid, taped interview, 1986.

Northern Pacific/Hartford Eastern Right of Way Engineering Drawings, 1904 and 1915.

Patty, Ernest N., *The Metal Mines of Washington.* Washington Geological Survey Bulletin 23, 1921.

Petrailla, Joseph F., *Gold! Gold!* San Francisco: Sierra Trading Post, 1980.

Pinkham, Daniel, *There's Gold in Them Thar Hills, Being the History of the ".45 Mines, Inc."* Lynn, Massachusetts, 1964.

Pitt, Dale L., *Report on the Sunset Copper Company,* Index, Snohomish County, Washington, 1919.

Poehlman, Elizabeth S., *Darrington, Mining Town/Mill Town.* Kent, Washington: Gold Hill Press.

Prater, Yvonne, *Snoqualmie Pass.* Seattle: The Mountaineers, 1995

Purdy, C. Phillips, Jr., *Antimony Occurrences of Washington.* Washington Division of Mines and Geology Bulletin 39.

Ream, Lanny L., *Gems and Minerals of Washington.* Jackson Mountain Press, 1985.

The Seattle Times, various dates.

Smith, Robert Earl, *Geology and Development at the Alexander Mine, Skykomish, Washington.* Unpublished thesis, University of Washington, 1953.

Snow, Eugene L., *The Silverton Mine and Mill.* Unpublished thesis, University of Washington, 1941.

Spring, Vicky; Spring, Ira; and Manning, Harvey, *100 Hikes in the Alpine Lakes.* Seattle: The Mountaineers, 1985.

The Sunrise Mine Proposal. A brochure produced by the Mount Baker-Snoqualmie National Forest to publicize the Bren Mac Mining Proposal.

"Sunset Mine's Sad Story." *Compressed Air Magazine,* May 1960.

Todd, W. A., *The Geology Plan of the Bald Hornet Claims,* King County, Washington, 1961.

Thyng, William S., and Landes, Harry, *Washington Geological Survey Annual Report Volume I for 1901.*

University of Washington Geology Department Staff, *A Geologic Trip Along Snoqualmie, Swauk, and Stevens Pass Highways.* Olympia: State Printing Plant, 1963.

Van Ornum, Maynard Howard, *Geology and Mining of Coney Basin Mine.* Unpublished thesis, University of Washington, 1937.

Warren, James R., *King County and Its Queen City: Seattle.* Woodland Hills, Calif.: Windsor Publications, Inc., 1981.

Washington Miner. Washington State Mining Association, 1907-08.

Washington: A Guide to the Evergreen State. Washington Writers Program; Portland: Binford and Mort, 1941.

Washington State Department of Natural Resources, unpublished data.

Weaver, Charles E., *Geology and Ore Deposits of the Index Mining District.* Washington State Geological Survey Bulletin 7, 1912.

The Westerner Magazine, December 1905.

Whitfield, William, *History of Snohomish County.* Chicago: Pioneer Historical Co., 1926.

Wilkie, Rosemary, *A Broad Bold Ledge of Gold.* Seattle: Seattle Printing and Publishing Company, 1958.

Wilmans, John MacDonald, *Remembrances,* 1910.

Wolgemuth, Helma, taped interview, 1988.

Woodhouse, Philip R., *Monte Cristo,* Seattle: The Mountaineers, 1978.

Maps

USGS 7.5 Minute Series Quadrangle Maps, United States Geological Survey:

Bandera	Monte Cristo
Baring	Mount Daniel
Big Snow Mountain	Mount Phelps
Chester Morse Lake	Mount Stickney
Chikamin Peak	Skykomish
Granite Falls	Snoqualmie Pass
Grotto	Sultan
Index	Whitechuck Mountain
Lake Philippa	

Anderson's Map of the Money Creek, Miller River, and Buena Vista Mining Districts. Seattle: The O. P. Anderson Map and Blueprint Co., 1897.

Anderson's Map of the Monte Cristo and Silver Creek Mining Districts; Seattle: The O. P. Anderson Map and Blueprint Co., Seattle, 1897.

Anderson's Map of the Stillaguamish Mining District. Seattle: The O. P. Anderson Map and Blueprint Co., 1897.

Huntting, Marshall T., Geologic Map of Washington. State of Washington Department of Natural Resources, Division of Mines and Geology, 1961.

Kennedy's Map of the Silverton Mining District. Kroll Map Company, Seattle, Washington.

Map of the 45 Mine: Snohomish County, Washington, 1910.

Map of the Underground Workings of the Bonanza Queen Mine. Colorado School of Mines, 1956.

Map Showing Location of the Virginia Agenda Mines and Town Site of Silverton and Northern Pacific Railroad, 1922-30.

Plan and Cross Section Maps of the Independent Mine Workings. Ore Recoveries Corporation, Silverton, Washington.

Stretch, R. H., *Index and Its Vicinity,* The Washington Map and Blueprint Company, 1903.

Glossary

adit   A horizontal mine tunnel that enters from the surface and can be of any length. Other special types of tunnels include crosscuts, drifts, and inclines.

aerial tramway   A device for transporting materials by means of buckets that travel over a suspended cable.

air receiver   A thick-walled metal tank used as a reservoir for compressed air. In the mines, the compressed air was used to power drills.

altimeter   A device that measures the elevation above sea level, usually by using the prevailing atmospheric pressure to generate its readings.

amalgam   A mixture of any metal with mercury. Mercury was often used to amalgamate free-milling gold and silver away from the fine rock dust in which it was dispersed.

argentiferous   Containing silver.

arrastra   An early device for crushing ore. It consisted of a flat, circular floor of stone about 20 feet in diameter. In the center was a vertical axle that was rotated by a long, horizontal arm attached to a mule, a horse, or other beast of burden. Water power was also used, when available. Also attached to the axle was a stone or stones that were dragged or rolled around the circular floor as the animal was driven in a circle around the axle. The ore was placed on the floor of the device and was gradually crushed by the action of the rolling or dragging rocks.

arsenopyrite   A mineral containing arsenic, iron, and sulfur.

assay   Chemical analysis of an ore to determine the values of metals it contains.

assessment work   The minimum amount of work required by the U.S. government as proof that a mine is not lying idle. One hundred dollars of assessment work (improvements) per year is usually considered adequate. Assessment work is required only on unpatented claims.

azurite   An ore of copper that exhibits a brilliant blue color.

ballast   In railroading, the crushed rock tamped between and under the ties to create a firm roadbed.

batholith   A large mass of igneous rock that was forced, under great pressure, into cooler rock layers. This normally happens deep below the earth's surface, which causes the mass to cool very slowly, giving rise to a moderately coarse rock structure similar to common granite. These structures can be very large and sometimes many miles across.

bleb   A small inclusion of mineral or other matter that has filled an air bubble or other cavity in the native rock.

Bleichert tram   A type of aerial tramway, patented by Theodore Otto and Adolph Bleichert in Germany in 1876, that uses a stationary carrying cable from which the cars hang and roll along on wheels. A second traction cable is clutched to each car as required to move it along the stationary cable.

blind vein   A vein discovered during tunneling that does not outcrop on the surface.

blocking out   The boring of tunnels or other activity to define the extent of an ore body. This is generally done prior to any commitment to production.

bond Similar to a modern lease. But in addition to the lease or bond payments, the lessee is usually required to put an agreed-upon amount of money into the property or make stipulated improvements to it over the life of the bond, which is usually one to three years.

bornite Also called peacock ore. A mineral containing copper, iron, and sulfur. It is similar to arsenopyrite but has a higher percentage of copper. The mineral is the color of shiny brass when first broken open but rapidly tarnishes to an iridescent peacock color.

boulangerite An ore containing lead, antimony, and sulfur.

breccia Rock that consists of broken pieces of rock cemented together by calcite or another matrix material.

bull wheel The wheel around which the moving cable of an aerial tramway passed at its terminals. A bull wheel usually had a system of grippers on its rim to keep the cable from slipping as it engaged with the wheel.

Carboniferous The geologic period that extended from 280 to 345 million years ago. Much of the earth's coal was formed during this period, hence the name.

cat road A rough road carved by a bulldozer.

chalcocite An ore of copper containing copper and sulfur.

chalcopyrite A mineral containing copper, iron, and sulfur.

chloanthite An ore of nickel containing nickel and arsenic.

chrysocolla Hydrous copper silicate containing copper, silicon, oxygen, and water.

cirque The head of a glacial valley where the glacier has carved a bowl-shaped hollow.

collar Also called a shaft collar. The wooden or concrete structure that defines the mouth of a shaft or winze. It is the uppermost tier of timbering.

concretion A solid mass formed by minerals deposited on the outside of a core, such as a grain of sand or a small rock. An example is a pearl.

concentrator A mill where the ore is crushed and the lighter nonmetallic material is separated from the heavier metallic pay dirt.

consist *(noun)* The makeup of a train; literally, the number and type of cars connected to the locomotive. The accent is on the first syllable.

contouring Walking along the side of a slope while staying at approximately the same elevation.

core drill *See* diamond drilling.

Corliss engine A steam engine that used a rather complex, but very efficient, valve system.

country rock Rock that already existed in a given area when other molten rocks intruded into it.

covellite A form of copper sulfide containing copper and sulfur.

Cretaceous The geologic period that extended from 65 to 136 million years ago.

crosscut A horizontal mine tunnel not bored along a vein.

crusher A device used to reduce raw ore particles to a smaller size determined by the design of the mechanism.

cubanite An ore containing iron, copper, and sulfur.

cuprite An ore of copper containing copper and oxygen.

deciduous trees Trees that lose their leaves in the winter.

development work The work required to ascertain the quality and extent of an ore body and to develop the roads and other transportation facilities needed to successfully operate a mine.

devil's club A plant with a hard, woody stem and large leaves, all of which are covered with sharp thorns.

diamond drilling Usually refers to hollow-core diamond drilling, the process by which a hollow, diamond-impregnated drill bit is used to drill holes through rock, forming a core sample inside the drill as the unit penetrates the rock. These cores are extracted and analyzed to determine the mineral value at various distances along the bore. Core holes can be driven for hundreds of feet, and the process is much less expensive than tunneling.

dike An igneous intrusion where the molten rock was forced into a vertical fissure.

dip The angle at which a vein of ore is tilted from the horizontal.

Doré bars The result of certain smelting processes. The bars consist of gold and silver of high purity, from which these metals are further refined.

drift A horizontal mine tunnel that follows a vein.

duplex In an air compressor, a dual-action cylinder that provides compression during both the push and the pull stroke.

dynamo A direct-current generator. Dynamos were often connected to Pelton wheels, steam engines, or internal combustion engines to supply electrical power at the mines. Normally used for lighting, dynamos also ran pumps, blowers, compressors, and, in a few mines, they powered electric drills.

electrical conductivity survey Measurement of the conductivity between two points on the surface of the ground. Since metallic ore conducts electricity better than the country rock, this process can indicate the amount of ore below. This is one of many geophysical methods for detecting the presence of ore bodies.

epidote A family of minerals described as "complex, basic silicates," which include zoisite and clinozoisite. These minerals contain calcium, aluminum, silicon, oxygen, and hydrogen, as well as iron and manganese.

erythrite A mineral containing a large amount of silica.

exploratory tunnel A mine tunnel driven in an attempt to locate a vein or veins or to block out a body of ore.

float Mineral samples found in the talus slope below a rock outcropping or mine tunnel. Usually a good indicator that an ore vein is exposed on the heights above.

flotation Also floatation. A process for concentrating metallic ore that blows air into the bottom of a large tank containing the ore as a fine slurry. The gangue, or lighter rock particles, cling to the bubbles, float to the surface, and are skimmed off and discarded. The heavier metallic particles settle to the bottom and are retained. Any mill called a flotation mill used this process to refine ore.

flume An open water conduit, usually built of wood, that conducts water from a source to either a mine or a mill.

Glossary

fool's gold Any of the many forms of pyrite that exhibit a brassy, golden color.

foot wall The wall of a mine cavity, usually a stope, that defines the bottom.

fraction claim A claim that is smaller than the allotted 20 acres of a normal-size claim.

freibergite An ore mineral containing copper, silver, antimony, and sulfur.

gad A pointed metal bar used to wedge and break pieces from an ore vein.

galena The sulfide ore of lead.

gangue The portion of the vein containing no mineral of value, which is separated from the ore during concentration.

garnierite An ore containing nickel, magnesium, silicon, oxygen, and hydrogen.

giant powder A mixture of nitroglycerine and a substance similar to black powder, which is formed into sticks and used for hard rock blasting.

glory hole The spot where a body of ore is stoped to the surface and opens into a large hole. Glory holes were generally created when miners dug upward through the ore body and broke out onto the surface.

goethite A hydrated iron oxide containing iron, oxygen, and hydrogen.

gossan A hydrated iron oxide formed by the contact of veins of iron sulfide ores (pyrites) with the atmosphere. This formed an "iron hat" over the vein that differed in color from the surrounding rock and was used by the early prospectors to locate these veins.

grizzly A coarse screen through which raw ore is passed. Whatever passes through goes to the concentrator, and whatever doesn't is run through a precrusher to reduce its size.

grossular A form of garnet mineral that often resembles gooseberries, as the name implies (from the Old French).

grubstake An agreement whereby a person buys supplies and food (grub) for a prospector in exchange for a certain stake in all minerals found by the prospector.

gyratory crusher A rock crusher that uses a vessel in the shape of a cone, inside which is positioned another conical-shaped device roughly the shape of a child's top. The internal piece is pivoted at the bottom and is slowly "gyrated" at the top, crushing the ore between it and the conical vessel.

Hallidie tram A type of aerial tramway, similar to a ski lift, in which the supporting cable and moving cable are the same.

hanging valley A side valley that does not merge with the main valley but terminates high up on the wall of the main valley, hence the name. Created when the glacier forming the main valley cut at a greater rate than the one forming the side valley, leaving the side valley high above.

hanging wall The wall of a mining cavity that defines the ceiling or roof.

haulage tunnel Usually the lowest tunnel, driven for the purpose of hauling ore from the mine. It is normally connected to the ore-producing workings of the mine through stopes or raises that allow gravity to bring the ore down for removal from the mine.

haulback tram An aerial tram that consists of a single, stationary, elevated cable on which rides a bucket suspended from a pulley. The bucket is lowered by gravity and raised or "hauled back" using a single cable attached to a winch at the top of the tram.

headhouse A building located at the adit or shaft of a mine. The headhouse usually contained the winding machinery, ventilation blowers, or other equipment needed to operate the mine.

hematite An ore containing iron and oxygen; the most common ore of iron. Specular hematite is a semiprecious gemstone.

hogback A mountain ridge, usually somewhat rounded on top, that begins at the bulk of the mountain and continues into the valley below.

hoist room The room in which the machinery was located to lower men and equipment down a shaft or incline and to hoist up the men, equipment, and ore. Such rooms were built on the surface or carved from solid rock within a mine.

hornfels A form of metamorphic rock in which a fine-grained rock consisting of three or more minerals has been reheated and slowly cooled so that phenocrysts (embedded crystals) of one of the mineral constituents form among the finer matrix (composed of the other two minerals) of the rock.

Howe truss bridge A railroad bridge that uses a lattice work of wood to carry the compressive stresses and uses steel tie-bolts to carry the tension. A Howe truss bridge can be used in two ways: On a deck-span bridge, the train travels over the top, or deck, of the truss; on a through-span bridge, the train travels through the truss structure.

igneous Fire-formed rock. Rock that has been melted and then cooled. Examples are granite, rhyolite, and basalt.

incline A mine tunnel that is neither horizontal nor vertical but angled.

intrusive rock Volcanic rock that has been forced into cracks in the country rock deep below the earth's surface. The intrusions can form any number of bodies, such as batholiths, laccoliths, sills, or dikes, depending on their size and shape; all are generally referred to as plutons.

jamesonite A complex ore containing lead, iron, antimony, and sulfur.

jaw crusher A rock crusher that consists of a fixed plate of metal (jaw), at the base of which another jaw is pivoted. The movable jaw is angled away from the fixed jaw at the top to create a hopper into which the ore is dropped. As the movable jaw is rhythmically moved toward and away from the fixed jaw, the ore is crushed to a size determined by the separation of the plates at the bottom of the hopper.

Jurassic The geologic time period that extended from 136 to 195 million years ago.

lagging Timbers placed within a mine tunnel to prevent its collapse, sometimes used in conjunction with planks between the timbers. Also called shoring.

ledge An approximately horizontal vein of ore.

lens Also called a lensatic ore body. A mineral deposit in the shape of a double-convex lens—thick in the center and tapering to very thin edges.

lode claim A claim made along the outcrop or suspected position of a vein or body of ore within the country rock. Extraction of the minerals usually requires tunneling or other means of excavation. *See also* placer claim.

mackinawite A unique form of iron sulfide.

magnetite An ore mineral containing iron and oxygen. The mineral is often magnetically charged, hence the name. If magnetized, it might also be called lodestone.

malachite A mineral containing copper, carbon, oxygen, and water, which forms a hydrated copper carbonate. This is the intensely green mineral stain often associated with copper-bearing ores.

matterhorn A type of mountain formed when glaciers carve away the lower slopes on all sides. It is usually very steep and snaggle-toothed in appearance.

marcasite A mineral containing iron and sulfur. Unlike the usual pyrites, the molecular structure of this mineral causes it to appear silvery white rather than yellow. Also called white pyrite.

metamorphic rock Rock that has been metamorphosed, or changed in form, from its original condition. This usually happens through the reheating of the rock, often while under enormous pressure at great depth beneath the earth's surface.

mill site claim An additional parcel of land, amounting to 5 acres, that can be granted to a holder of an unpatented mining claim. A mill site claim does not need to be adjacent to the mineral claim, although it is generally as close as possible so that the ore doesn't have to be transported far. Minerals cannot be exploited on a mill site.

native metal Metal that has been naturally reduced to its metallic state, as opposed to metal that must be extracted from ore.

ore Mineralized rock that contains metals of interest to miners. This is usually found in veins or irregularly-shaped bodies within the matrix of the country rock.

orpiment An ore that contains arsenic and sulfur.

outcrop The point at which an ore vein becomes exposed on the surface.

Paleocene The geologic time period that extended from 53 to 65 million years ago. The oldest portion of the Tertiary time period. *See also* Tertiary.

patent The deed to the land on which a mine claim is located. This differs from an unpatented claim that conveys only the mineral rights to the miner.

Pelton wheel An impulse water turbine that uses a powerful stream of water played against wheel-mounted buckets to create rotary power.

penstock The pipe that carries water from a dam or other diversion structure to a power plant.

pentlandite An ore containing iron, nickel, and sulfur.

placer claim A claim made across or near a stream bed with the intent of washing valuable metals, usually gold, from the sand and gravel deposits in the area.

plat The map of a town showing its layout plan with streets, lots, and so forth.

pluton Any of a number of types of rock structures caused by igneous rocks being forced into the native rock of an area deep under the earth's crust.

pseudomorph Literally meaning false form; in mineralogy, a particular mineral that has been altered through oxidation or some other process but retains the crystalline shape of the original material.

puncheon The split planking used in early pioneer road construction.

pyrite Also called pyrites or iron pyrite. A mineral containing iron and sulfur. Also known as "fool's gold" because of its brassy, golden color.

pyrrhotite A form of pyrite.

raise A tunnel bored upward from below.

range *See* township.

receiver *See* air receiver.

realgar An ore of arsenic containing arsenic and sulfur.

retort A large vessel for roasting ore to drive off the mineral it contains. A retort is usually used to extract mercury.

reverberatory A smelting furnace in which the flames are deflected downward off the roof.

roasting The heating of ore to temperatures just short of smelting to drive off impurities such as arsenic and sulfur.

rockfall Any area where rocks have tumbled down from above. This term can apply either on the surface or underground in the mine workings.

rolls Two large rollers rotating almost in contact with one another to crush ore. The ore is dropped between the rolls and crushed to a size determined by the distance between the rolls.

scheelite An ore containing calcium and tungsten.

screens Wire mesh or perforated steel plates used to classify (separate) ore particles of a specific size from the rest of the ore.

section In mapmaking, technically 1 square mile. However, because the surface of the earth is curved, a section is often smaller than 1 square mile.

shaft A mine tunnel driven vertically downward from the surface.

shaft collar *See* collar.

shoo-fly curve In railroading, a curve built around an obstacle such as a collapsed tunnel or a washed-out bridge.

shoring *See* lagging.

siderite A form of the mineral hornblende.

silica A mineral containing silicon and oxygen. Most sand is a form of silica.

sinusoidal Having the form of a sine wave. A sine wave looks like the cross-section of a series of ocean swells, rising and falling at regular intervals.

smelter A plant containing a smelting oven in which base ore is reduced to its metallic content.

sphalerite Also known as blende or zinc blende. An ore of zinc containing zinc and sulfur.

stannite An ore mineral containing copper, iron, tin, and sulfur.

stibnite A mineral containing antimony and sulfur.

stope A mining cavity created when the ore is removed from the vein. It follows the contours of the vein and is irregular in shape. *See also* underhanded stope.

stringer A very thin vein.

stull Large timbers wedged between the hanging and foot walls of a mine.

Glossary

sulfide ore An ore that contains one or more metals in combination with the element sulfur. Thus the sulfide ore of lead is galena, of iron is pyrite, of zinc is zinc blende, of iron and copper is chalcopyrite, and of iron and arsenic is arsenopyrite. Also known as sulfurets.

switchback A method by which a railroad gains altitude without gaining distance. The train is stopped, a switch is thrown behind it, and the train is backed up a grade. A switch is then thrown in front of the train, and the train moves forward on a track higher in elevation than the one it arrived on. Also, a road or trail that follows a similar pattern up a slope.

tailings Fine particles of gangue that have been removed from the ore—the result of the concentration process. Also, the waste material dumped at the mine adit because it was not considered to be of sufficient value to ship to market. Often called a mine dump.

tailrace The water discharge from a water wheel or turbine.

talus The broken rock that piles up at the base of a steep mountain slope or cliff.

Tertiary The geologic time period that extended from 7 to 65 million years ago.

tension station An aerial tramway structure containing massive weights and pulleys, which maintained tension on the tram's cables.

township In surveying and mapmaking, a township and range are location descriptions for a square nominally 6 miles on a side, thus nominally containing 36 square miles. Township and range are usually described as "township north or south, and range east or west" and are usually abbreviated. For example, "T24N, R6E" means the 24th township north of a reference latitude and the 6th range to the east of a reference meridian.

tram An aerial or ground tramway.

tramway An aerial or ground conveyance that uses buckets or cars to transport bulk materials.

tourmaline A mineral best described as a complex borosilicate. It presents many colors, depending on the chemical makeup of the specific specimen. Red, clear, green, and black are common.

underhanded stope A stope cut downward from the tunnel. These stopes were not often cut because they tended to flood and were difficult to work.

unpatented claim A mine claim that allows the miner to remove minerals but does not convey ownership of the land to the miner. Ownership of the land remains with the government.

vein The mineralized fissure along which the minerals of the area have been deposited and concentrated.

vug A rock cavity in which crystals or other mineral forms sometimes grow.

windlass A winch, powered by either motor or hand cranking, that winds the rope or cable around a drum. Windlasses were used to lift small loads from shafts or winzes. When heavier lifting was required, a geared winch or large winding machinery was used.

winze A vertical mine shaft bored downward from a horizontal tunnel. The entire length of a winze is underground.

wood-stave pipe Pipe that is constructed like a long barrel, with closely fitted slats of wood forming the body of the pipe and hoops of steel wire tightened around the pipe to resist the pressure.

wye In railroading, a pattern of switches and curved track that resemble the letter Y from above. The layout allows a locomotive or cars to be turned around without the use of a turntable.

Resources

In almost all cases, you need permission or a permit to excavate on public and private lands, cross rivers and streams, or release water from mine tunnels. The following organizations can assist you in determining which lands are public and which are private, what kind of permission and/or permits are required, and other helpful information.

King County and Snohomish County Assessors
Located in the county courthouses.
Information on patented mine claims.

Monte Cristo Preservation Association
P.O. Box 471
Everett, Washington 98206
Information on the history of the Monte Cristo area.

No Name Prospectors Club
P.O. Box 2872
Woodinville, Washington 98072

Northwest Underground Explorations
P.O. Box 386
Monroe, Washington 98272

U.S. Bureau of Land Management, Oregon State Office
P.O. Box 2965 (1300 NE 44th Ave.)
Portland, Oregon 97208
Information on unpatented mine claims.

U.S. Forest Service, Mount Baker Snoqualmie National Forest
21905 64th Ave. West
Mountlake Terrace, Washington 98143
Maps, information on trails, campgrounds, weather, fire and road conditions.

University of Washington Libraries
Reference books and theses.

Washington State Department of Fish and Wildlife
16018 Mill Creek Blvd.
Mill Creek, Washington 98012
Information on rivers and streams, hydraulic permits, and placer mining regulations.

Washington State Department of Natural Resources
Division of Geology and Earth Resources
Natural Resources Building, Room 148
1111 Washington St. SE
Olympia, Washington 98501
Information on mines, mining claims, and minerals, and an excellent library.

Washington Prospectors Mining Association
10002 Aurora Ave. N, Suite 1193
Seattle, Washington 98133

Index